The Leopard's Spots

The Leopard's

Spots

SCIENTIFIC

ATTITUDES

TOWARD RACE

IN AMERICA

1815–59

BY WILLIAM STANTON

THE UNIVERSITY OF CHICAGO PRESS

CHICAGO AND LONDON

THE UNIVERSITY OF CHICAGO PRESS, CHICAGO 60637
The University of Chicago Press, Ltd., London W.C. 1

TO MY MOTHER

AND TO

THE MEMORY OF

MY FATHER

Preface

Traditionally, Americans have been dedicated to the idea of equality. At the same time circumstances have caused them to be peculiarly concerned with race. Their dedication and their concern were never greater than in the eighteen-forties and fifties. Some believed that only science could resolve the dilemma and so they asked, in the only way they knew to put the question, whether the races of men sprang from one creation or many. It was only another way of inquiring about the origin of species. This book is about the efforts of American scientists to provide an answer.

Their efforts resulted in a war of ideas. I have attempted to examine merely the grand strategy of that war, not to survey contemporary attitudes toward race, nor even to list all those who offered opinions on the scientific aspects of the problem. There were many—one thinks of the pious scholar James Lawrence Cabell; the perpetually indignant New York editor John H. Van Evrie, Copperhead-to-be; the brutal Louisiana physician and publicist Samuel A. Cartwright, with his banana-skin humor—who appeared only on the periphery of the controversy to comment, cheer, or make impolite noises of disapproval. Because they did not influence the tide of battle, I have thought it best to leave them where they lie.

In writing a book of this kind one feels most keenly one's debt to the community of scholars who, at the lectern and in print, have endeavored to thrust back the gloom of ignorance. This debt I gratefully acknowledge. Of the many individuals who have personally assisted me, I wish to express appreciation to librarians in general and to these in particular: Mrs. Venia T. Phillips of the Academy of Natural Sciences of Philadelphia, and E. Milby Burton and Miss Emma B. Richardson of the Charleston Museum, who accorded me the most valuable privilege in the gift of the librarian—freedom of the stacks; Mrs. Gertrude Hess of the American Philosophical Society; Wayne Andrews and Wilmer R. Leech of the New-York Historical Society; Barney Chesnik and his staff of the Library Company of Philadelphia; the staffs of the College of Physicians of Philadelphia and the Manuscripts Division of the Library of Congress; and Frank Haber, then of the Peabody Library. I wish also to thank Edward Lurie and Hunter Dupree, who, working in adjacent fields of historical research, offered many helpful suggestions regarding manuscript letters. I am indebted to my former colleague, John A. Garraty, for reading the manuscript, and like many another student of history in this generation, to Oscar Handlin, whose interest in this work has been of a value known only to me.

To my former professors at Brown University I owe many debts of gratitude—particularly to Edmund S. Morgan, now at Yale, who gave warm encouragement when I first proposed investigating the mystery of what happened to the Jeffersonian concept of equality, and to Donald Fleming, now at Harvard. Professor Fleming has been an unfailing source of guidance and enthusiasm. His sharp eye for illogic and evasion has righted many an awkward sentence in these pages. Whatever excellencies are to be found here they inspired. The blunders are mine. Finally, this book could not have been written without the generosity of the donor of the President's Fellowship at Brown University, a grant which enabled me to devote a year entirely to research.

Contents

"An Universal Freckle"

On the evening of February 8, 1848, the distinguished members of the Academy of Natural Sciences of Philadelphia gathered in their new hall to hear their most eminent scientific member, the craniologist Dr. Samuel George Morton, report on his examination of a Hottentot boy then in the city "under the kind and paternal auspices" of the United States consul at the Cape of Good Hope. Morton confined his report to "a very few interesting points," with the intention only of guiding the members in their own examinations, for the consul had kindly agreed to bring his charge to a future meeting.

The boy was about eighteen years old, almost six feet tall, and slender, with a complexion resembling "that of a dried leaf." Morton thought he could discern "the osseous framework" of the famous upswept buttocks of the "Hottentot Venus" and hoped he might have an opportunity "to examine this structure more carefully, and report the facts to the Society." The head, in which Morton expressed particular interest, was "flattened on the coronal region, full behind, and rather broad between the parietal bones," displayed a very flat nose, and was crowned with hair "arranged in delicate tufts, of a straight and cylindrical form, each tuft being inserted separately into the scalp." Morton's friend Dr. Charles D. Meigs, the Philadelphia authority on women's diseases, secured a few hairs as a memento of the occasion and noted in passing that each had "the precise appearance of an ordinary steel watchspring."[1]

Dr. Morton's report is not without a touch of humor to modern eyes, but the dry, matter-of-fact minutes contain no hint of a smile, no echo of laughter. The assembled scientists heard his report with sober interest.

To account for this gathering, to explain the interest of such men in a visiting Hottentot is to uncover the violence of a curious and all but forgotten battle that once raged between science and the American Dream. It had its inception in the Declaration of Independence, a document which, though its author was at considerable pains to make it meaningful and lucid, was nevertheless to trail confusion in its wake through generations.

The heart of the Declaration was the "self-evident" truth "that all men are created equal." These words did not mean to Jefferson simply that men ought to enjoy equality of opportunity or equality before the law. They meant precisely that men had been *created* equal, that equality of rights derived from the biblical Creation. Jefferson's friend Dr. Benjamin Rush expressed the same idea when he wrote, "The history of the creation of man and of the relation of our species to each other by birth, which is recorded in the Old Testament, is the . . . strongest argument that can be used in favor of the original and natural equality of all mankind." To the great prophet of natural rights, John Locke, there had been "nothing more evident, than that creatures of the same species and rank, . . . born to all the same advantages of nature, and the use of the same faculties, should also be equal one amongst another without subordination or subjection." Locke knew that men were of the same species because they descended from the same creation. But Locke had never lived in proximity to Negroes or Indians. Americans did, and many wondered just how far the concept of equality extended. Though some stiff-necked New Yorkers or Charlestonians might cavil at the notion, most Americans probably admitted that all white men were created equal. But did the phrase in their Declaration mean that the Negro was the equal of the slaveholder or the Southern poor white? The slaves, not one of whom had ever written a book, worked with brush and palette, or, in fact, done anything requiring more mental application than suckering tobacco, hoeing corn, or perhaps in a burst of endeavor, shoeing a horse or waiting table—were these slaves the white man's equals? What of the Indian? The Indian who stalked the plains and forests of the West in search of food like the veriest beast, who was taciturn and vindictive and stubbornly shunned the blessings of civilization—was the Indian created the equal of the white? Each race possessed peculiar and distinctive physical characteristics—were Negro, Indian, and white descended from the same creation?[2]

These were portentous questions, for as Jefferson remarked in perhaps the most equivocal passage to be found in his writings, to conclude that the Negro was inferior would be to "degrade a whole race of men from the rank in the scale of beings which their Creator may perhaps have given them." The present state of knowledge offered scant evidence with which to solve the problem, for "to justify a general conclusion, requires many observations." Jefferson begged to be excused. Devoutly hoping that it would entitle the races of men to an equal place in the scale of being, he left to science final confirmation of his profound belief in the doctrine of equality, to which the Negro posed so disturbing a threat.[3]

Anthropology was in its infancy. Like so much else in natural history, its beginnings lay in the revolutionary work of the great Swede Linnaeus (1707–78). In his *Systema naturae* of 1735 Linnaeus classified all the races of men as one species of the animal kingdom. His concept of species as an unchanging category created by God was his outstanding contribution. For it marked the end of the old notion of spontaneous generation of higher organisms; it took the species problem away from those metaphysicians who denied that species had objective existence (only the individual was real); and it gave the naturalist a tool for observation and experiment. Though in the next century Darwin was to show that species do change, he could hardly have done so without using the objective categories established by Linnaeus. In the intervening period, naturalists working with the immutable species of Linnaeus sought unceasingly to explain the evidences of change in nature that confronted them on every hand. Those who studied man noted that certain biological types were peculiar to their own geographical areas and that each exhibited a peculiar culture. It was thus clear that men differed as to "race." The more elaborate the classification, the greater the emphasis placed on differences rather than affinities, and because classification, after the stimulus from Linnaeus, became a universal endeavor in the eighteenth century, soon the question was asked, "If the differences revealed by classification really exist in nature, then in what ways, if any, are men alike?"[4]

The Reverend Dr. Samuel Stanhope Smith, professor of moral philosophy at the College of New Jersey (Princeton) and later its president, attempted to answer the question for believers in equality and disciples of the Christian faith—indistinguishable groups in

Smith's mind. His *Essay on the Causes of the Variety of Complexion and Figure in the Human Species,* first published in Philadelphia in 1787 and republished in 1810 in a greatly expanded form, was the first ambitious American treatise on ethnology and long a standard work in the United States. It even attracted the attention of European savants—no mean accomplishment for an American book in the eighteenth century.[5]

The object of his book, Smith announced in the advertisement in 1810, was "to establish the unity of the human species." Too many of those who argued for the diversity of human species had spoken of "the spirit of piety" as "hostile to profound researches into nature." These "superficial smatterers in physical science" had insinuated that the "friends of piety" were ever ready to rest their opinions on revelation, rather than on "well ascertained facts," in order to avoid "the hazard of inquiries so dangerous to contented superstition." Smith hoped to refute the unphilosophical theory of "these self-dubbed naturalists." The theory of distinct human species offended not only the piety of Samuel Stanhope Smith: it offended the sense of order and economy in nature that pervaded eighteenth-century thought. If "the Great Contriver" had created man in separate species, then He had violated laws of His own making and wantonly thrown confusion into a simple and orderly universe. For example, Linnaeus and others before him had held that the laws of nature did not provide for the interbreeding of different species. Yet it was readily observable that the varieties of men did interbreed, that, consequently, their characteristics blended and became indistinguishable. "Were the species of man made capable of being blended together," Smith asked, "contrary to the nature of other animals . . . ?" Had the Master Craftsman rendered "the end unnecessary for which they were supposed to be created"? A disorderly universe implied slovenly craftsmanship.[6]

There were species criteria other than those dictated by one's sense of the fitness of things. The German anatomist, J. F. Blumenbach (1752–1840), had proposed ascertaining whether extremely different individuals were connected by intermediate varieties; if not, then those individuals must constitute distinct species. Applying Blumenbach's criterion to man, Smith concluded that men did not radically differ, that there were many gradations between the extremes. Yet the argument was not complete. To successfully defend the accepted theory of the unity of *homo sapiens,* Smith was compelled to explain away the many differences that defined the races. In doing so, he came upon a principle of nature that disposed of racial differences as superficialities and at the same time provided a criterion which bound all the races together as a single species distinct from all others of the animal kingdom.

The anthropological past as President Smith re-created it for Americans seemed an epic of which Mr. Jefferson's Declaration was the final act. Man was created in the form of a single pair somewhere in the "middle regions of Asia," where "all the earliest monuments of nations" are found. Because these monuments presented man in a civilized state, Smith concluded that "man, originally formed by a wise and beneficent Creator, was instructed by him in the duties, and the most necessary arts of life." In other words, man was created with not only an opposable thumb, erect posture, and intelligence, but also with a ready-made civilization. As population increased, groups wandered away from the original homeland into new environments. At this point in history changes began to occur, the effects of which some present-day "spurious" pretenders to science were ascribing to separate creations. To Smith's mind, however, it was "unphilosophical" to rely on assumption when investigation revealed that the phenomenon of race could be "accounted for by the ordinary laws of nature." Color was a prime example. Noting "a gradation in the complexion nearly in proportion to the latitude of the country," Smith concluded that color was the effect of climate. "Even the blackest Negro, when first born," did not exhibit his "true complexion" until he had been "some time exposed" to the atmosphere. Everyone knew that the sun caused freckles, and color might "be justly considered as an universal freckle." The universal freckle was deepened by "the putrid exhalations that copiously impregnate the atmosphere in warm and uncultivated regions," which acted to produce the secretion of "a redundancy of bile," which, in turn, darkened the skin. The "excessive heat of a vertical sun" produced an excess of perspiration, which, evaporating, left the skin dry and contracted and so imparted a tight curl to the hair of the Negro.[7]

As proof of this theory, Smith cited the celebrated case of Henry Moss, which presented the kind of evidence that in any age is the answer to a scientist's dream. The name of Henry Moss, Dr. Charles

Caldwell recalled many years afterward, was once "almost as familiar to the readers of newspapers and other periodicals" as that of "John Adams, Thomas Jefferson, or James Madison." Born a slave in Virginia, Moss had joined the Continental Army and fought through the Revolution. About 1792, spots began to appear on his body and within three years he had become almost entirely white.[8]

Able to recognize a good thing when he saw it, Moss went to Philadelphia in 1796, armed with letters of introduction, and advertised himself in the public prints:

A GREAT CURIOSITY

There is a black man at present at Mr. LEECH's Tavern, the sign of the BLACK HORSE, in Market-Street, who was born entirely black, and remained so for thirty-eight years, after which his natural colour began to rub off, which has continued till his body has become as white and as fair as any white person, except some small parts, which are changing very fast; his face attains more to the natural colour than any other part; his wool also is coming off his head, legs and arms, and in its place is growing straight hair, similar to that of a white person. The sight is really worthy of the attention of the curious, and opens a wide field of amusement for the philosophic genius.[9]

Despite the substantial admission price of "one Quarter of a Dollar each person" (children half price), which Moss used to purchase his freedom, the philosophic genius of Philadelphia nevertheless turned out at the sign of the Black Horse to view this phenomenon. Samuel Stanhope Smith, finding Moss to be in good health, announced that he was living proof of the unity of the human species. He noted that "wherever there were rents in the thin clothes which covered him there were generally seen the largest spots of black." This was a sure indication that sun was responsible for color. Moreover, Moss's hair was becoming "fine," "straight," and of a "silky softness." That he had not changed color earlier in life was probably due to a little-understood law which provided that "where any dark colour has been contracted by the human skin, the solar influence alone, and the free contact of the external air, will be sufficient to continue it a long time even in those climates which are most favorable to the fair complexion."[10]

Jefferson's friend and colleague in science, Dr. Benjamin Rush, also visited Henry Moss and afterward reported to a special meeting of the American Philosophical Society that "the Black Color (as it is called) of the Negroes is derived from the LEPROSY." The disease was congenital and appeared in so mild a form that excess of pigment was its only symptom. Moss, he noted, appeared to be undergoing a spontaneous cure.[11]

Having taken up the cudgels against the theory of separate creations, Smith was obliged to explain away other racial characters as the results of climate and custom. The catalogue of differences was so great that his efforts sometimes seemed like attacking a colony of ants with a hammer. Some "superficial observers," seeking to avoid this tedious business, had asserted that the races of men, like the lower species of animals, were confined by their physical constitutions to a limited range of climate; at the Creation the various "species" of man had been adapted by the Creator for the environments they were to inhabit. Smith did not deny that these observations, however superficial, were valid in regard to the lower animals, but they led him to a far different conclusion regarding man. Man was not "confined in his range" as the lower species were, for the "peculiar flexibility" of the human constitution enabled it to adapt itself "with wonderful facility" to "every degree of temperature from the extreme heats of the torrid, to the perpetual rigors of the frozen zone." One writer, attempting to show that the races of men were descended from originally different stocks, had cited the greater amount of fat carried by Arctic peoples to protect them from the cold. Smith had little patience with such poor reasoning. It was evident to him that the fact supported a contrary conclusion. In the "wise arrangements of divine providence," animals which are "destined to run wild in the forest" increase their coat of hair and "augment their fat" at the approach of winter. In southern latitudes "provision has been happily made" for cooling the body with "a more profuse perspiration." If so close a relationship existed between climate and constitution among the lower animals, how much greater must be the effect of climate upon man, whose geographical range was so much greater? The cause of this phenomenon, Smith concluded testily, ought to be "no secret to a philosopher who treats of human nature."[12]

Many other differences could be explained in the same manner. The Negro's skin was said to be thicker than the white's. This was due to the action of the sun, which made a man sweat and release

7

the "hydrogene" which had diluted the "bilious mucous," leaving that fluid "more glutinous," and thereby imparting "a greater density to this integument." The Negro was more capable of enduring heat because he could reduce the temperature of the body by perspiring more profusely. One observer had innocently thought "facility of parturition in black women" a specific character of the Negro, only to receive Smith's rebuke that this was certainly "a very inconsiderate suggestion coming from an author so well acquainted with the economy of the human body." Smith added for good measure that "this operation of nature is ever easier to the inhabitants of warm than of cold climates," and easier for active women of all varieties. If many women in both Ireland and Africa did indeed carry "long and leathern dugs," as so many travelers had said, this was merely the effect of long "suckling of children," age, "poverty, great hardships, and exhausting toils," not only on savages but on "poor women in the lowest classes of civilized society" as well.[13]

Just as climate and the state of society imparted physical attributes to various groups of men, so did it impart mental characters. The "apparent dullness of the Negro," for example, was ascribable to environment, which in Africa was savagery and despotism, and in America, slavery. Savagery itself was the result of too rapid a dispersion. Smith explained that some individuals had fallen away from the high state of civilization given to the species in the original homeland. Savage life arose from "idle, or restless spirits, who, shunning the fatigues of labor, or spurning the restraints and subordinations of civil society, sought, at once, liberty, and the pleasures of the chase, in wild, uncultivated regions remote from their original habitations." Here, "forgetting the arts of civilized life," they and their descendants "degenerated in a course of time, into all the ignorance and rudeness of savagism." The process could be reversed only with the "greatest difficulty." As proof of his theory, Smith called attention to those occasional restless and irresponsible citizens of the Republic who "voluntarily" renounced "all the conveniences of civilization to mingle with the savages in the wilderness" and remarked the failure of the Americans to introduce their arts among the Indians.[14]

Thus, Smith's most potent argument for his contention that man was of one species was that, in contradistinction to the other animals, man possessed adaptability. The human constitution, although "the most delicate of all animal systems," was also "the most pliant, and capable of accommodating itself to the greatest variety of situations." While the lower animals had little protection against the shattering impact of a new environment, "the arts of human ingenuity" were a "protection to man against the dangers which surround *him* in every region." The principle of adaptability explained the differences among the varieties of men, it accounted for the dispersal of men from one common center, and it offered in one peculiar attribute the criterion by which man could be distinguished from all other animals. This was an argument the anti-equalitarians had to refute.[15]

It was pure environmentalism. Contemporaries who believed inheritance to be a factor of importance were on the defensive. Thus Dr. Samuel Latham Mitchill (1764–1831) of New York, though he was a thoroughgoing believer in the unity of the human species, did not think that the physical differences between "tawny man," "white man," and "black man"—the three types of humankind he recognized as races—could be explained as the results solely of the action of climate. He admitted that it was "generally supposed, and by many able and ingenious men too," that the "combination of circumstances" called climate had "wrought all these changes in the human form." He himself, however, felt that there was "an internal physical cause of the greatest moment," which had "scarcely been mentioned." This was "the generative influence." "If by the act of modelling the constitution in the embryo and foetus," he reasoned, "a predisposition to gout, madness, scrofula and consumption, may be engendered, we may rationally conclude . . . that the procreative power may also shape the features, tinge the skin, and give other peculiarities." That Mitchill felt it necessary to state that a "generative influence" helped to mold the physical constitution speaks volumes for the American faith in environment.[16]

Smith himself had no clear notion of how the effects of environment became hereditary. When unthinking critics asked why, if men were all of one species, the natives of a single region were not identical, Smith replied, "It is for the same reason, whatever that may be, that other resemblances of parents are communicated to children." At one point he almost came to grips with the subject of inheritance and its function, but went skittering evasively away. "Experience demonstrates," he wrote, "that figure, stature, complexion, features, diseases, and even powers of the mind may become hereditary. To those who find no difficulty in acknowledging that these properties may be communicated to offspring according to the established laws of nature, the transmission of the climatical or national differences among men . . . can contain nothing which ought to appear supernatural, or incredible."[17]

Smith's evasion of this issue did not lessen the popularity of his book, for Americans were not alone when they took their stand on the unity of the human species. Indeed, they could summon to their aid all the great names in anthropology and allied sciences: Linnaeus, Buffon, John Hunter, Blumenbach, Zimmermann, Kant, Cuvier, Lamarck, and even the German professor of medicine, S. T. von Sömmerring, who found by his dissections that the Negro was anatomically much closer to the ape than was the white. Moreover, America, with its Indians, its Negro slaves, and its varied population of whites, tended to make every citizen, if not an ethnologist, at least a speculator on matters of race.

Thus there was almost no end to the number of books and theories purporting to show how the Indian arrived in America from the site of the Creation. Dr. James Haines M'Culloh of Baltimore in his early youth became interested in "the manner by which America had been supplied with men and animals," and wrote a paper on the subject which interested no less a figure than Dr. Benjamin Rush. In his charming—and highly imaginative—*Researches on America,* which appeared in 1816, M'Culloh put forth the theory that the world was once widely populated by civilized men but that since that time, "our earth has suffered under some great convulsion, that has destroyed the communications that once existed between the new and old continents." He thought it unnecessary even to consider "the opinion, which supposes two or more different creations of men," for, he noted, "the best naturalists have agreed in the identity of the human race," and their observations, "concurring with the Pentateuch, should be considered conclusive." In 1822 Richard Harlan of Philadelphia, one of the founders of vertebrate paleontology in America, told the Academy of Natural Sciences that it was now "satisfactorily proved by modern zoologists, that all the diversities of mankind are but *varieties of one original stock.*"[18]

The presence of the curious earthworks in the Mississippi Valley caused much speculation. M'Culloh thought the builders of the mounds were "ancient white aborigines of America." The widely respected Dr. Samuel Latham Mitchill, having examined bits of cloth and artifacts found with mummified bodies, concluded that "colonies of Astralasians, or Malays" settled in the middle of the continent and erected "fortifications, mounds, and other structures." They were finally overcome by Tartars who crossed from northeast Asia, Mitchill explained, and it was from the latter that the Indians descended. Caleb Atwater, in the first volume (1832) of the *Transactions* of the American Antiquarian Society, agreed that the Indians were Tartars but thought that the Mound Builders, a highly civilized people, were Jews. The erratic but eminent naturalist Constantine Rafinesque concluded (1824) that America had been peopled by a group of Noah's descendants, who from their powerful empire in North Africa followed the trade winds to the West Indies and thence discovered the continent of North America. In his *American Antiquities* (1837), a conglomeration of credulities, superstitions, and miscellaneous traditions, Josiah Priest insisted that America had been peopled immediately after the Flood by the sons of Shem, who were later joined successively by Romans, Egyptians, Norwegians, Welshmen, Greeks, and various other travel-worn national groups. John Delafield believed (1839) that the mounds had been built by civilized tribes related to the Egyptians, who, driven northward by the savage tribes, developed the civilizations of Mexico and Peru. Alexander Bradford stated it as his opinion (1843) that the Mound Builders were a separate and more civilized race than the Indians.[19]

Smith, who followed and often cited Blumenbach, founder of the five-race theory of anthropology, did not attempt to delineate the races of men. Blumenbach, Leibniz, Linnaeus, and Buffon had done this, and although Smith listed their classifications, he accepted none. On the contrary, he remarked that "the conclusion to be drawn from all this variety of opinions" was that it was "impossible to draw the line" between the races of men, "or even to enumerate them with certainty." It was a "useless labor to attempt it."[20]

The eighteenth-century concept of equality was a scientific concept; it rested upon biology, the descent of all men from the Creation; it rested upon morphology, the similarity of men's bodies; and it emphasized the importance of environment in shaping men's biological and mental structure. Its political implications extended far beyond the immediate object of separation from the British Empire. It is therefore not surprising that, drawing political conclusions from the fact that the sun had turned the Negro black, Smith, Rush, and Jefferson himself attacked slavery.

Smith's assault was based on his own observation of the workings of Nature's laws. "The form and expression of the countenance . . . being principally affected by the state of society, are constantly receiving some modification from that cause, to improve the negro visage." The "countenance of the domestic slaves" of the third and fourth generations, and not infrequently the second, afforded "a striking example of the influence of the state of society upon the features." In New Jersey, where the "hardships of slavery" were "scarcely felt," Smith had seen many Negroes who had "the nose as much raised from the face, the forehead as well arched, and the teeth as perpendicularly set in their sockets, as the whites." Every day in the vicinity of Princeton he saw Negroes who had noses "turned with a handsome aquiline curve." There was thus reason to believe that if all "these people were perfectly free" and "admitted to all the civil privileges of their masters," they would soon "have few of the distinctive traces of their African ancestors remaining."[21]

Jefferson had favored the abolition of slavery, but he had hedged on the equality of the Negro. His indecision brought a sharp retort from Smith, who complained that Jefferson's "remarks upon the genius of the African negro," had "little foundation in true philosophy." Jefferson had noted, rather sadly, that though many of the slaves had been so placed that they might have enjoyed the society of their masters, they had failed to profit by the association. This was no argument, Smith replied. "What society, alas, can subsist between a master, and a slave?" And he concluded that among the many causes which might "prevent the faculties of the human mind from arriving at full maturity" or "totally restrain" the "powers of genius," slavery was "the principal."[22]

Dr. Benjamin Rush, having determined that the Negro's color was a symptom of endemic leprosy, drew three conclusions. First, whites should cease "to tyrannise over them," for their disease "should entitle them to a double portion of our humanity." However, by the same token, whites should not intermarry with them, for this would "tend to infect posterity" with the "disorder." (Rush was quick to assert that this was not to question "the sameness of descent, or natural equality of mankind.") Finally, attempts must be made to cure the disease. "Nature has lately unfurled a banner upon this subject," Rush announced. "She has begun spontaneous cures of this disease in several black people in this country"—in Henry Moss, for example. Effective treatment would "produce a large portion of happiness in the world," by destroying "one of the arguments in favor of enslaving the negroes, for their color has been supposed by the ignorant to mark them as objects of divine judgements, and by the learned to qualify them for labor in hot, and unwholesome climates." A cure would also add to the happiness of the Negro himself, for "however well they appear to be satisfied with their color, there are many proofs of their preferring that of the white people." And finally, Rush wrote, "We shall render the belief of the whole human race being descended from one pair, easy, and universal, and thereby not only add weight to the Christian revelation, but remove an obstacle to the exercise of the universal benevolence which is inculcated by it." Thus Dr. Rush prescribed pressure from "cloathing," which tended to absorb "the coloring matter," friction, depletion through "bleeding, purging, or abstinence," fear, "Oxygenated muriatic acid," and "the juice of unripe peaches" as well-tested remedies for the Negro's color. Constantine Rafinesque shared Rush's sentiments in regard to the unity of the human species and also denounced the "unholy and dangerous bonds" of slavery.[23]

As early as the publication of Smith's original essay, one could hear the firing of distant guns. It is hardly surprising that early in the 1770's slaves in the New England states should have begun to sue in courts of law for their freedom. One, with the assistance of lawyers, successfully brought suit against his master in Plymouth County in 1770.

Other opponents of slavery began to use the argument of equality and natural rights. The town of Worcester instructed its representative in 1765 to use his influence "to obtain a law to put an end to that unchristian and impolitic practice of making slaves of the human species." Leicester instructed its delegate to act for the prohibition of the slave trade, for "as we have the highest regard for (so as even to revere the name of) liberty, we cannot behold but with the greatest abhorrence any of our fellow creatures in a state of slavery." In 1776 the Massachusetts House of Representatives passed a resolution "to prevent the sale of two negro men lately brought into this

State, as prisoners taken on the high seas, and advertised to be sold at Salem" at "public auction." The House thereupon resolved that "the selling and enslaving the human species" was a "direct violation of the natural rights alike vested in all men by their Creator."[24]

As the House resolved, so most naturalists in these years also resolved, and the few who disagreed with Smith were inclined to voice their dissent privately.

"Either a Philosopher
or an Infidel"

Attacks on Samuel Stanhope Smith's theory were slow in coming, for the Jeffersonians had a near monopoly on equalitarianism and, because their science agreed with the scriptural account of the Creation, on piety as well. Thus Smith's reviewers and commentators for many years were timid, shy of aligning themselves with slavery and subjection, wary of contradicting revelation.[1]

Smith's defense of the unity of man was inspired in large measure by the views of the Scottish judge and dabbler in metaphysics, Lord Kames (1696–1782), whose *Sketches of the History of Man* (1774) went through so many editions that Smith became alarmed. Less reluctant than most men to take up an unpopular position, Kames denied the unity of the human race. He found the differences between the races of men so great as to override Buffon's opinion that all the races were of one species because when crossed they produced fertile offspring. The races must have sprung from different stocks, for climate could hardly account for the "copper colour and smooth chin" of the Indians,[2] "the black nipple" among "female Samoides," the short stature of the Eskimo, the "ugly visage" of the Laplanders, the black color, "thick lips, flat nose, crisped wooly hair, and rank smell" of the Negroes, and certainly not for such moral characters as the "cowardice" of the American Indians and the courage of the inhabitants of the Celebes. These considerations pressed Kames dangerously near the point of infidelity, almost leading him to conclude "that God created many pairs of the human race, differing from each other both externally and internally; that he fitted these pairs for different climates, and placed each pair in its proper climate; that the peculiarities of the original pairs were preserved entire in their descendants." Fortunately, however, he got command of himself at this point, remembering that "this opinion, however plausible, we are not permitted to adopt; being taught a different lesson by revelation, viz. That God created but a single pair of the human species." To reconcile Scripture with science, Kames was forced to conclude that racial distinctions must have been implanted by God at a later period, namely, at the time the Tower of Babel was erected, when God impressed upon men "an immediate change of constitution" in order to prepare them for their dispersion and the regions in which they were thenceforth to live.[3]

The prominent English surgeon, Charles White (1728–1813) of Manchester, agreed with Kames that mankind constituted more than one species. White had observed Professor John Hunter's (1728–93) cabinet of skulls and had seen Hunter place a number of his specimens "upon a table in a regular series, first showing the human skull, with its varieties, in the European, the Asiatic, the American, the African; then proceeding to the skull of a monkey, and so on to that of a dog; in order to demonstrate the gradation." Contemplating this arrangement, White was suddenly struck with the idea that "Nature would not employ gradation in one instance only, but would adopt it as a general principle." Investigation confirmed that gradations among the races of men were not confined to the skull, for he found gradation also in many other parts of the anatomy ("That the PENIS of an African is larger than that of an European, has I believe, been shown in every anatomical school in London"). White concluded in his *Account of the Regular Gradation in Man* (1799) that the human race was graded just as was all nature, and that "the various species of men were originally created and separated, by marks sufficiently discriminative." It was these distinctions which determined that man was made up of different species. The fact that all the races interbred meant nothing, for by the species criterion of interfertility, "not only the various kinds of dogs, but even foxes, wolves, and Jackalls, must be considered as of one species." Carried to its logical conclusion, the notion that climate produced the distinctions between groups of men and animals would lead one to derive the entire animal kingdom from one pair. A more "degrading notion" than this, he added in disgust, "certainly cannot be entertained."[4]

White was not certain just how many species of men there were, remarking only that "the Negro, the American, some of the Asiatic tribes, and the European, seem evidently to be different species." But whatever the number of human species, the "white European" was the first link in that "immense chain of beings, endued with various degrees of intelligence and active powers, suited to their stations in the general system," which extended from "man down to the smallest reptile, whose existence can be discovered only by the microscope."[5]

Contemplation of this superb first link led White into one of the earliest, and surely the most amiable, of the innumerable paeans to the "white European," the Caucasian, the Aryan, the Teuton, that these groups, lost in admiring wonder at their own magnificent gifts, have crooned to themselves over the last two centuries. None would doubt the white European's intellectual magnificence—surely superior to that of "every other man," he intoned. Where else shall we find, he asked,

that nobly arched head, containing such a quantity of brain ... ? Where that variety of features, and fulness of expression; those long, flowing, graceful ring-lets; that majestic beard, those rosy cheeks and coral lips? Where that ... noble gait? In what other quarter of the globe shall we find the blush that overspreads the soft features of the beautiful women of Europe, that emblem of modesty, of delicate feelings ... ? Where, except on the bosom of the European woman, two such plump and snowy white hemispheres, tipt with vermillion?

Dr. Smith and his colleagues held the white European in no less esteem than did Dr. White, but in their esteem, vermillion or no vermillion, there was room for the entire human species.[6]

White conceived of his investigations and conclusions as having only scientific (and evidently aesthetic) importance and denied that either religious or political conclusions could be drawn from them. As for revelation and Scripture, "Revelation was given to man for a different purpose than to instruct him in philosophy and natural history." Like "most rational Christians," he believed the Mosaic account of the creation to be "allegorical." As for the objection that his book was untimely in view of the fact that humanitarians were in the midst of their fight to abolish the slave traffic, White obliged them with a condemnation of that trade in human misery and asserted that "the negroes are, at least, equal to thousands of Europeans, in capacity and responsibility; and ought, therefore, to be equally entitled to freedom and protection. Laws ought not to allow greater freedom to a *Shakespear* or a *Milton*, a *Locke*, or a *Newton*, than to men of inferior capacities; nor shew more respect to a General Johnstone, or a Duchess of Argyle, than the most unshapely and ill formed."[7]

With the weight of scientific and scriptural authority, and political sentiment as well, on the side of the equalitarians, few Americans raised their voices in dissent. Samuel Stanhope Smith's first American critic, and the only American to attack directly the first edition of his *Essay*, was Dr. John Augustine Smith, lecturer in anatomy and surgery in the College of Physicians and Surgeons of the University of New York. Born in Virginia in 1782, he graduated from William and Mary in 1800, studied medicine in England, and then became successively president of William and Mary and president of the College of Physicians and Surgeons in New York. In 1808, having just returned from his tour of study in Europe and already a fellow of the Royal College of Surgeons, young Dr. Smith delivered an introductory lecture to his class in anatomy.[8]

He told them frankly that his purpose was "to prove that the anatomical structure of the European, whatever . . . the cause," was "superior" to that of the other races of men, or, at least "farther removed from the brute creation." He rested his proof on the differences between the European and the African, because these races, occupying "opposite extremes of the scale," presented differences "more numerous, and more strongly marked." In noting the anatomical differences he admitted that qualitative interpretations were relative, a position unusual among early nineteenth-century ethnologists. Although he found the features of the European "more elegant," he did not deny that "the African may not be of the same opinion."[9]

Not wishing to quarrel with Scripture, he confessed that unity of human descent was "indeed clear from Revelation, the best of all authority." His objection was that too many writers had attempted to support this best of all authority by assuming that racial distinctions were the result of environment. Revelation should not be made to depend on so inconclusive a proposition as this. "But what satisfies me," he wrote, "that the colour does not depend upon climate and mode of life solely, is, that we find persons of such different complexions in the same latitude, and under nearly the same circumstances, and such similitude of appearance in the inhabitants of such extensive countries."

Seeking to prove that all men were descended from the same stock, these scriptural commentators among the naturalists asserted another untenable argument: races of men interbred; groups descended from separate stocks did not. This, Smith objected, was no valid test of the unity of descent, for there were too many exceptions to the rule. The crossing of foxes and dogs, wolves and dogs, wolves and foxes, produced fertile offspring, whereas the crossing of the common and muscovy ducks, for example (which resembled one another more closely than did the dogs, wolves, and foxes) produced infertile offspring. Consequently, "this pretended rule" had no relevance "to the human race." So much for the argument of Samuel Stanhope Smith: "The execution does less credit to his head, than the intention to his heart."

What then were the causes of the differences between the races of men? Smith confessed his ignorance. He believed them to be "secondary" (i.e., operating only after the Creation) and, "perhaps, like the causes which have produced small-pox and syphilis, they may have ceased to operate." "But on this subject," he told the class, "I hold it my duty to lay before you all the facts which are relevant, all the opinions which are plausible, leaving you then to judge for yourselves. . . . Far be it from me to fix the bounds of your faith."

Another different mind from Samuel Stanhope Smith, and one not so tenderly concerned with the faith of young men, was Dr. Charles Caldwell (1772–1853). Old President Smith had done his best, and what his effort lacked in scientific fact was more than compensated for in dogmatic assertion. But in this latter quality, as well as in talent for sustained invective, Smith was no match for the lordly Caldwell, who attacked his theory first in two magazines, then in a book. Caldwell, a native of North Carolina, studied medicine under Dr. Benjamin Rush and received his medical degree from the University of Pennsylvania. At the time of his attack on Smith, Caldwell was practicing medicine in Philadelphia and was professor of natural history at the university. He was a close friend of Thomas Cooper and acquainted with Joseph Priestley and Jefferson. He was later, by his own modest admission, to be "the first introducer of true medical science into the Mississippi Valley," by establishing the medical department at Transylvania University in Lexington, Kentucky. Proving too strong a dose of magnificence for the medical faculty, he moved on to Louisville to establish the medical school at the university there.[10]

Dignified, pompous, and vain, Caldwell throughout life was out of step with the medical profession. His mind was like a steel trap which, under the weight of an overweening ego, slammed shut in early youth, never to open again except to fads. His vanity "jutted out upon all occasions, in season and out of season—in his manners, in his walk, in his conversation, in his writings." Addressing a large audience at Lexington on the subject of phrenology, he told his hearers, "There are only three great heads in the United States: one is that of Daniel Webster; another that of Henry Clay; and the last . . . modesty prevents me from mentioning."[11]

Caldwell opened his assault on Smith anonymously in the pages of the *American Review*. Several theories, he wrote, had been propounded in the attempt to account for color, for "it is rare that the mind puts the finishing touches to absurdity at once." He admitted that environmental influences worked an effect on the human frame. "The scorching sun" of tropical climates would "efface, in time, the fair tints of the European skin," and some races which closely resembled one another might become identical under the influence of a common climate. The Spaniard and the Italian, for example, having emigrated to northern latitudes, would eventually "exchange their olive for the carnation of the north." But these influences produced only limited effects. Neither climate nor state of society could ever change the African into a European. The examples of racial transformation cited by Samuel Stanhope Smith—Hungarians into Laplanders, Portuguese into Hottentots, and the like—were due not to the influence of climate and the state of society but to intermarriage. Climate could not "erase the true and distinctive characters of the race." The American Indians, though they ranged from pole to pole, displayed "a striking uniformity" in color, and, on the other hand, the Moors, the Negroes, and the Caffres, though all lived in the tropics, displayed three shades of complexion.[12]

Caldwell was not content with having destroyed Smith's arguments. It was necessary also to point out their deleterious influences on both science and true religion. Smith's book struck him as "unbecomingly authoritative and dogmatical," lacking in "that liberal sentiment and tolerant spirit without which, argument is apt to degenerate into invective, and discussion to be converted into angry vituperation." Caldwell was disturbed by the "harshness of language" and the "unseemly asperity" of the book and indignant at Smith's practice of denouncing "as an infidel at heart, and hostile to the interest of our holy religion," everyone who disagreed with him. This practice was damaging to science, for it had "a direct and powerful tendency to check investigation and defeat argument, by blackening his adversary's character, consigning his case to general detestation, and thus depriving him of an impartial hearing."[13]

Indeed, Caldwell himself was to feel the brunt of bigotry. Whatever the reason, the second portion of Caldwell's criticism did not appear in the pages of the *American Review* but in the *Port-Folio,* a Philadelphia magazine of which he had recently become editor. It began with the pained announcement that he had been misunderstood. Despite his statement that the discussion was "not intended to have the slightest reference to the original identity of the human race," a doctrine which he did "not presume to question, much less to deny," nevertheless he still heard "slight and half-suppressed, yet audible murmurings." Caldwell could not abide a murmurer. With a sigh of outraged patience he reiterated his avowal that he had only the greatest respect for the Mosaic account of the creation of man. The distinguishing characteristics of the races were not the result of climate, and he knew of no cause short of an act of the Deity capable of effecting those distinctions, and that His interposition was immediate and miraculous was a doctrine which was "neither contrary to philosophy, nor inimical to religion." Indeed, it was Smith's argument, not his own humble questionings, which subverted Scripture. Caldwell charged that the doctrine which ascribed the varieties of men to environmental influences was "much more strongly marked by the pride of science than by the humility of religion." It was "a bold attempt to explain what, to our limited capacities, is wholly inexplicable." It was probably "dangerous" to "belief in revelation," for Smith was plainly asserting, "You must either adopt the belief, that all the varieties of complexion and figure which now prevail among the human race, are derived from the influence of climate, the state of society, and the manner of living, or you must admit that a plurality of races was originally created, and that more than Noah and his family escaped the deluge. There is no alternative; you must be either a philosopher or an infidel."[14]

Caldwell, however, refused to be intimidated. He was "neither the one nor the other." Rather he was "the simple unassuming christian." Smith, indeed, had attempted to attribute racial distinctions to mere natural causes, whereas, Caldwell assured his readers, "we honestly state the differences of physical man as we find them, acknowledging their production to the power of God. To that power we set no limits." It was with the intention to present this belief in the power of God, "and not from any abstract love of controversy," that Caldwell "ventured" to criticize Smith's *Essay*.

It is difficult, in view of Caldwell's turbulent career and his surpassing talent for vituperation, to accept these pious utterances at face value. The "simple unassuming christian" was manifestly attempting to steal the sword of righteousness from the hand of President Smith. But whatever the measure of his modesty, Caldwell's criticisms had some validity. Smith *was* dogmatic and he did attempt to stigmatize as infidels those who denied the power of climate and state of society to effect racial distinctions. Such bigotry produced an intellectual climate which had a corrosive effect on individual scientists, making them either reluctant to voice their conclusions or so eager to martyr themselves in the name of science that their conclusions tended to soar out of sight of the facts. Caldwell was himself affected and, like Kames before him and many another to come, was forced to compromise between denial of environmental influences and the scriptural account, between the concept that man was descended from many Adams and the orthodox doctrine that he was descended from one. For years to come scientists were forced to find their repose between the horns of this dilemma. However, Caldwell's pious professions offered no better alternative, for in affirming his adherence to Scripture and true religion and in his denunciation of Smith's attempt to explain the manner in which secondary causes operated to produce variations in the human race, Caldwell was closing off large areas to scientific endeavor. He failed to recognize that to restrict the ethnologist to the observation of physical man only, to insist that he not be concerned with the manner in which phenomena occur, with processes or developments, is to prevent the formulation of scientific laws which, in turn, serve to stimulate discovery.

Samuel Stanhope Smith was unable to appreciate the virtues of Caldwell's criticism. According to his family, the shock of criticism was too much for his hitherto robust health. Injured in his fundamentals, President Smith suffered a lingering attack of paralysis and died in 1819.[15]

Though these criticisms had gone hard with President Smith, Jefferson remained unshaken in his confident faith that science, by proving men equal, would banish subjection from the world. Regretfully declining an invitation from the citizens of Washington to join the other Signers in attendance at their celebration of the fiftieth anniversary of the Declaration of Independence, Jefferson wrote what was to be his final will and testament to his countrymen. Surveying the contemporary scene, he found everywhere evidences of the beneficent effects of the Declaration. "All eyes are opened or opening to the rights of man," he noted serenely. "The general spread of the light of science has already laid open to every view the palpable truth, that the mass of mankind has not been born with saddles on their backs, nor a favored few, booted and spurred, ready to ride them legitimately, by the grace of God. These are grounds of hope for others; for ourselves, let the annual return of this day forever refresh our recollections of these rights, and an undiminished devotion to them."[16]

But the light of science was shortly to develop a new intensity, and in pushing back the shadows it was to lay open to view shapes that Jefferson would have been hard put to recognize as truths.

"White Pepper Seed"

In the early years of the nineteenth century the study of man was coming to acquire the earmarks of a science in the modern sense. Its zoological foundation was acquiring form and mass. The basis of modern classification had been established by Linnaeus' binomial nomenclature, with which a specimen could be classified promptly by genus and species. From time to time earnest attempts were made to break away from the Linnean conceit of immutable species. But these were firmly put down, and the prophets paid for their folly. Lamarck's reputation was destroyed. William Lawrence (1783–1867) spoke out once (1817), then when shown the error of his ways shrewdly lapsed into silence and a brilliant career in surgery. Scientists laughed and theologians raged at the anonymous author of the *Vestiges of Creation* (1844), Robert Chambers.

Baron Cuvier (1769–1832), foremost zoologist of the age, brought his knowledge and prestige to bear against all theories of organic transformation. He defeated Geoffroy St. Hilaire in debate before the French Academy and ridiculed Lamarck before the world. Cuvier did not deny change in the organic world. Indeed he saw it all around him in the geological strata of the Paris Basin and brought it to the attention of the scientific community—an important contribution. But to a mind steeped in teleology, such change was the result neither of the chance appearance of hereditary deviation, nor of hereditary characters acquired by volition of the organism. Rather, it represented the exercise of the Creator's will through geological catastrophe and repopulation. In time, Cuvier's catastrophism gained intellectual ascendancy, and zoological thought hardened into a brittle and doctrinaire structure. It was generally conceded that Cuvier's great debate with St. Hilaire (1799–1853) had lowered the final curtain on the interesting and novel concept of evolution. The innovators had been given a fair hearing, their notions had been disproved, and it was best now to forgive and forget: there were still many species to be discovered and classified. Caught up in this conservative climate of opinion, those scientists to whom classification was not an end in itself were forced to reconcile as best they could the evidence of zoology with the immutable species of Linnaeus.

In anthropology the techniques of classification proceeded apace as calipers replaced aesthetics. The Dutch anatomist Pieter Camper (1722–89), who approached anthropology through painting, had contributed the "facial angle," the interior angle which the face makes with the horizontal. The Belgian astronomer Quetelet (1796–1874) subjected man to quantitative analysis by introducing the statistical method and the "average man," and by 1842 the Swedish anthropologist Anders Retzius (1796–1860) had perfected a measuring technique which provided the cephalic index, the ratio of the length to the width of the head. Retzius also provided the criteria of prognathism and orthognathism, based on the configuration of the skull produced respectively by projecting and non-projecting jaws. To head shape he applied his own terms "dolichocephalic" (long-headed) and "brachycephalic" (broad-headed). He thus had four possible divisions of all mankind. Man was being fitted into a system of immutable law.[1]

In the midst of the confused speculation about the origin of the races there appeared in 1839 a book that was hailed as a solution to the whole problem, Dr. Samuel George Morton's *Crania Americana*. A gentle, courteous Philadelphia physician and professor of anatomy, Morton possessed an astonishing ability to inspire loyalty among his associates. Completely dedicated to his scientific interests, he could have had little conception of the storm of charges and countercharges that was to rage about him from the publication of this volume until his death.

A lifelong resident of Philadelphia, Morton was born there in 1799. His father, an Irish immigrant, died when the boy was six months old, and his mother then married Thomas Rogers, a Quaker who had a lively interest in mineralogy. In his youth Morton became aquainted with the anatomist and naturalist Richard Harlan (1796–1843), who further stimulated his interest in natural science. Educated in various Quaker schools, Morton was only seventeen when his mother died. He then entered the office of a prominent local physician, Dr. Joseph Parrish, and attended lectures at the University of Pennsylvania Medical School, receiving his degree in 1820. In the same year he began his lifelong membership in the Academy of Natural Sciences of Philadelphia. In 1823, with financial assistance from a wealthy uncle in Ireland who was inclined to disparage American degrees, he received a second degree in medicine at Edinburgh and attended Robert Jameson's lectures on geology. After the conventional tour of the Continent, he returned to Philadelphia in 1824 to begin practice.[2]

Morton's scientific reputation came with the publication of his *Synopsis of the Organic Remains of the Cretaceous Group of the United States* (Philadelphia, 1834), in which he described the fossils collected by Lewis and Clark. He thus became the founder of invertebrate paleontology in America. Benjamin Silliman of Yale, editor of the *American Journal of Science,* thought so highly of Morton's ability as a geologist that he asked Morton to keep him "informed of the progress of this branch of knowledge of which," he added, "I . . . regard you as the particular guardian & supervisor." This work brought him into contact with the English geologist Gideon Mantell (who named a new species of fish after Morton) as well as the Americans Edward Hitchcock and Amos Eaton, who were not above seeking his advice on geological matters. Like most scientists of the period, Morton never concentrated his energies in any one field of investigation. Plagued by ill health all his life, probably the result of a liver ailment, he nevertheless was able to take time from his large practice and from his duties as professor of anatomy at Pennsylvania Medical College to publish books and articles in various scientific journals on anatomy, medicine, and vertebrate paleontology, as well as geology and craniology. The diversity of his interests seemed only to increase his energies; certainly it enhanced his reputation. Thus he became well known as an anatomist. When Dr. Robert S. Holmes of St. Louis learned that "the famed San Martin, (Dr. Beaumonts case) with the hole in his stomach" was to honor the medical profession of his city with a visit, he asked Morton to suggest whatever experiments he might think proper. And when Dr. Washington L. Atlee, the distinguished gynecologist and expert in ovariotomies, found a young man "possessing the extraordinary faculty of producing music of the softest and sweetest kind within the larynx without any aid from the organs of the mouth," he asked Dr. Morton to examine him and "show him to your scientific friends."[3]

In 1831 Morton was elected corresponding secretary of the Academy of Natural Sciences, a position which, through the scientific reputation that the Academy was acquiring in these years, brought him into correspondence with the leading scientists of many nations. His custom of holding "weekly soirées" to which he invited friends and "strangers distinguished in the various departments of learning and philosophy," increased his already wide acquaintance. A lucrative practice, together with an inheritance received upon the death of his uncle in Ireland, enabled him to live with some ease and to finance publication of his books. Tall, cadaverous, and "of a large frame, though somewhat stooping," with "bluish grey eyes, light hair, and a very fair complexion," of an urbane, though somewhat retiring nature, Morton was an altogether improbable person to foment revolution in American science, to provide the boots and saddles and spurs with which to ride the mass of mankind.[4]

About 1820 he became interested in crania. He later explained that his interest was aroused when, in preparing a lecture for his class in anatomy, he could find no information on the subject. A friend recalled that "among the earliest recollections of my visits to his office is that of the skulls he had collected." By 1832 he was asking Edmund Ravenel of Charleston for an alligator skull, and the physician-naturalist Zina Pitcher was sending Osage crania from Arkansas. No thanks were due him, Pitcher added; it was "sufficient compensation" to know that he had ministered to "the gratification of a gentleman whose published essays have impressed me no less favorably with regard to his zeal, than his powers of discrimination, when applied to some of the most difficult departments of Natural Science." Opening a correspondence the following year with Dr. Samuel P. Hildreth, the Ohio physician, meteorologist, paleontologist, and historian, Morton remarked that his collection now numbered nearly one hundred and "of many 'kindreds, tongues & peoples.'" It had, he wrote, cost him "great pains and expense to add to this series, and now, after years of fruitless toil," he had "got matters in a fair train," and friends "in all quarters of the world" were contributing to the collection. He hoped someday to write a "monograph on this (to me at least) interesting subject," and offered to exchange with Hildreth anatomical preparations (making these was a hobby with Morton) for Indian crania. His wide scientific correspondence, especially with army surgeons stationed at remote frontier outposts, brought him crania from every state, territory, and nation—from Pitcher in Arkansas, from Judge Benjamin Tappan in Ohio, from Douglass Houghton, the Michigan geologist, from Joseph Sullivant, Ohio naturalist. Henry Piddington, the English meteorologist, sent Hindu skulls from India in exchange for samples of American cotton and tobacco. Alexander Nasmyth, the English painter, exchanged crania. William S. W. Ruschenberger, naval officer and member of the Academy sent skulls from Peru. The American consuls at Constantinople and Cairo forwarded their contributions, and the explorers Isaac G. Strain and T. J. Page added their discoveries to Morton's collection.[5]

These, to name but a few, recognized Morton's pre-eminence in the study of crania and were proud to contribute to his famous cabinet. In this manner Morton was able to gather at the Academy of Natural Sciences the largest collection of crania in the world—"the American Golgotha," it was called in scientific circles. That army surgeons stationed at remote western outposts and explorers of the world's deserts took the trouble, often at great hazard to themselves (for some tribes had strong taboos against the desecration of the dead), spoke eloquently of the wide reputation that Morton's collection had acquired.[6]

In collecting crania, Morton was entirely dependent upon others, for he never went into the field himself, probably never in his life traveling west of Pennsylvania. Thus he had to rely upon correspondents for the circumstances of the discovery of a particular skull, its situation in the earth, the geological conformation of the site, and their opinion as to the tribe to which it belonged. This practice, inexcusably lax in a modern anthropologist, was not considered untoward in the early part of the nineteenth century. At any rate, Morton's experience in craniometry enabled him to name, without knowing the circumstances of its discovery, the tribe to which any given cranium belonged. The information he sought was simply of a corroboratory nature. He was attempting, like any scientist worth his salt, to collect as much information as possible before drawing conclusions. In the event that his findings did not agree with the opinion of the man in the field, Morton faithfully stated both views.[7]

Skulls were not an unusual collector's item in this period. Aside from the compulsion of the true collector to collect anything, the romantic interest they stimulated, and their use in medical schools, the rage for phrenology in the first half of the nineteenth century led many people to collect crania, for by "reading" their contours the accomplished phrenologist could explain the rise and fall of nations. It was his absorbing interest in phrenology which motivated the eccentric Joseph Rodes Buchanan of Cincinnati to build a collection which probably rivaled Morton's in size. The only other collection in America which was used for serious craniological research was the much smaller one belonging to Dr. John Collins Warren of Boston, who occasionally exchanged specimens with Morton.

In beginning his collection Morton was not interested in the phrenological study of crania—as has been alleged—although he did have a certain romantic interest in the persons upon whose shoulders these skulls once rested. Thus, Number 14 in his *Catalogue of Skulls of Men and the Inferior Animals* (Philadelphia, 1840) is listed merely as "Anglo American Female. Died insane, 1830." But on a sheet of interleaving opposite, Morton wrote in his own copy of the work,

14. Skull of the celebrated Mrs. Fortesque, who was in succession seduced, thrown upon the town & abandoned. She became melancholy, entered the Alms house & died insane in one of the cells of that institution, in the 30th year of her age. She was of respectable family & had been remarkably beautiful.

Whatever his original reasons for collecting skulls, Morton's study convinced him—as Tiedemann and Blumenbach before him had been convinced—that the different races displayed different head shapes. Cranial capacity and conformation, like color, was a distinctive racial character. When his collection numbered upwards of a hundred he began to plan a craniological work on the American Indians, modeled more or less on Blumenbach's *Decades Craniorum* (Göttingen, 1790–1838). In 1837 he sent out a prospectus describing his contemplated work and asking for more skulls, for of the 140 crania in his collection, only sixty-three represented American tribes, and but twenty-three of these were North American. Although the collection was "the most extensive of its kind in this country," it was "yet very inadequate" for the purpose of a craniological work.[8]

The prospectus brought a favorable response, and two years later the work was ready for the press. With the financial backing of his uncle in Ireland and aid from William Maclure, the geologist and angel of the Academy of Natural Sciences, Morton published the book by subscription in 1839. *Crania Americana* consists of an introductory essay on the various races of men, a long chapter on the crania and customs of the Indian nations, seventy-one beautifully executed lithographic plates of life-size which John Collins of Philadelphia spent two years in making, a phrenological chart, and an essay by the eminent phrenologist George Combe, then touring the United States.[9]

The work opens with the traditional observation on the well-nigh universal distribution of man: "The extremes of heat and cold, and the intervention of seas and mountains, have presented but trifling barriers to the peopling of the earth." But Morton noted another fact, one which had escaped earlier investigators. "The oldest records," he wrote, "seldom allude to an uninhabited country." Nations of men from the "remotest ages" had been marked by "certain physical and moral peculiarities" which distinguished them from all other peoples.

The Arabians are at this time precisely what they were in the days of the patriarchs: the Hindoos have altered in nothing since they were described by the earliest writers; nor have three thousand years made any difference in the skin and hair of the Negro. In like manner the characteristic features of the Jews may be recognized in the sculpture of the temples of Luxor and Karnak, in Egypt, where they have been depicted for nearly thirty centuries.

Since Morton was reasoning within the confines of the biblical, or "short" chronology, a period of thirty centuries was significant. Because Egyptian monuments showed that the Negro and the Caucasian were as "perfectly distinct . . . upwards of three thousand years ago as they are now," it was "evident that if the Caucasian was derived from the Negro, or the Negro from the Caucasian, by the action of external causes, the change must have been effected in at most a thousand years," a theory, Morton added, which "the subsequent evidence of thirty centuries" proved to be "a physical impossibility."[10]

He noted that the antiquity of the races had occasioned much speculation and that most observers had solved the problem to their own satisfaction by relying on the Scriptures, which, "in their literal and obvious interpretation" taught that all men had "originated from a single pair." But these observers had too "hastily and unnecessarily inferred" that present racial differences were the result of environmental factors only. It was really "more convenient with the known government of the universe" to suppose that an all-wise Creator had adapted man "at once to the physical, as well as to the moral circumstances in which he was to dwell." Having destroyed with the Deluge all mankind except the family of Noah, surely He would not then have left that hapless group to combat the elements with "uncertain and inadequate means." Hence, Morton arrived at the "reasonable conclusion" that "each Race was adapted from the beginning to its peculiar local destination" and that the physical characteristics of races were "independent of external causes." This method of solving the problem, typified by the "reasonable conclusion," was precisely that which had led Smith to conclude that racial characters were dependent upon external causes. Morton, like Samuel Stanhope Smith, was arguing from economy and sound craftsmanship, the attributes of a wise Creator.[11]

The difference was that Morton did not have to depend upon a priori reasoning alone. He had made painstaking measurements of the skulls of Blumenbach's five races, and in the *Crania Americana* gave generally thirteen separate measurements for each cranium, including the internal capacity, which he felt was of particular importance. His description of his method indicates the great care he took to insure accuracy:

... A tin cylinder was provided about two inches and three-fourths in diameter, and two feet two inches high, standing on a foot, and banded with swelled hoops about two inches apart, and firmly soldered, to prevent accidental flattening.—A glass tube hermetically sealed at one end, was cut off so as to hold exactly five cubic inches of water by weight, at 60° Fahrenheit. A float of light wood, well varnished, two and a quarter inches in diameter, with a slender rod of the same material fixed in its centre, was dropped into the tin cylinder, then five cubic inches of water, measured in the glass tube, were poured into the cylinder, and the point at which the rod on the float stood above the top of the cylinder, was marked with the edge of a file laid across its top; and the successive graduations on the float-rod, indicating five cubic inches each, were obtained by pouring five cubic inches from the glass tube gradatim, and marking each rise on the float rod. The graduations thus ascertained, were transferred to a mahogany rod fitted with a flat foot, and these subdivided, with compasses for the cubic inches and parts. In order to measure the capacity of a cranium, the foramina were first stopped with cotton, and the cavity was then filled with white pepper seed poured into the foramen magnum [The large opening through which the spine enters the skull] until it reached the surface, and pressed down with the finger until the skull would receive no more. The contents were then transferred to the tin cylinder, which was well shaken in order to pack the seed. The mahogany rod being then dropped down with its foot resting on the seed, the capacity of the cranium in cubic inches is at once read off on it.

This painstaking process, repeated with each of the seventy-one crania depicted in the work, gave the results set forth in Table 1.

TABLE 1*

Races	No. of Skulls	Mean Internal Capacity (cu. inches)	Largest in Series	Smallest in Series
Caucasian.......	52	87	109	75
Mongolian......	10	83	93	69
Malay..........	18	81	89	64
American.......	147	80	100	60
Ethiopian.......	29	78	94	65

* Reproduced from *Crania Americana*, p. 290.

These measurements, together with the others (the horizontal periphery, the various diameters and arcs of the skull) led Morton to three conclusions: "The American race differs essentially from all others, not excepting the Mongolian." Analogies drawn from language, arts, religious institutions, and modes of government to show that America had been peopled from Asia indicated at the very most nothing more than "casual" communication between the continents. The similarities of the two peoples were probably due instead to the "mere coincidence" that they inhabited similar latitudes and thus had "similar wants and impulses." Second, "The American nations, excepting the Polar tribes, are of one Race and one species." Third, the Mound Builders belonged to the same race. Morton did not explicitly state that the Indians constituted a distinct species of man. Indeed, he drew no conclusions on this subject other than to state that the physical distinctions between the races did not result from climate, and to hint that they were imparted at the time of the Dispersion. This was characteristic. The quiet, dignified Morton never willingly entered into controversy. The question of specific unity or diversity was left to the reader. But, on the evidence presented, who could decide for unity? One might still insist that climate could change color, but who could say that climate could change the osteological character of the individual, determine the capacity of the skull or the angle the face makes with the horizontal? Here was a portion of the human frame which, protected from the rays of the sun and the fetid air of marshes, could not be influenced by environment. Here was the line of demarcation between the old anthropology and the new: mathematical measurement was supplanting aesthetic judgment.[12]

The Jeffersonians had not been concerned with classifying the races, for in the light of their environmental philosophy, there was, in the long run, no such thing as race. Samuel Stanhope Smith had declared that it was impossible to differentiate the races with anything approaching precision. With the appearance of the *Crania Americana,* however, the impossibility became accomplished fact. Morton evaded the question of whether the varieties of men were separate species by dividing mankind into twenty-two "families," and, for the larger divisions, adopting Blumenbach's classification of five races. Morton's "families" differed from races in that whereas races displayed "primitive distinctions," some families displayed "the peculiarities of the aboriginal races to which they belong," while others were mixed "and of comparatively recent origin." Thus the Caucasian race was composed of seven families, the Mongolian of five, the Malay and American of two, and the Ethiopian of six.

Morton described the chief physical and "moral" characteristics of each race. The Caucasian was distinguished for "the highest intellectual endowments"; the Mongolian was "ingenious, imitative, and highly susceptible of cultivation"; the Malay, "active and ingenious," as well as "predaceous"; the American, "averse to cultivation, and slow in acquiring knowledge; restless, revengeful, and fond of war"; the Ethiopian, "joyous, flexible, and indolent," presenting "a singular diversity of intellectual character," some tribes constituting "the lowest grade of humanity." Morton then considered in detail each of the twenty-two families, and, as was still typical of the anthropologists of the period, he was not averse to drawing cultural and aesthetic judgments. Thus the "Circassians," a nation of the Caucasian family of the Caucasian race, "in exquisite beauty of form and gracefullness of manner" surpassed "all other people," while the "Ossitinians" of the same family were "a mere horde of rapacious banditti." The "Usbecks" were notable for speaking "one of the sweetest dialects of the Tartar language."[13]

Like Jefferson, Franklin, Samuel Stanhope Smith, and others before him, Morton stoutly defended the American Indian from Buffon's old charge, popularized by William Robertson in his widely read *History of America* (London, 1777), that the Indian was a lower order of man because life tended to degenerate in America. But to Morton, in contrast to the Jeffersonians, the charge was simply a scientific fallacy without political meaning. The Jeffersonians had thought it necessary to refute the theory because it meant men were unequal; Morton was compelled to refute it because it meant that men were influenced by climate. There was, he declared, "ample evidence to disprove the hypothesis of some closet naturalists, that the physical man of the new world is of a defective and degenerate organization." Many American nations were "remarkable for their perfect symmetry." The Indians were renowned for their "endurance of fatigue, of hunger, of thirst and of cold. . . . By day and by night, in summer and winter, over mountains, and through rivers and forests, they pursue their determined course, whether the object be revenge on an enemy, or food for their families at home." A "moral influence" rather than their own inherent weakness had destroyed the Indians of Hispaniola. The Indian was "incapable of servitude, and thus his spirit sunk at once in captivity, and with it his physical energy," while "the more pliant Negro, yielding to his fate, and accommodating himself to his condition, bore his heavy burthen with comparative ease." It was idle, therefore, to attribute to these people "less hardiness of constitution than belongs to the European." Morton was defending the Indian for a reason vastly different from Jefferson's. Morton was ready enough to point out decided differences—differences primordial, not acquired—between Indian and white, between Indian and Negro. Though he defended the Indians from charges of cowardice, treachery, and physical deformity, he did not hesitate to ascribe to them lack of intelligence and incapacity for "a continued process of reasoning on abstract subjects," and did not cavil at the discovery that "their proximity, for more than two centuries, to European institutions" had made "scarcely any appreciable change in their mode of thinking" or "manner of life." Jefferson had found the differences few, and these few he had ascribed to environment. Where the old science had found equality, and therefore, "natural" liberty, the new found inequality and, incidentally, the appropriateness of suppression.[14]

By means of his cranial measurements Morton could grade the varieties of men. Although he did not press the point, it quickly became evident that Morton's quantitative distinctions were also qualitative. Thus George Combe, in his "Phrenological Remarks" appended to *Crania Americana,* declared that the capacity of the skull influenced national character. Phrenologists had "in vain called on their opponents to produce a single instance" of high intelligence manifested "by a very small brain." It was a cardinal principle of phrenology that "individuals and nations distinguished for great aggregate force of mind, animal, moral and intellectual," had "large brains." Although Morton himself never equated cranial capacity and intelligence, his followers certainly assumed a close relationship.[15]

The appearance in *Crania Americana* of the essay by George Combe has no doubt contributed to bringing the whole work into the same oblivion into which phrenology itself descended. Phrenology had been developed by Dr. Franz Gall (1758–1828) of Vienna and was popularized by Gall and his disciples Johann Spurzheim (1776–1832) and George Combe (1788–1858). Founded on the assumption—by then generally recognized as valid—that the brain is the seat of the mind and that each of the various parts of the brain has its own function, phrenology taught that the size of the part determined the degree of the function and that since the brain is closely encased by the cranium, the size of the various parts could be determined by the contour of the skull. Phrenological "charts," like that supplied by Combe in the *Crania Americana,* displayed the various "organs" and indicated the function of each. The phrenologist, by "reading" the surface of the head, could describe the individual's personality.

Combe found that the Negro brain showed "proportionately less Destructiveness, Cautiousness, Self-Esteem, and Firmness, and greater Benevolence, Conscientiousness, and Reflection, than the brain of the native American," and concluded that the Negro was "naturally more submissive, docile, intelligent, patient, trustworthy, and susceptible of kindly emotions, and less cruel, cunning, and vindictive, than the other races." The brains of both the Negro and the American Indian, he noted, were "inferior in size" to that of the Anglo-Saxon. These qualities made the Negro docile in slavery and the Indian impatient of restraint. Unequal distribution of phrenological attributes did not, however, constitute specific distinctions. The Negro and the white were one species because they produced offspring when crossed. Moreover, these attributes, unlike specific characters, were not permanent. The exercise of Benevolence increased the size of the organ of Benevolence, thereby increasing one's capacity to be benevolent. Thus Combe condemned slavery as "a canker in the moral constitution of the country, that must produce evil continually." In slavery the brain of the Negro remained small, whereas "the greater exercise of the mental faculties in freedom" caused the brain to "increase in size," for it was a "general rule in physiology, that wholesome exercise favours the development of all organs." Combe complained that even in freedom the brain of the American Negro could not receive wholesome exercise. He was struck by the fact that in Philadelphia, "so intense" was the "aversion even of many humane and educated persons" to Negroes that "apparently they would shrink back from the gate of Heaven, if it were opened by a coloured man and showed coloured people within. Only the warmly philanthropic view them as men, and treat them with real regard."[16]

Combe arrived in the United States during the heyday of phrenology. When Johann Spurzheim died in Boston during a tour of the Republic, the citizens of that enlightened metropolis erected a statue in his memory, and the local Phrenological Society kept his brain and skull locked up in a safe. Although he gave promise of leaving no such memento, Combe was hardly less handsomely received when he arrived in 1838. Lecturing in the larger cities, he drew big crowds. During his first series of lectures in Philadelphia, where he found audiences particularly eager to learn the principles of phrenology, the average attendance was 520, and even during the second course the average was 357. Such prominent citizens and men of affairs as Nicholas Biddle, Dr. Joseph Hartshorne, Dr. William Gibson, Alexander Dallas Bache, and Dr. John Bell indorsed his lectures and testified that they recognized "many important suggestions for the improvement of education and jurisprudence, and the consequent happiness of mankind." At the close of Combe's lectures in New Haven, Governor Edwards himself offered a series of resolutions in appreciation, which Professor Benjamin Silliman supported in a rather lengthy address, telling the audience that he had "attended four courses of lectures on phrenology" and was "satisfied that the great principles of the science were well founded." Doctors Charles Caldwell, Samuel Gridley Howe, and Isaac Ray were eager phrenologists, and Horace Mann was an enthusiastic convert.[17]

There was some opposition of course. Old John Quincy Adams classed phrenology "with alchemy, with judicial astrology, with augury; and," he continued, "as Cicero says that he wonders how two Roman Augurs could ever look each other in the face without laughing, I have felt something of the same surprise that two learned Phrenologists can meet without the same temptation." His urbanity only slightly ruffled, Combe replied that "the only revenge which I shall take on Mr. Adams for the aspersion, is to mention that Phrenologists *do laugh* when they meet, in his presence, and perceive his own head, which is bald and strongly marked, proclaiming, in forms so distinct that those who run may read, the truth of the science which he employs that head in denying."[18]

In view of the popularity of phrenology and its acceptance by such men as these, it is not surprising that Morton devoted to the subject a chapter in his *Crania Americana,* a work which by its nature was most susceptible to interpretation by the phrenologist. It is only surprising that he did not interpret all his crania phrenologically, as some had suggested. On the contrary, Morton was most cautious. He took no part in the phrenological interpretation of the results and took none of the measurements of the organs of "Amativeness," "Constructiveness," "Benevolence." All this was done by Combe, who, himself owning a collection of crania and interested in the phrenological interpretation of skulls, had heard of Morton's forthcoming work, had seen Dr. Warren's collection in Boston, and at the end of 1838 had examined Morton's collection. Impressed by its size, the quality of the crania, and by Morton's painstaking measurements, Combe decided to "draw up some remarks" for the work. He modestly suggested that his essay appear at the beginning of the book, but Morton somehow tactfully vetoed this suggestion and placed Combe's essay at the end of the text, though before the plates.[19]

Although he acknowledged in the foreword "a singular harmony between the mental character of the Indian, and his cranial developments as explained by Phrenology," Morton made no use of phrenology in his interpretation of the races or of the Indian nations. Indeed, when he noted that despite their small heads the "ancient Peruvians" had developed an aboriginal civilization which rivaled that of the Egyptians, he merely remarked, "It would be natural to suppose, that a people with heads so small and badly formed would occupy the lowest place in the scale of human intelligence. Such, however, was not the case." Here Morton dropped the matter, for he was not concerned with proving that there existed a causal relationship between cranial capacity and intelligence. This was very disturbing to George Combe, who objected that such heads could not have conceived the monuments found in Peru. Either these crania must have been artificially compressed, or this people did not erect the monuments attributed to them. Combe, who was writing a review of the *Crania Americana* for Silliman's *American Journal of Science,* was anxious for an explanation, and, dissatisfied with those Morton proffered, he finally supplied one himself in the form of a postscript to the review, in which he explained that examination of other Peruvian crania had led Morton to the conclusion that the one depicted was not the "type of their nation."[20]

All this was Combe's work. Morton permitted the addition of this chapter on phrenology because he was able neither to prove nor to disprove the principles of that "science." In his foreword, he stated that rather than base the work on phrenology, he had thought it "the wiser plan to present the facts unbiassed by theory, and let the reader draw his own conclusions." He had "long admitted the fundamental principles of Phrenology, . . . that the brain is the organ of the mind, and that its different parts perform different functions," but had been "slow to acknowledge the details of Cranioscopy as taught by Dr. Gall, and supported and extended by subsequent observers." Anders Retzius wrote Morton that he believed *Crania Americana* to be "the strongest argument" against phrenology. Morton's research was not motivated by interest in phrenology, and he did not attempt to prove its principles.[21]

Morton of course relied to a great extent on the accounts of various countries and the customs and traditions of inhabitants written by travelers; these were the only descriptions available of some exotic peoples. It was precisely these accounts from which cultural anthropology, then in its "anecdotal stage," was to emerge. Morton's work and reputation rested chiefly upon his methodical research in his own collection. It was this which made him the founder of the new anthropology in the United States.

Crania Americana received favorable reviews. Professor Jeffries Wyman, appraising the work in the *North American Review*, found it "by far the most valuable addition" which had been made to "the natural history of man since the learned and philosophical works of Blumenbach and Prichard" and directed the reader's attention to Morton's conclusion that the Egyptians were not Negroes, but Caucasians. The assumption that they were Negroes had "been seized upon with avidity" in order "to place the African race in a different position from that which it is usually considered to occupy." But Morton's careful investigations had now destroyed the myth. Wyman found no flaw in the work.[22]

Charles Caldwell, reviewing the work for Daniel Drake's *Western Journal of Medicine and Surgery*, for once in his life was moved to almost unqualified admiration. He found it "the product of a bold and . . . original enterprise in the highest branch of natural science," anthropology, and was immensely pleased with its "freedom" from "self-glorifying theories and doctrines, and more especially from iron dogmas, and air-woven hypotheses." Instead of broaching "crude opinions," or presenting a "premature and ephemeral system," *Crania Americana*, Caldwell noted with satisfaction, consisted "almost exclusively of an immense body of facts" from which "substantial and lasting . . . systems" would be constructed. The work indicated that the American Indian was everywhere the same, and Caldwell found in the fact "evidence in refutation of the *temperature and climate hypothesis*, which is but the ricketty offspring of ignorance and prejudice; and the nurseling of error, superstition and obstinacy." Having hailed the book as an unrivaled contribution to the science of man, Caldwell then swung off into a wild digression on the great enthusiasm of his life, phrenology.[23]

There was surprisingly little opposition. Probably the only genuine attempt to refute Morton's arguments in the early forties was made by Dr. Samuel Forry (1811–44) of Pennsylvania. Before his early death Forry became an accepted authority on geographical medicine. Evidently suspicious of Morton's orthodoxy, Forry vigorously defended the Mosaic account of the unity of man. Assuming a position similar to Samuel Stanhope Smith's, he contended that varieties differed through adaptation and cited the blind fishes of the caves of Kentucky. He argued that the racial inheritance of all men was the same and that differences within the human species—sociological as well as biological—were due only to "local causes." The obvious flaw in Morton's argument, Forry said, was that if the Creator had originally adapted the Indian for the various American climates, the Indian would consist of several races instead of only one. Forry's objections went largely unheard. None foresaw where Morton's investigations were to lead. He was even praised for assuming the unity of the human race, and Forry thanked him for refusing to "grapple with the question of the *unity* or *multiplicity* of the species of men."[24]

In *Crania Americana,* Morton, like Lord Kames before him, found the little-trod path which allowed him to account for observed differences among the races without denying their unity of origin. To do so, he was forced to fall back on miraculous intervention. But simply pushing the problem onto the lap of the Deity and so beyond the bounds of scientific investigation was of course no solution. It was, rather, the very negation of science and was soon, when practiced by others, to be ridiculed by Morton's own followers. So flimsy a structure stood no chance of weathering the positivistic winds of nineteenth-century science. It provided at best a temporary refuge for those who were to conduct a revolution in instalments. Morton's conclusion left open the question of whether miraculous meddling in the mechanism of nature had sundered the specific unity of mankind. But in denying the effect of climate upon man, he had emphasized the permanence of racial characters, and when others found the time propitious to abandon the halfway doctrine of divine interposition, permanence could be explained only by taking the long stride that Morton was not yet prepared to take. It was indeed a long journey from scriptural authority to empiricism, from exciting assumption to dry observation, from fertile generalization to minute prying loose of fact, a journey not undertaken without occasional doubt, not completed without some returnings for glimpses of the old faith, certainly a journey not made in a day.

To those looking for an answer to the question of the unity or multiplicity of the species, *Crania Americana* was indecisive. Morton had merely raised the curtain on the turbulent drama that was to follow. If his scientific caution made the book ambiguous on this point, nevertheless his conviction was steadily growing that man consisted of several "distinct races." Encouraged by the accuracy of his improved method of ascertaining cranial capacity—the use of lead shot in place of pepper seed—he set about to measure his specimens anew and informed the Academy of Natural Sciences that the average capacity of the Caucasian skull was seven cubic inches greater than that of the Negro skull. In 1840, in a lecture delivered before his class in anatomy, he stated that although his observations had been made on an as yet "comparatively limited scale," they indicated "that the brain in the five races of men," Caucasian, Mongolian, Malay, American, and Negro, was "successively smaller in each." Some part of this difference was perhaps due to climate, for he had noted that the northern latitudes were more conducive to mental development than the corresponding southern latitudes, and much more so than the tropical regions. Nevertheless the prime cause, he insisted, lay in "those primeval attributes of mind, which, for wise purposes, have given our race a decided and unquestionable superiority over all the nations of the earth." The Caucasian could not otherwise have survived in America; he would have been destroyed by the "lawless tribes of Barbarians" which, despite their modest cranial capacities, had zealously guarded their continent against the encroachment of the white men. But on the contrary, and in the face of an unaccustomed and unfriendly climate, the white man had overspread the earth. "In Asia, in Africa, in America, in the torrid and in the frigid zones, have not all the other races of men yielded and given place to this one . . . ?"[25]

As intellect was not determined by climate, neither was color. Everyone knew that the rays of the sun darkened the skin, but color thus acquired could not be inherited. And surely climate could not be responsible for the color of both the Negro of the tropics and the Negro of Van Diemen's Land, which was nearly as cold as Iceland.[26]

These observations led irresistibly to the conclusion that racial distinctions were permanent, that there was "a primal difference among men." The monuments of Egypt testified to the truth of

Morton's conclusion, for there were depicted the same races of men familiar to the nineteenth century. If climate had not changed these races in the 3,500 years since the monuments were erected, how could it have changed them between that time and the period of the Deluge, a span of only 3,000 years? We can only conclude, said Morton, "that these diversities of organization were coeval with the dispersion of our species."[27]

The strongest evidence against the impact of climate was drawn from Morton's own collection of crania. Invited in 1841 to deliver the annual address before the Boston Society of Natural History, he chose to speak on the "Distinctive Characteristics of the Aboriginal Race of America." Skulls from all parts of the Western Hemisphere, he told the society, displayed a remarkable conformity. At the beginning of his researches the elongated heads of the ancient Peruvians had led him to divide the American aborigines into two great families, the savage tribes and the "Toltecans," but his recent discovery that the elongations were the result of artificial compression had led him to conclude that the Indian, "from the southern extremity of the continent to the northern limit of his range," was "the same exterior man." There were variations in stature and complexion, but the Indian's "distinctive features" were "never effaced: he stands isolated from the rest of mankind, identified at a glance in every locality, and under every variety of circumstance; and even his dessicated remains which have withstood the destroying hand of time, preserve the primeval type of his race, excepting only when art has interposed to pervert it." This discovery seemed to deal the death blow to the theory that climate created the races by modifying the original stock of mankind and to its corollary, the theory that America was peopled by immigration from Asia. The Indian remained an Indian despite great variations in climate, and if these were incapable of modifying man, one could hardly suppose that the slight climatic variations encountered by a hypothetical group of wandering savages, moving generally along the same lines of latitude, would have produced the distinctions observable between the Mongolian and the American Indian.[28]

Here again, Morton stopped short of asserting that the races were distinct species. In concluding that the Indian was a distinct "race," Morton had relied upon the method, developed by Linnaeus and virtually sanctified by Cuvier, of separating both varieties and species by tabulating their anatomical differences or affinities. This was sound scientific practice and it provided a working definition of zoological categories. To have concluded on this basis that the American natives were not only a distinct race but also a species to themselves would have required Morton to surmount two formidable obstacles. The morphological definition of species, the result of applying the mechanistic concepts of Newton to organic nature, was closely related to another species criterion, unity of descent, which of course derived from teleology. Unity of descent, or community of origin, as the idea frequently appeared, long antedated the concept of fixed species, having in fact once shared the spotlight, compatibly enough, with the long since exploded notion of spontaneous generation. Appearing now in conjunction with the morphological concept of species, it tended to reinforce the latter by emphasizing permanence of type. Rarely questioned in zoology, it had a special and even more rigorous application in anthropology: The Book of Genesis distinctly stated that all men were descended from one pair placed upon the earth on the sixth day of Creation. Effective refutation of this law of anthropology required the amassing of sufficient scientific evidence to establish that passages relating to natural phenomena should be read as examples of poetic license, figuratively expressing a divine idea, instead of descriptions of facts.[29]

The second obstacle to the demonstration that the American race constituted a separate species was another species criterion, popularized by Buffon (1707–88) but recognized earlier by the English naturalist John Ray (1627–1705). This was the concept of specific interfertility: organisms which cross and produce fertile offspring are of the same species. Now everyone knew that the Indian produced fertile offspring when crossed with the white man, and in the great ethnological laboratory south of the Mason-Dixon Line it was a notorious fact that the crossings of Negro and white were fertile. Judged by this criterion, all races in America must be of the same species.

Consequently, the anthropologist interested in classifying the varieties of mankind had to submit his findings to three criteria. Morton's tabulation of cranial characters convinced him that the Indian and the white man were separate species, yet they were descended from the same pair and they were interfertile. Caught in this anomalous position, he needed more evidence.

Thus far, Morton had given his attention chiefly to the Indian; his published work and the papers he had read before the Academy of Natural Sciences, of which he was now vice-president, were devoted largely to that race. But a new acquaintance, the United States vice-consul at Cairo, was to broaden his horizons.

"A Grand Theme of Conversation"

For two years before the publication of *Crania Americana* Morton had been in correspondence with George Robins Gliddon, the United States vice-consul at Cairo. When Gliddon came to the United States in 1837, Morton had sent him a prospectus of his forthcoming work and had requested that Gliddon keep an eye out for Egyptian crania, little aware of the zeal with which his new acquaintance would take up the search. In March, 1839, Gliddon wrote, "I have gone on collecting, and putting by, without thinking of the number, until I have 93 skulls in my house . . . 93 relics of humanity, 'grinning horribly their ghastly smiles,' out of Cupboards . . . and Shelves." His servant was horrified and "greatly scandalized at his Master's abominations."[1]

The Master's turbulent life began in St. Thomas, Devonshire, where he was born in 1809, the eldest son of John Gliddon, a merchant. When the boy was two, he went with his mother to Malta, where his father had recently established a mercantile business, and in 1818 the family moved to Alexandria, Egypt. After schooling and business training in England, Gliddon assisted his father, then director of the Alexandrian Insurance Company, serving as his agent in Greece, Syria, and Cairo, where in 1832 young Gliddon was appointed United States vice-consul. Here he entertained many distinguished American travelers, among them John Lowell, Jr., founder of Boston's Lowell Lectures, John Lloyd Stephens, the American travel-writer, and Richard K. Haight, a wealthy New Yorker who was to become his close friend and financial backer. In 1837 Mohammed Ali, viceroy of Egypt, sent Gliddon to America to purchase machinery for cotton, rice, and oil mills. Gliddon became enamored with the Republic and afterward wrote Morton from Egypt that he had left his "heart in America" and was building "Castles about a speedy return." He supervised erection of the mills and interested himself in plans for a Suez canal and an overland route to India. Financial reverses and disgust with the tyrannical rule of Mohammed Ali brought him in 1840 again to the United States, where, opening the first of a series of lecture tours which lasted until 1852, he became the first to lecture to Americans on Egyptology.[2]

A name-dropper, a sponger, a swinger on the shirttails of the great, a braggart, pretender, and scatologist, Gliddon was also courageous, generous, warm-hearted and loyal, and a friend worth having. The pendulum of his frenetic personality constantly swung between boundless joy and utter despair. Proclaiming himself the eternal and implacable foe of humbug, he was himself a master of the art of puffing. Hopelessly addicted to the polysyllable and relishing the ponderosities of Victorian prose, he never blighted with boredom the life of anyone. Devoted to his family, he found in it more worry than repose. Loyal and frank, closely attached to his friends, he died alone in the jungles of a foreign land. A generation of the godly knew him as a baiter of the orthodox, yet he is today forgotten by believer and infidel alike. With delusions of profundity, his mind was as shallow as a mountain stream, and, except when clouded by his turgid rhetoric, as clear. Gliddon would have fascinated Huck Finn much as the Duke and the Dauphin did, for he brought to the cities and towns of America—

ILLUSTRATIONS, BRILLIANTLY COLORED, AND COVERING MANY
THOUSAND SQUARE FEET OF SURFACE, COMPRISING—

Hieroglyphical, Hieratic, Enchorial, Greek and Roman Texts, *Steles*, Inscriptions &c., from the Sculptures, Paintings and Papyri, including the *Rosetta Stone*, the *Funereal Ritual*, the *Turin Genealogical Papyrus*, the *Tablet of Abydos, Ancestral Chamber of Carnac*, the *Zodiac of Dendera*, and all important historical documents of the Egyptians from the earliest times to the Christian era. A complete series of all the *Pyramids*. . . . Panoramic views of the *Temples, Palaces* and remarkable *Tombs*. . . . Plates, illustrative of the art of embalment, human and animal. . . . Portraits of the Pharaohs in their chariots, and royal robes—Queens of Egypt in their varied and elegant costumes—*Likenesses* of forty-eight Sovereigns of Egypt. . . . Priests and Priestesses offering to all the Deities of Egyptian Mythology—Battle Scenes on the monuments. . . . In short, Diagrams of every kind, illustrating every variety of Egyptian subjects, during a period of human history far exceeding 3,000 years, and terminating with the Romans in the 3rd century A.D.[3]

Gliddon arrived in America at the opportune time, for the citizens of the Republic were displaying a widespread romantic interest in Egypt. Several American explorers, with the able assistance of P. T. Barnum and Peale's Museum, had popularized Egyptian relics, and during the thirties and forties the Egyptian influence became apparent in American architecture. Alexander Jackson Davis, John Haviland, Robert Mills, Solomon Willard, and Thomas S. Stewart experimented with the Egyptian style, and the Washington Monument, the Tombs prison, the Newark Court House, and the Egypt Building of the Medical College of Virginia testify to their industry. At the same time, well-to-do Americans began to include Egypt as a part of the Grand Tour. One American visiting that country wrote home that he had met twenty-four of his countrymen in Cairo and Alexandria, all tourists like himself. Another remarked "a great passion among the ladies" traveling in the East for ancient jewelry from the tombs. He had seen many "wearing the jewelry of thirty centuries ago." Thousands who could not afford the journey traveled vicariously with the indefatigable John Lloyd Stephens. The wholesale descent upon Egypt of wealthy Americans seeking to gratify their romantic curiosity by pondering the inscrutable Sphinx, or peering among the mummies of the catacombs in search of material for drawing-room narratives, induced the American government to open diplomatic relations with Egypt. Accordingly, in 1832 John Gliddon was appointed United States consul at Alexandria and his son George, vice-consul at Cairo.[4]

In order to bring to Americans news of the latest developments in the archeology and chronology of Egypt, Gliddon studied for several months annually under the great Egyptologists of England and the Continent—Samuel Birch, Karl Richard Lepsius, Jean-Antoine Letronne, Baron Bunsen, Prisse D'Avenne. While working at the British Museum and conferring with its director, Samuel Birch, Gliddon resided in a notorious old house in Queen's Road, Bayswater, which, as a kind of conjugal experiment station, titillated fashionable London society. There was no reason why he should not have felt himself entirely at home in this congenial group, for there lived his brother John, who was married to a daughter of Leigh Hunt; his sister Catherine—or Kate, as she was perhaps more appropriately called—whose husband was that outrageous young rip, Thornton Hunt, Leigh Hunt's son; another sister, Anastasia, with her husband Samuel Lawrence, the portrait painter; and a scattering of female cousins (one of whom, the talented Anne, Gliddon later married) together with George Henry Lewes and his wife. Life could hardly have been dull even without the regular visits of the old warhorse of reform, Robert Owen, still vigorous, still talking; the popular Frank Stone, painter friend of Thackeray and Dickens; Mrs. Milner Gibson, a London social leader who kept her political and literary salon open to the distinguished exiles of the Continent, probably in the hope of converting them to mesmerism and spiritualism; the Reverend E. R. Larkin, whose fame rested on the solid basis of his having been the first English clergyman to wear a beard in the pulpit; and a select host of the fashionable in flight from convention. London society, pleasantly aghast, referred to the establishment as "that notorious group of Freelovers," the "most notable example of matrimony void of contract" of the day. All in all, life in Queen's Road was happy enough for "that handsome Egyptologist, George Gliddon," as a regular Sunday visitor remembered him.[5]

Escaping the fleshpots of Bayswater, Gliddon lectured in the major American cities. After soliciting information from acquaintances on the scene regarding audience prospects and rental fees, he drew up an itinerary which carried him yearly by steamship, riverboat, and stage, from New York to New Orleans and as far west as St. Louis. Arriving in, say Baltimore, he hired a hall and placed an advertisement in the local newspaper in order to raise a subscription for a series of from three to eight lectures, for he delivered as many as the local traffic would bear. In 1848, with farseeing eyes fixed firmly on the box-office, he obtained a "GRAND MOVING TRANSPARENCY," or panorama, of the Nile, which he displayed to induce audiences to attend his lectures. Making the most of the drama inherent in the subject and exploiting to the full his own flair for histrionics, Gliddon lectured between two large tables, one piled high with copies of the chief works on Egyptology, the other with relics of Egypt, some of them borrowed from one or more of the various Egyptian collections in this country, while majestic scenes of ancient Egypt moved slowly along the walls and soft strains of appropriate oriental music filled the hall. "Once placed within a hall thus adorned," wrote one enthusiastic viewer, "the visitor found himself in a new and magic region; the present vanished, and the men, and the events of thirty and forty centuries back arose before his gaze. In such a scene, the most dull could not fail to be impressed, the coldest could not resist the contagion of enthusiasm." Enlightened and entertained at once, Americans flocked to hear the young Egyptologist. Arriving in numbers from two hundred to two thousand, his hearers averaged "in the large cities, 500 of the elite of American Society," and by 1849, it was estimated, more than a hundred thousand had heard him. Extensive newspaper coverage—the reports often written by Gliddon himself—and the publication of his *Ancient Egypt: A Series of Chapters on Early Egyptian History* extended his audience far beyond the range of his actual hearers. Gliddon turned over this work, copyright and all, to that vitriolic pirate of the public prints, Park Benjamin, who then published it at a low price in his *New World* as one of that magazine's famous "extras." By bringing out twelve editions, Benjamin was able to sell 24,000 copies within five years.[6]

Gliddon's career as a lecturer was given a pronounced boost by an invitation to deliver the Lowell Institute Lectures in Boston in 1843. The Lowell Lectures, begun in 1839, had already become a distinguished series, for Gliddon's predecessors had been Edward Everett, then governor of Massachusetts; Benjamin Silliman; John Gorham Palfrey, author, editor, minister, and opponent of slavery; and the naturalist Thomas Nuttall. The appointment of Gliddon was ironical, for John Lowell, Jr., had suggested in the bequest establishing the Institute that "infidel opinions" were "injurious to society" and had stipulated that every lecturer must "declare his belief in the divine revelation of the Old and New Testaments, leaving the interpretation thereof to his own conscience." How Gliddon met this qualification is not known; doubtless his conscience rose to the occasion.[7]

Although he tempered his remarks to the winds of doctrine locally prevailing—and always dressed in black to lend decorum to his performance—Gliddon nowhere lacked in audacity. He told the Boston audience that the "inclined height" of the Grand Pyramid was "a few feet more than twice the height" of their new Bunker Hill Monument. The two subjects foremost in his mind were ethnology and chronology, and he used these to place ancient Egypt in as favorable a light as possible. He stoutly denied that the ancient Egyptians were Negroes, and pointed out to the Bostonians "40 heads of Nations known to the Egyptians 2000 B.C., to prove that mankind, in proportion to the population of the earth, were just as distinct 4000 years ago, as at the present day." Some had pretended to see Negroid lineaments in the Sphinx, but whatever resemblance it bore to the Negro physiognomy resulted from its having been peppered with grapeshot and musket balls for five centuries. The Egyptians were not Negroes but whites, and because the races were distinct even at that early date, because the passing centuries had not "whitened the Negro, or darkened the Caucasian, from their primitive types," Gliddon's audience could only conclude that racial distinctions—either at the Creation or at some time subsequent—were impressed upon man by the hand of God. Gracefully enticing the unwary into the halls of modern hieroglyphical science with his awe-inspiring panorama, Gliddon mentioned that man had probably been on earth longer than hitherto thought possible. Egyptian civilization, believed to be the world's first, from which all subsequent civilizations were derived, could hardly be reconciled with the commonly accepted chronology, that of Archbishop Usher—who by means of biblical exegesis had determined to a nicety the date of the Creation as 4004 B.C. Offering a second bait, Gliddon suggested the possibility, and no more than the possibility, that the Septuagint, or Jewish, chronology might allow sufficient time for the construction of the Pyramids, which manifestly were built after the Deluge. Then, slamming the door behind his victims, Gliddon announced to his Boston audience, "If the advocates for Archbishop Usher's chronology deem such opinions heretical, it should be borne in mind distinctly, that 'the charge of heresy cannot destroy hieroglyphical facts.'"[8]

Dr. Morton's improbable friendship with the bumptious Gliddon was of great value, for he was able now to verify his growing suspicion of the great antiquity of the races through his own researches on Egyptian crania and through Gliddon's knowledge of Egyptian chronology. By pushing chronology beyond Usher, Gliddon was challenging the position Morton had taken in the *Crania Americana*. Under Gliddon's tutelage, however, Morton himself abandoned the Archbishop. In the spring of 1843 he displayed to the members of the American Philosophical Society "twenty embalmed heads from the Egyptian catacombs" sent by Gliddon, and reported that measurements of these crania showed that the Caucasian head had a mean internal capacity of eighty-five cubic inches, the mulatto eighty, and the "unmixed Negro but seventy-one." Although these capacities were smaller for each race than were characteristic of the races in 1843, the differences in capacity had remained the same. These results, he said, showed, "by direct and unequivocal contrast," that these differences were "as old as the oldest records of our species."[9]

Gliddon's generosity also enabled Morton to solve the problem of the origin of that mysterious people on the banks of the Nile who so early in human history had developed a culture which was to be "the parent of civilization, the cradle of the arts, the land of mystery." Internal capacity and cranial conformation showed that the Egyptians had been neither Caucasians—as was later to be asserted by those who stood in the alleys of science beating the drum of race— nor Negroes, but, rather, a blend of "several distinct branches of the human family," the Caucasian, the Semitic, the "Austral-Egyptian" (whose skull-type was displayed in the nineteenth-century Hindus), and the Negro.[10]

These results were embodied in 1844 in *Crania Aegyptiaca*, a much smaller volume than *Crania Americana*, but the product of mature research. *Crania Aegyptiaca* discovered to anthropology the great age of the races and noted that slavery was "among the earliest of the social institutions of Egypt." The social position of Negroes had been the same as it was in the nineteenth century, that of servants and slaves.[11]

The book quickly caught the attention of anthropologists throughout the world. Anders Retzius, Morton's Swedish correspondent whose fame was ultimately to outdistance Morton's own, wrote, "*You have done more for ethnography than any living physiologist;* and I hope you will continue to cultivate this science, which is of so great interest." The venerable James Cowles Prichard (1786–1848), who had devoted a lifetime to ethnological research and was the foremost champion of the unity school, paid the American scientist the highest of all compliments. He noted that "a most interesting and really important addition" to our understanding of the "physical character of the ancient Egyptians" had lately issued "from a quarter where local probabilities would least of all have induced us to look for it." French scholars aided by government patronage, English scientists with the advantage of their nation's wealth, German and Italian students working in their museums and academies—all had long been investigating Egyptology. But, said Prichard, "in none of these countries" had "extensive collections been formed of the materials and resources" which alone could provide a "secure foundation" for the science. "It is in the United States of America that a remarkable advancement of this part of physical science has been at length achieved." This was music to American ears. It was good for a change to hear the tune played by a foreigner, especially an Englishman.[12]

Gliddon was delighted upon learning that Morton had dedicated the *Crania Aegyptiaca* to him. Having just arrived in Charleston from Savannah, where he had had to compete with Henry Clay for audiences, he thanked Morton for having "handed me to posterity," hailed the work as the beginning of "a *new era* in Ethnography," and added that he had displayed his own advance copy in Savannah, where it had "formed the theme of endless conversations." Resolving to do all in his power to promote its sale, he noted that of the three unbound copies which Morton had sent, he had given one to his friend William Brown Hodgson, had kept one for himself, and had had the third copy bound. This copy Hodgson was taking with him to Washington "to present it either to Calhoun, or the Nat. Institute," as Morton should prefer. Hodgson was sure that Calhoun would "appreciate the powerful support" it offered to the South's "peculiar institutions." Because its "conclusions as to the unvarying physical characteristics of races" exploded the "one-sided arguments" for unity, the South would no longer be "so much frightened" by the "voices of Europe or of Northern America." Morton "need not fear for the sale" of the book, for the "great and novel science" would be "taken up" by Southerners. In his reply, Morton suggested that the copy be given to Calhoun, but his letter did not reach Hodgson in time, and the latter, who was to read a paper on paleontology before the National Institute, seized the occasion to review the work. He "detailed its merits," read Morton's conclusions, and laid it upon the table for the members to examine at their leisure. "A rush was made at it—It was admired, and all sorts of inquiries made as to where it was for sale!" It "took amazingly and excited the Southerners to the astonishment of the Northerners." Within a few days Hodgson was receiving "personal applications" for the book.[13]

One notable to whom Hodgson introduced the work was Governor James Henry Hammond of South Carolina, flushed with his recent triumphant defense of the South's "peculiar institutions" against the carping criticisms of English and Yankee abolitionists and now apparently bearing up well under the enthusiastic acclaim of his countrymen. Hammond, long a close friend of Hodgson, was visiting with him in November, 1845, and their conversation, Hodgson informed Morton, "frequently turned upon your researches." Hammond was "collecting materials in continuation of his Slavery letters," and as his next article would be on the subject of "*Race,*" he would find it necessary to "draw from the Aegyptiaca." Hammond had read Prichard's arguments for unity and, "convinced that the philosophy of subjugation" lay in "the doctrine of Races," had deprecated them as "illogical." At Hodgson's urgent recommendation Hammond "immediately bought a copy" of the *Aegyptiaca.*[14]

Gliddon introduced the not-yet-published book in Charleston, where he was lecturing in April, 1844. He lent it to Judge Mitchell King, a civic leader who took a great interest in scientific matters. King in turn called it to the attention of the Charleston Literary Club, a meeting place for science-minded Charlestonians. There "it formed a grand theme of conversation." Dr. John Edwards Holbrook, the herpetologist, expressed great enthusiasm for the work, Gliddon reported, for he was "the only combatant for *Diversity* of Races in this City, and was constantly attacked about this Doctrine, till he carried the war into the enemy's Camp, by bringing up the absurdity of sending *Missionaries.* The orthodox now let him alone." All in all, Gliddon thought *Crania Aegyptiaca* would soon be "fairly launched down South," where Morton's findings would "draw plenty of customers." Thus the new anthropology reached the American South.[15]

"Less in Love with Freedom"

The South of 1844 was not the South the Jeffersonians had known, the South whose leaders had deplored slavery as a cancer on the body politic and whose zealous antislavery societies had outshone those of the North. Yet even in 1830 the continuation of slavery in Virginia had hung upon only one vote in the Constitutional Convention. While in the early years of the century the majority of slaveowners had retained their property, they had tended to look upon slavery as an evil in the abstract. They were, so to speak, philosophical libertarians. The Englishman Thomas Hamilton, who had traveled in the South in the 1830's, recalled that during the course of his tour, he had "never conversed with any American on the subject of slavery without his at once admitting the magnitude of the evil. The planters uniformly speak of it as a noxious exhalation, by which the whole atmosphere is poisoned." Saddled with "an inevitable evil, for which the collective wisdom of mankind has yet discovered no cure," they explained that they were "slaveholders by compulsion alone." Hamilton admitted that the slaveholders favored a peculiar form of abolition, one which would be "at once cheap and profitable," which would "peril no interest, and offend no prejudice; and which in liberating the slaves," would "enrich the master." But this is the way with gentlemen reformers, who, well-propertied, wish reform to augment their holdings. They hated slavery and regarded "those States where this curse is unknown with envy."[1]

By the early thirties there were other voices on the wind. New prophets with new doctrine were gaining honor in the land, "politicians, philanthropists, ministers, suddenly starting up to find they had been all along in error in thinking that slavery was an evil, and hoping that some day it would be removed, that they had been wrong in speaking of being 'opposed to slavery in the abstract.'" Although the new doctrine did not spread with the speed that William Aikman, writing during the heat of the war that was to follow, attributed to it when he stated that it "swept over the whole Southern States in a few months," moving with "telegraphic speed," still it moved rapidly enough.[2]

Its acceptance is nowhere more clear than in the career of the ghost of Thomas Jefferson, which all through these troubled years was to stalk the pine-scented land of the South. Although the Declaration he had written was to become the cornerstone of the abolition edifice, even during his lifetime, Jefferson was quoted, now with glee and again with rancor, as an advocate of subjection. Thus Representative William Smith of Maryland read to the First Congress in 1790 "some extracts from Mr. Jefferson's Notes on Virginia, proving that negroes are an inferior race of beings; and that the whites would always feel a repugnance at mixing their blood with that of the blacks." Smith noted with satisfied approval that Jefferson, although he favored emancipation, "was, on a consideration of the subject, induced candidly to avow that the difficulties appeared insurmountable."[3]

The bitter campaign of 1800 raised the question anew. While at least one Southerner objected to Jefferson's election on the ground of his opposition to slavery, others considered him unfit because he had "degraded the blacks from the rank which God hath given them in the scale of being! You have advanced the strongest argument for their state of slavery!" one of them raged. "You have insulted human nature! You have contemned the word of truth and the mean of salvation!" Jefferson's uncertainty as to the equality of the Negro was seized upon as ammunition against him by the Federalists. It was alleged that in his letter to the Negro almanac-maker Benjamin Banneker, Jefferson had attempted to renounce his former opinion of Negro inferiority by stating that Nature had granted equal talents to the blacks and that appearances to the contrary were owing solely to their enslavement. He had, however, betrayed his true feeling in the same letter when he expressed a wish "to see a good system commenced for raising the condition both of their *body and mind* to *what it ought to be, as fast* as the imbecility of their present existence . . . will admit." Federalist writers pounced upon the passage with alacrity. How, they asked, was one to raise the condition of an equal to a plane of equality? This was certainly an "artful salvo," a "piece of gross hypocrisy calculated to filch a little popularity from a few free negroes, and the friends of emancipation, at the expense of his own character and of the peace of his country." Charges of sexual irregularities with his slaves—not an unpardonable sin in Southern eyes but considered damning by the opponents of slavery —were circulated against Jefferson. Whispers of "Dusky Sal," reputed favorite among "Mr. Jefferson's Congo Harem," of her son "Tom," who was said to bear a striking resemblance to Jefferson, and of a mulatto "daughter" whom Jefferson was said to have freed— these vicious rumors wound their tortuous way through political alleyways. It was said that Jefferson had fathered a total of five mulatto children.[4]

After the election of 1800, Jefferson was alternately praised and damned by every group that took a stand on slavery, the praise and denunciation increasing in fervor with the growth of sentiment for and against slavery. Jefferson's equivocations on the question of Negro equality acted as a powerful corrosive on his reputation. Thus the "daughter" had a long life and proved to be particularly useful to some of the abolitionists, with whom, despite his authorship of the Declaration, Jefferson was coming into ill-repute.

Malodorous slanders—early a commonplace of American politics— again were hurled against him in the thirties as the abolition cause gained strength. Thomas Hamilton heard them during his visit and solemnly recorded them as fact for the edification of his countrymen. "The moral character of Jefferson was repulsive," he wrote. "Continually puling about liberty, equality, and the degrading curse of slavery, he brought his own children to the hammer, and made money of his debaucheries. Even at his death, he did not manumit his numerous offspring, but left them, soul and body, to degradation, and the cartwhip." The contrasting attitudes of the antislavery group toward the man and toward the document were exemplified in a passage writted by Dr. David Francis Bacon, who went to Liberia as a physician for the American Colonization Society in 1836. On his first day in Monrovia Bacon found "two long-standing cases of melancholy, or hypochrondrias." One "was an object of rather singular interest, being the daughter of no less a person than THOMAS JEFFERSON, the exemplary apostle of American democracy" and "author of a well-known document" which laid down "as a 'self-evident truth' —'that all men are created *equal*, and endowed by their Creator with certain inalienable rights; that among these are life, *liberty,* and the pursuit of happiness.' " Yet he made "profitable traffic in the children of his own body, in spite of their 'inalienable rights' " and thus "completed the glorious work of exemplifying in his life, the 'self-evident' truths of that early 'declaration.' "[5]

Many of the new defenders of slavery dismissed the principles embodied in the Declaration as nothing more than "the effusions of the speculative philosophy of his young and ardent mind," the mere vagaries of a youth who, ripening in age and wisdom, came to rest his political thought on a sounder basis. Some argued that the Declaration was "a pretty piece of poetry" intended only for the export trade, that, seeking allies, the fathers of the Republic had judiciously colored the document with the radical equalitarian sentiment then rampant in Europe. Anyway, the Declaration had not been intended to apply to slaves, for had not the author himself owned slaves? Were he and his supporters "so ignorant of the purport of their own language as to write themselves down asses in the face of the civilized world"? Few of the new political theorists of the South ignored the Declaration. All either vociferously repudiated its principles or otherwise paid their respects to the document by warping its principles to suit their all-pervading purpose. New and imposing political edifices were erected to explain its "true meaning."[6]

These speculative enormities provoked Charles Francis Adams disingenuously to remark to the citizens of Fall River in 1860: "I know not whether you have been made aware of the fact . . . that the Declaration of Independence is no longer received with unqualified favor in all parts of the United States alike. The reason is that it enunciates certain propositions touching human liberty as maxims beyond a contradiction, the truth of which is no longer convenient in some quarters to acknowledge. Hence . . . on almost every day of the year, new and strange theories of construction are advanced." This development must have had "its origin in some powerful cause" for, Adams suggested, "it is not the natural tendency of men to grow less in love with freedom." Replying to Douglas in Springfield in 1857, Abraham Lincoln noted the same phenomenon. There was a time, he said, when "our Declaration of Independence was held sacred by all, and thought to include all; but now, to aid in making the bondage of the negro universal and eternal, it is sneered at and construed, and hawked at and torn, till, if its framers could rise from their graves, they could not at all recognize it."[7]

In its new desire to place slavery in as favorable a light as possible, the South seized eagerly upon the Census of 1840. This, the Sixth Census, was the first to enumerate the mentally ill and the feeble-minded—the "insane and idiots," as they were then classified. When all the reports were in, Dr. Edward Jarvis (1803–84), a young physician from Massachusetts who was interested in the new study of vital statistics, made a startling discovery. He found that while there was no appreciable difference between the incidence of insanity among the whites of the North and those of the South, the incidence among Negroes of the Free States was 1 in 162.4, whereas in the South it was only 1 in 1,558. In the North the ratio of insanity between Negroes and whites was 6 to 1. In the South it was 3 to 5. Although inclined to question some of the figures, Jarvis was struck by the divergence and deduced that slavery must have "a wonderful influence upon the development of moral faculties and the intellectual powers" of the individual, for in "refusing many of the hopes and responsibilities which the free, self-thinking and self-acting enjoy and sustain, of course it saves him from some of the liabilities and dangers of active self-direction." The "false position" of the Negro in the North had a disturbing effect on his "character."[8]

This confident assumption was somewhat shaken three months later by the results of further investigation. Disturbed by the strikingly large number of insane reported for the Northern states, Jarvis examined the reports made by every city in the North and found that several were "reported to have as many colored lunatics as people." Although he felt sure that these errors arose in Washington in the arrangement of thousands of reports written by as many marshals, he was "disappointed and mortified" at "having unconsciously sent forth error" but hopeful that the mistake in the census would quickly be remedied.[9]

Jarvis was oversanguine in hoping promptly to remedy error, conscious or unconscious, for embarrassing though it was to rectify his own mistaken conclusions, it was far more difficult to purify a government document draped in the cloak of official sanctity. The census revealed not only a greater frequency of insanity among Northern Negroes than among Northern whites, and among Northern Negroes than Southern, it also revealed a correlation between insanity and latitude: there was apparent a steady decrease in frequency from Maine to the Deep South. In Maine every fourteenth Negro was found to be either a lunatic or an idiot, in New Hampshire, every twenty-eighth, in Massachusetts, every forty-third, in New Jersey, every two hundred and ninety-seventh. Proceeding into the salubrious South, it was found that in neighboring Delaware the rate suddenly dropped by half. It appeared that Mason and Dixon had surveyed a line not only between Maryland and Pennsylvania but also—surely all unwitting—bewteen Sanity and Bedlam.[10]

Many, though momentarily puzzled by the figures, quickly regained presence of mind and suggested various explanations. One writer, in a letter to the editor of the newly formed *Hunt's Merchants' Magazine,* inferred that "the rigors of a northern winter, which have no influence on the temperament of the whites, affect the cerebral organs of the African race," and suggested another explanation by adding that slavery probably kept down insanity among the Negro population. A writer in the *Southern Literary Messenger,* denying that climate had anything to do with it, painted a dark picture for Virginians should they ever subscribe to the tenets of Northern propagandists. The census showed, he noted, that Negroes grew "more vicious in a state of freedom." Imagine half a million of these beings "suddenly turned loose in Virginia . . . ; all sympathy on the part of the master to the slave ended; the white population employed in vigilantly guarding their own property. . . . Where should we find Penitentiaries for the thousands of felons? Where, lunatic asylums for the tens of thousands of maniacs? Would it be possible to live in a country where maniacs and felons meet the traveller at every crossroad?" This picture of the Old Dominion overrun by black madmen, its gracious citizens frightened out of their genteel wits by faithful slaves turned maniacs, was no mere figment of the imagination, for the census showed that the Negro could not compete with the white. Cultivation over "many successive generations" was necessary before man's mind could rise effectively to "the difficult task of self-direction, amidst the dangerous temptations and ardent rivalries of civilized life. To go lightly armed into the conflict" was "like opposing the bow and arrow to the rifle." The writer confessed to disapproving of slavery, but not for the sake of the contented Negro—for who is happier, "those among whom moral causes produce an insane person in every 143 of their number, or those among whom a case of insanity occurs in only one in 1,605"?—but for the sake of the white, to whom the great mass of Negroes, if disaffected by the ill-considered suggestions of Northern philanthropists, posed a threat terrifying to contemplate.[11]

Thirteen months after he first noted its errors, Dr. Jarvis published in the *American Journal of the Medical Sciences* a complete refutation of the census. Its errors were so many, he said, that "nothing but a document, coming forth with all the authority of the national government, and 'corrected in the department of state,' could have gained for it the least credence among the inhabitants of the free states, where insanity was stated to abound so plentifully." Wondering at the vigor of error, he remarked that statistics on insanity from the census had been published in America and in Europe and that "throughout the civilized world" word had gone forth that, according to American experience, slavery was "more than ten-fold more favorable to mental health than freedom." Slaves were consoled with the assurance that though they were denied liberty, they were "not bound with insane delusions, nor crushed in idiocy" as their free brethren were. This discovery, Jarvis added, might well "become not only a fundamental principle in medical science, but also one of the elementary principles of political economy." Unable longer to restrain himself, Jarvis resorted to ridicule. Finding that in many instances there were listed cases of deafness and muteness among Negroes of a town in which no Negro lived, he reported that "these disorders exist there in a state of abstraction, and, fortunately for humanity, when they are said to be present, there are no people to suffer from them. But in others the entire colored population are overwhelmed with these calamities, and now and then they are all afflicted, not with one disease only, but with both blindness and insanity." Once again he called for a correction of the census. It was, he declared, "due to the honour of our country, to medical science, and to truth."[12]

Old John Quincy Adams, leader of the antislavery forces in Congress, now took up the cause. Since the census was then conducted under jurisdiction of the State Department, Adams discussed the matter with Secretary Abel Upshur, of Virginia, and proved to him the general falsity of the document. Specifically, he pointed to "the error of the return of one-hundred and thirty-three insane colored persons in the town of Worcester, Massachusetts." A week later, at

Adams' motion, the House asked the Secretary whether there actually were errors in the census, and if so, what had been done to correct them. Two days later, Upshur was killed in the "Princeton" explosion.[13]

Among the unfinished business which incoming Secretary John C. Calhoun inherited were two matters of particular interest. It was necessary to make some kind of response to the request of the House for information regarding alleged errors in the census, and, too, there was the curious letter to Upshur from the British Foreign Secretary, Lord Aberdeen. The controversy over the annexation of Texas was raging at the time, and Aberdeen had expressed it as Britain's hope that slavery would be abolished throughout the civilized world, including Texas, which Britain also hoped would remain independent.[14]

In reply to Aberdeen, Calhoun announced that a treaty of annexation had already been concluded. Anyway, he wrote, slavery in Texas was no concern of Britain's nor even of the federal government's. Abolition might have been a philanthropic enterprise in Britain, but it could not be in the United States. To prove his point, Calhoun unblushingly cited the late census. "If the experience of more than half a century" meant anything, abolition would be "neither human nor wise" in the Southern states, for "the census and other authentic documents" proved that in the free states "the condition of the African, instead of being improved," had become worse. There, Negroes had "invariably sunk into vice and pauperism, accompanied by the bodily and mental afflictions incident thereto—deafness, blindness, insanity and idiocy—to a degree without example." In the states which had "retained the ancient relation" between the races, Negroes had "improved greatly in every respect—in number, comfort, intelligence, and morals." Calhoun buttressed his compassion for the Negro with a great array of figures from the census. In short, slavery was necessary to preserve the Negro race, and the annexation of Texas necessary to preserve slavery.[15]

Calhoun had no sooner set this matter at rest than he began to fear that France was going to support Britain in protesting the annexation of Texas. Foreseeing the possibility that he might have to deliver a little lecture on ethnology to the French foreign minister, as well as the likelihood of having to continue the correspondence with Aberdeen, Calhoun wisely sought the latest scientific information on the subject. Fortunately, the man to provide it was at hand. George R. Gliddon happened to be in the city, having just arrived from Charleston, where he had introduced the *Crania Aegyptiaca*. Calhoun therefore summoned him. A little taken aback by the signal honor of having his advice sought by the Republic's leading statesman, Gliddon nevertheless rose to the occasion. He informed Calhoun of the "true state of the case" and referred him to the authorities in the field—especially to his "distinguished friend, Saml. Geo. Morton Esq. M.D." On his return to Philadelphia, Gliddon told Morton of this development, and, in his next letter to Calhoun, inclosed one from Morton. Morton sent Calhoun his *Crania Americana* and *Crania Aegyptiaca,* and Gliddon quickly followed these with three of his own pamphlets which, he remarked, contained "many *Oriental* facts, bearing on some of those vast Southern interests, which may be said, to centre in your name and person," for "points relating to *Slavery* in *modern* Egypt are scattered throughout." Morton's researches, he added, proved that "Negro-Races" had "ever been *Servants* and *slaves,* always distinct from, and subject to, the *Caucasian,* in the remotest times." With a touch of the sycophancy that was never far below the surface of his personality, Gliddon confessed to having been "excited" by the "depth" of the Secretary's "Statesmanlike remarks"; and any time Calhoun should "desire the solution to any ethnographical problem, in respect to *African*-subjects," he and his colleagues (engaged "in a new branch of Science of which Dr. *Morton* is the master-mind") would be most happy to assist him. "In short," Gliddon concluded, "we have any amount of *facts* at our disposal to support and confirm all those doctrines, that, for so long and bright a period, have marked the illustrious career of John C. Calhoun." Gliddon did not wait for Calhoun to express his need, but quickly followed up with a dissertation on chronology.[16]

Secure in the new knowledge acquired from Gliddon and Morton and the late census, Calhoun informed the American minister at Paris, William R. King, that to abolish slavery in areas where Negroes were few would not "raise the inferior race to the condition of freemen," but "deprive the negro of the guardian care of his owner," leaving him "subject to all the depression and oppression belonging to his inferior condition." This was a prospect gloomy enough, but, he continued, to abolish slavery in areas where Negroes were many would result in "a deadly strife," nothing less than a "war of the races" all over the western hemisphere. The conflict would include the Indian as well and "make the whole one scene of blood and devastation." Great Britain's was truly a "stale and unfounded plea of philanthropy."[17]

Calhoun was a little disappointed that the promising correspondence with Aberdeen was not continued, for his two letters, he said, "were intended but as the beg[inn]ing of a long correspondence with the British Government" which would have laid open the entire question of British policy in regard to American slavery. The British government would perhaps have learned something from the social arrangements of ancient Egypt.[18]

Abbreviated though it was, the correspondence of the new secretary had created something of a stir. It was applauded by Southrons and denounced by antislavery groups. Gliddon was "delighted" that Calhoun had "thrown a hand-grenade" into the "canting camp" of English abolitionists, and James Henry Hammond expressed his gratification. John Quincy Adams, disgusted, remarked that Calhoun's conduct betrayed "so total a disregard of all moral principle" that it could only be attributed to "absence of honesty or of mental sanity. 'Tis the fanaticism of the slave-monger," he added.[19]

Calhoun turned now to the other matter of unfinished business, the report to the House concerning alleged errors in the much maligned census. Having used the census to justify his foreign policy, he had now to justify the census. To his good fortune, Calhoun was able to take advantage of a typographical error in his copy of the House resolution and so evaded a direct answer. The Secretary's report, Adams commented, was "at once insulting to the House, evasive of the enquiry, and false by equivocation."[20]

Edward Jarvis, meanwhile, had not given up the fight. He was joined now by the Massachusetts Medical Society, which, investigating the number of insane Negroes in Massachusetts, found many additional errors in the census figures, and by the American Statistical Association. The latter organization submitted a memorial to Congress asking that the census be either corrected or disowned, "as the good of the country shall require, and as justice and humanity shall demand." Adams moved a suspension of the rules so that he could present the memorial to the House, but the vote failed to sustain him. He then, not very hopefully, instructed the Clerk to refer it to the select committee on statistics. "The slave oligarchy," he predicted, "will yet prevail to suppress this document." The next day he took the matter up with Calhoun personally. The Secretary "answered like a true slave-monger," Adams recorded in his diary. "He writhed like a trodden rattlesnake on the exposure of his false report to the House that no material errors have been discovered in the printed Census of 1840, and finally said that there were so many errors they balanced one another, and led to the same conclusion as if they were all correct." While the memorial from the American Statistical Association was dying a quiet death in committee, Adams took a copy of it over to the offices of the *National Intelligencer,* as he was in the habit of doing with antislavery petitions denied a hearing by the gag-rule.[21]

By this time, however, the House was coming to the realization that there was little to be gained by trying to gag John Quincy Adams. At the next session, Adams moved, and the House resolved that the Secretary of State should inform the House "whether any gross errors" had been discovered in the Sixth Census "and, if so, how those errors originated," what they were, and what, "if any," measures had been taken to rectify them. The House thereby left the Secretary to his own devices—devices of no mean order, as it turned out.[22]

The august Calhoun then asked William A. Weaver, superintendent of the Census of 1840, to investigate himself. After Weaver had conducted a "thorough and impartial investigation," Calhoun reported in his ponderous fashion that "great and unusual care was taken in order to insure accuracy" in the census and that "many items charged as errors in it by the memorialists" were "errors on their part," and the others only seemed to be errors. Seeing here a chance to further his own great object, the Secretary suggested that "the great object" in imputing "gross and glaring errors" in the census was "to destroy its credit," because it showed the condition of Negroes in the free states to be much worse than that of Southern slaves "in reference to the greater prevalence of insanity, blindness, deafness, and dumbness." Why Negroes suffered so terribly in freedom, Calhoun did not pretend to know, but he was willing to assert that the cause "must be deep and durable." (Deep and durable since the days of the Pharaohs, anyway, Morton and Gliddon had informed him.) Making the most of his opportunity, the Secretary added that "so far from bettering" the condition of the African race, changing the relation between the races of the South would "render it far worse." To the African, freedom would be "a curse instead of a blessing."[23]

Dr. Jarvis continued to protest for over a decade, but though he helped with the censuses of 1850, 1860, and 1870 and became the nation's leading authority on vital statistics, the Census of 1840 continued to bear the sanction of Congress. A dozen years later, readers were still discovering "Startling Facts from the Census." "Who would believe," asked a belatedly astonished New Yorker in 1851, "without the fact, in black and white, before his eyes, that *every fourteenth colored person in the State of Maine is an idiot or lunatic?*"[24]

From the vast amount of conjecture on the remarkable Census of 1840 which appeared in the periodicals of the time, one article caught the attention of Dr. Josiah Clark Nott of Mobile. A physician of considerable reputation, Nott is remembered today chiefly for his speculations concerning the transmission of yellow fever and the germ theory of disease. Walter Reed gave him credit for having first suggested that yellow fever could only be spread by an intermediate host. But Dr. Nott's contemporaries took little note of this contribution to medical science. Outside the medical profession he was known solely as one of the founders of the "American School" of anthropology.[25]

Tall and angular, with a high forehead and a smart goatee, an eye for good horseflesh as well as for a neatly turned feminine ankle, the popular Dr. Nott was in many ways the very archetype of the Southern gentleman of the thirties and forties. Born in Columbia, South Carolina, in 1804, into the generation of Southerners which reached manhood in the disturbed intellectual atmosphere of the prewar years, Josiah Nott came of good family. Eliphalet Nott, founder of Union College, was his cousin, and Judge Abraham Nott, who served in Congress in 1800, his father. One of his brothers, Henry Junius, attained some reputation in Southern literary circles, then greatly enhanced his fame by going down with the steamer "Home." After receiving the bachelor's degree from South Carolina College in 1824, Nott studied at the University of Pennsylvania, where he was awarded his medical degree in 1827. There he served as demonstrator of anatomy to Dr. Philip Syng Physick for two years before returning to Columbia to begin practice. In 1832 he married and three years later went to Europe to travel and to study medicine and natural history. On his return, Nott settled in Mobile, where he wrote articles for the medical journals of the day. He was a frequent contributor to the best of them, the *American Journal of the Medical Sciences,* and early gained both a reputation as a surgeon of considerable skill and a lucrative practice. Always a man who kept at least one eye on the eagle, in 1836 he was "going ahead very cleverly &," he reported to a friend, "I think next year I shall make from 8 to 10 thousand dollars."[26]

In Mobile, Dr. Nott strenuously applied himself to the care of his patients and his horses, until in 1842 his attention was diverted by an anonymous letter to the editor of the *Boston Medical and Surgical Journal* on the "Vital Statistics of Negroes and Mulattoes." In this letter—based on the Census of 1840—"Philanthropist" showed by means of statistics that of all peoples the "pure Africans" enjoyed the greatest longevity, that mulattoes were shorter lived, and that the death rate of mulattoes increased proportionately faster with age than did that of whites or "pure Africans," that the mortality of free Negroes was "more than 100 percent greater than that of the slaves," and that this high mortality was due entirely to the presence among them of large numbers of mulattoes. Realizing that this explanation of the census figures was a new corollary to the widely accepted axiom that the welfare of the Negro was dependent upon the protective mantle of slavery, the writer hoped this information would interest readers of the *Journal* and would prove of "much assistance" in deciding a question which was being "agitated with intense interest through the whole length and breadth of our Union." "Philanthropist's" wish was soon to be fulfilled.[27]

Nott called attention to the letter with an article of his own in the ultra-respectable *American Journal of the Medical Sciences.* Entitled "The Mulatto a Hybrid—Probable Extermination of the Two Races If the Whites and Blacks Are Allowed To Intermarry," this was Nott's first venture into anthropology. He "rejoiced," he wrote, "to see light breaking from this point of the compass as the writer cannot be charged with sectional prejudice, or the influence of self-interest," and reprinted "Philanthropist's" article almost in its entirety, adding a few observations of his own which he had made during fifteen years of practice among the mixed races in the South. He had found that mulattoes were less intelligent than whites but more intelligent than Negroes, less hardy and shorter lived than either of the parent races, mulatto women being "particularly delicate" and "subject to many chronic diseases," and hence "bad breeders and bad nurses—many of them do not conceive at all—most are subject to abortions, and a large portion of their children die at an early age." The union of mulattoes, he had noted, was less prolific than the union of mulatto with white or Negro. In New Orleans, for example, he remembered "many instances" in which families had "run out so completely as to leave an estate without an heir to claim it." In view of the fact that today the preponderance of American Negroes number whites, Indians, or both among their ancestors, the relative infertility of race crosses was a curious notion. But it was commonly accepted doctrine among "progressive" agriculturalists of the South. Josiah Nott did not infer from these observations, as Benjamin Rush might have, that the mulatto suffered from congenital tendency to abortion. Instead, he concluded that the mulatto was a hybrid, the product of "two distinct species—as the mule from the horse and the ass." He did not attempt to explain how the Caucasian and the Negro became separate species but only remarked that it had "pleased the Creator at some period of time, so to make or change them."[28]

There was nothing extraordinary in classifying the mulatto as a hybrid, he said, for there were many hybrids "running through the whole chain of animated nature, from man down through both animal and vegetable kingdoms." Some of these hybrids did not breed, but others propagated "perfectly, as in the offspring of the he-goat and ewe—the goldfinch and Canary birds, the Cygnoides (Chinese goose) and common goose &c &c." There were degrees of hybridization, that is to say, some species crossed more successfully than others, and it was common knowledge that mulattoes tended to return to either of the parent stocks. Thus he found in Mobile families which had both white and black children, yet there was "every reason to believe" that the mothers had been "faithful to their husbands."

Nott's conclusions did not depend only upon the physical and mental characters of the mulatto. The parent races themselves exhibited specific differences. During the great yellow fever epidemics to which Mobile fell prey in 1837, 1839, and 1842, Nott had noted the peculiar immunity to yellow fever of any individual "in the remotest degree allied to the Negro race." There were also anatomical differences: the Negro had larger nerves, head of a different shape, a smaller brain and facial angle, and "intellectual powers comparatively defective." In view of these distinctive differences, was it any cause for wonder that the hybrid mulatto was "a degenerate, unnatural offspring, doomed by nature to work out its own destruction"?

Nott hoped his remarks would interest others who had more leisure to study the phenomenon of hybridization. "If I can start the ball my object is accomplished." How well he had accomplished his object became clear when in August, 1844, he received a cordial letter from Dr. Morton in Philadelphia, together with specimens of the doctor's ethnological works and a request for alligator skulls. Morton had read the article with "much pleasure and instruction" and agreed "that no physical causes, excepting direct amalgamation of races," could have produced "the different grades of colour, conformation, etc.," which formed the "links between the Caucasian and Negro races." Nott replied that the theory perhaps contradicted Scripture, but argued that if the Bible was divinely inspired it surely was not intended to include "the whole range of natural science," for it showed "no knowledge beyond the *human* knowledge of the day."[29]

Nott next delivered before a group of gentlemen in Mobile who had "a taste for literary and scientific pursuits," "Two Lectures on the Natural History of the Caucasian and Negro Races." He opened his lectures by declaring that the question of the unity or diversity of mankind was a scientific question and was to be decided by facts alone. Hitherto, those scientists who had been "bold enough to speak truth" had been persecuted by religious bigots. Just so was Galileo punished and his science proscribed, Nott charged—drawing here the analogy that was to inspire intimations of martyrdom in the hearts of those American scientists who upheld diversity. He himself did not expect to escape persecution; he was well aware that he would "have anathemas heaped upon my head, and wrong motives imputed to me—false issues . . . made and the true points for discussion evaded," but, consoled by the firm conviction that truth and its handmaiden Science must ultimately prevail, Dr. Nott stepped briskly along the brambly path that led away from the comfortable road of true belief.[30]

The question of unity, he noted, could not be decided by Scripture, for theologians themselves could not agree on a suitable interpretation of a document so at variance with observed fact. His words overlaid with a patina of scientific detachment, Nott, much in the manner of Thomas Paine, derided the many absurdities of the Mosaic account. Geological investigation revealed that there had been "several *creations* and destructions in the Animal and Plant kingdoms" before the creation described by Moses. And because existing species of animals differed from the antediluvian species, undoubtedly there were others later—unless, lost in a veritable quagmire of unthinking belief, one assumed the twin absurdities of a universal deluge and Noah's success in coaxing into the Ark pairs of all species now existing. This conclusion was verified by the fact that islands newly emerged were soon covered with plants "differing from all others in other parts of the globe." These were, Nott remarked, only a few of the imperfections of the Mosaic account.

His task, as Nott conceived it, was to prove "that there is a genus, Man, comprising two or more species—that physical causes cannot change a White man into a Negro, and that to say this change has been effected by a direct act of providence, is an assumption which *cannot be proven, and is contrary to the great chain of Nature's laws.*" If this proposition were true, the reader could draw only one conclusion: there had been at some period separate creations of man. There were, as has been remarked, three theories by which one might account for racial differences: Either environmental influences operating after the Dispersion gradually turned the sons of Adam red, yellow, black, and white; or racial characters were the result of miraculous intervention; or else in the beginning God created separately the different races. The believers in unity clung to the theory of environmental conditioning. Most of those who divided mankind into species, while continuing the attempt to reconcile science and Scripture, invoked divine interposition. Nott was probably the first American scientist to take up publicly the third position, of professing belief in the separate creation of different races. He criticized those who, hanging back, sought the comfortable warmth of Scripture, on the ground that their assumptions were not susceptible to scientific investigation. Nott well knew that such assumptions when voiced by recognized authority were obstacles to the pursuit of knowledge. He thus drew abreast of the flimsy structure Morton had erected, flung it a contemptuous glance, and passed on to heights of heresy not attained since Larmarck's famous assent.

To prove that Negro and Caucasian were separate species it was necessary, Nott believed, to show that Egypt, the earliest of known civilizations, was peopled by two distinct races, Caucasian and Negro. It was not necessary to show that the Egyptians proper, the people that conceived and built the pyramids, were Caucasians, but evidently Nott wished to show that a qualitative difference also existed at this early period in man's history.

Champollion, Rosellini, and Gliddon, scientists who had spent many years studying the monuments of Egypt and might be supposed to "know more of these subjects than Oxford and Andover professors," had given positive dates as early as 2272 B.C. to some of the monuments, a time "*within* 72 *years* of Usher's date of the flood," and Champollion and Rosellini had placed Menes, "the first King of Egypt," at 2750 B.C., or four hundred years before Usher's date for the Deluge. These dates were "positive facts" and "just as much to be relied on as the inscriptions on the Bunker Hill, or Battle Monument at Baltimore."

Dr. Morton had shown, said Nott, that the heads of mummies from Egypt were Caucasian heads and that Negroes, who were depicted as a separate race on monuments dated as early as 2000 B.C., occupied then the position they occupied in the nineteenth century, "that of Plebians, Servants and Slaves." Morton's conclusion was borne out, in his opinion, by the notorious fact that no people other than Caucasians had ever developed a great civilization. Even the civilization of Egypt had collapsed when the Egyptians mingled their blood with that of "various inferior tribes." Nott himself had observed the inferior descendants of that once illustrious people when he was a student in Paris. He had attended the hospitals in company with Egyptian students, some of whom, he recalled, "looked like mulattoes, others like the cross of Indian and white races." When he saw "the material with which Mehamet Ali had to work," he was "convinced that Egypt's sun of glory was set, never again to rise."[31]

Nott pointed out that the argument for separate origins need not rest on Egyptology alone. There was analogous evidence in the general laws of natural history. The genera of the vegetable and animal kingdoms were divided into species. The genus *Equus,* for example, consisted of five species. There were twenty-eight species of cats. Thirty different species of apes, "the nearest link to man," had been described. In view of the all but universal compartmentalization of nature, it "would be almost an anomaly in nature if man should be restricted to one species."

Another natural law stated that certain species of plants and animals were "suited to certain climates and soils and no other." Many species were restricted to a single continent. Australia, for example, had "a stock of plants and animals altogether peculiar" and an "entire genera of Animals" unknown elsewhere. Many animal species—lions, tigers, hyenas, elephants, giraffes, camels, horses— were not found in the America of the fifteenth century but were restricted exclusively to Europe, Africa, and Asia. Was it natural that man should form an exception to the law?

The Negro had been created for hot climates, the Caucasian for temperate. The late census of the United States showed as much. It proved that the Negro could not exist in the northern states, for in Maine every fourteenth Negro was found to be either insane or feeble-minded. Nott reprinted almost the whole of his article on the hybridity of mulattoes to show that both climate and hybridization were responsible for this shocking state of affairs.

Nott had shown that racial characters, physical and "moral," had been the same for four thousand years, indicated that the races were created for different regions, and emphasized that this was in complete conformity with the general laws of natural history. He now defined *species* as "a race of Animals or Plants, marked by peculiarities of structure" which had "always been constant and undeviating." He took no account of the traditional test of specific identity, the ability to produce fertile offspring.

The question of the specific unity of man, Dr. Nott solemnly assured his readers, was one of "deep Political, Moral and Religious import," for "if there be several *species* of the human race—if these species differ in the perfection of their moral and intellectual endowments—if there be a law of nature opposed to the mingling of the white and black races—I say if all these things be true, what an unexplored field is opened to the view of the Philanthropist!! Is it not the *Christians duty* to inquire into this subject?" The implications for the philanthropist were that Americans must not attempt to force their Caucasian civilization upon the Indian or the Negro and that Caucasians must not mingle their blood with that of "the inferior races." Probably no pure race existed as late as the nineteenth century, but there was no need, Nott thought, to add further to the deterioration of the Caucasian race.

Science was not what it had been in the days of Samuel Stanhope Smith: it was beginning to look as though science had deserted the Jeffersonian dream.

"A Hell of a Rasping"

Thus far, Morton, Gliddon, and Nott had had things pretty much their own way. True, a small skirmish erupted in 1844 when the Reverend Orville Dewey, only recently returned from a trip to England, complained in the pages of the *Christian Examiner* that Englishmen, observing the democratic experiment across the sea, were concluding that democracy tended to corrupt the morals of its citizens. They had noted the repudiation of public debt, "an excessive and demoralizing love of pursuit and gain," and finally, the supreme irony of American democratic life, African slavery. Like Jefferson, Dewey was opposed to slavery yet uncertain of the equality of Negroes. Thus the prospect of their freedom presented almost as many problems as did the reality of their present status. "Scattered among us and separated by impassable physical, if not mental barriers; refused intermarriage, refused intercourse as equals, be it ever so injustly," the Negroes, Dewey suggested, should be freed gradually as they saw "it to be for their advantage to retire to Hayti or the West Indies."[1]

Dewey's article came under the notice of Prichard's fellow towns-man, Dr. William Benjamin Carpenter of Bristol, a distinguished naturalist whose *Principles of Human Physiology* was an authoritative textbook of the time. An avowed Lamarckian, Carpenter considerably broadened the issue when he declared in a letter to the *Examiner* that Negroes and Caucasians could not constitute separate species, because there were "no *definite* and *constant* anatomical or physiological differences" between them. What differences there were sprang from "various external circumstances" such as those which had produced "the various breeds of our domesticated races." Some animals possessed little or no power of adaptation, were therefore limited in distribution, and retained their original physical character. Others possessed the power of adaptation in abundance, diffused themselves over the earth, and came to differ widely. Of this latter group, he pointed out, "man unquestionably stands first." The characters which man acquired through adaptation were then transmitted to his offspring.[2]

Carpenter bridled at the notion of their being "impassable physical barriers" between the white and the black. "The best answer to this objection," he remarked with acerbity, "is furnished . . . in your own country; for it is notorious that, though *marriages* are prevented by law or by the force of public opinion, illicit connections are common proof that the barrier is *not* impassable; and that however distasteful may be the idea of a marriage between individuals of different races, on account of the present relative social position of the two, it is no more than would exist in this country between the daughter of a peer, and the son of a ploughman. No one who is not prejudiced by the pride of descent, would look upon this as impassable. . . ." Dr. Carpenter could not "but believe that, even in one or two generations, the daughter of an American merchant might find the descendant of the despised Negro not unworthy of her attachment." This was putting the issue bluntly enough and was, for Americans, the unkindest cut of all. For Carpenter, an Englishman, was accusing them of manufacturing class distinctions and of objecting to marriage with Negroes on grounds not of racial but of social prejudice. For all their vaunted equality, he was saying, their society retained the old class system of the erstwhile mother country.

It was too much for Dr. Samuel Henry Dickson of South Carolina, who fired off a letter to the *Examiner* in reply. He asked the old question, heard today chiefly though not exclusively in the southern portions of America and Africa, whether Dr. Carpenter had a sister or daughter whom he would care to "sacrifice to philanthropy." Referring the reader to Morton and to Nott, he noted that the Negro's condition was static, that he had been a slave even in ancient Egypt. Intermarriages produced only the enfeebled mulatto, who would in a few years become extinct. Because of these distinctions, because the Negro was an inferior race, abolition was impossible: "We cannot remain as equal co-occupants of the soil. . . ."[3]

This was only a small passage of arms, and it hardly touched Morton and Nott. There was other sniping during the early forties, but, generally, the usually sensitive ears of the orthodox failed to detect the distant rumblings of heresy. Yet the peace was uneasy.[4]

It was shattered in 1845 with the publication of Nott's *Two Lectures on the Natural History of the Caucasian and Negro Races*. Nott's outspoken denial of the omniscience of Moses and his equally frank avowal of diversity of human origin angered Moses Ashley Curtis. Born in Massachusetts, Curtis (1808–72) had moved to North Carolina in 1836 to teach in an Episcopal school at Raleigh. In 1841 he went to Hillsboro, where he spent the rest of his life, becoming as true a Southron as any native Carolinian. As both an Episcopal minister and an important American botanist, he was doubly impelled to reply to Nott. Upon the advice of Asa Gray (1810–88) he had at first determined not to answer Nott. However, when the editor of the *Southern Quarterly Review* referred in the October issue to Nott's effort as "a very valuable disquisition on a subject of much curiosity and interest," and expressed the intention of reviewing it in a future number, Curtis explained to Gray that he "could not stand it." He did not believe "that such a publication should be intelligently reviewed without great severity," and accordingly, "administered a stern rebuke to the author."[5]

Curtis' review appeared in the April, 1845, issue of the *Southern Quarterly Review*. He strongly objected to Nott's contempt for those who accepted Scripture as fact, ridiculed his intimations of martyrdom, and chided him for his pretensions as a naturalist. Curtis did not attempt to defend the Usherian chronology, which, he said, was not inspired. Indeed, Curtis could not see that chronology had anything to do with the question of the unity of the human species, but it is evident that he did not believe that chronology could be pushed much beyond the Septuagint. Nott, he said, had acquired just enough knowledge of natural history to think it strange that man should be the only species of his genus. A little firsthand investigation in that department of science would have shown him that there were "many instances in the vegetable and animal kingdoms, of genera with single species." Like all novices in science, Nott had placed too strict an interpretation on some of the laws of nature and had imputed infallibility to a rather vague law of geographical distribution. There were so many exceptions to this rule that while in some instances genera were restricted in their distribution, in others species ranged widely over the globe.

Many species of plants and animals were "actually 'adapted by nature' to great varieties of climate," and "capable of undergoing great changes of constitutional habit." The dog, cat, sheep, goat, ox, horse, and ass existed and propagated "from the frigid zone to the equator." And as for Nott's assertion that the Caucasian could not live in Africa, why, colonies of Portuguese had been settled there for centuries, and Curtis had not yet been informed that the climate of that continent was deleterious enough to bring the Arabs to extinction. Even if there were climates in which some races of man could not live at the present it would only show that "a kind Providence" had endowed the human constitution with the power of adaptation to varying climates." It was true, he noted, that no one knew precisely the effect that climate had upon the organism; probably man would never know. Nevertheless, variations constantly appeared: many animals, when subjected to new environmental influences, "swerved from their original type of form and color" to such an extent that they came to display greater differences than appeared among the races of men. The phenomenon was so common that Curtis believed "a susceptibility to change, both of form and color," was inherent in "the animal constitution." Thus the Negroes of Africa, like the Indians of America, varied greatly from region to region.[6]

He passed over Nott's argument of hybridity in a few paragraphs. In the first place, so far from hybrids being common, a hybrid in the wild state was an extreme rarity, and in the second, hybrids did not propagate. Mulattoes did, and despite Nott's notions about their limited fertility, they were prolific. Therefore, mulattoes could not be hybrids; Negroes and whites could not be distinct species. "Dr. N.," Curtis explained, in "attempting to prove two or more species in the human race," would have to rest his proof on evidence other than the falsely alleged hybrid condition of mulattoes. The rule that hybrids, when they did propagate, returned ultimately to one of the original parent stocks, applied also to varieties and, hence, might be of no relevance whatever. Whether the mulatto was short-lived had no bearing on the question of hybridization, for Curtis had "never heard that the mule was shorter lived than its parents." Nott had stated that "if a hundred white men and one hundred black women were put together on an island, and cut off from all intercourse with the rest of the world, they would become extinct." To this curious conjecture Curtis promptly replied that in 1790 Pitcairn's Island was settled by English sailors and Tahitian women, and that the population had since steadily increased. Curtis apologized for his long review but "considered it due to truth and science, that such a publication should not pass without merited rebuke."

Upon learning, with some surprise, that "a Revd. Mr. Curtis of Hillsboro North Carolina was about to make an onslaught" on his "INFIDEL pamphlet," Nott wrote to Morton to ask for "any facts, or statistics connected with the question of Hybrids, the effect of Climate on Races &c," for in Mobile he had access to few books. He had "got into a scrape with a parson" and intended to "give him a hell of a sweat." He was not disappointed at opposition from this "Massachusetts man . . . 'come south' as a school master," for, as he told his friend Hammond, who had just recently left the governor's chair in South Carolina, his object was to give the people a weapon with which to oppose abolition, "one of those unfortunate questions," he remarked, "which present one face to the philosopher & another to the mass—reason or religion can never decide it." Only religious prejudice stood in the way of general acceptance of a scientific answer to abolition, and all that was necessary now was to "get the dam'd stupid crowd safely around Moses & the difficulty is at an end." His *Two Lectures*, despite the novelty of the theories presented, had created favorable interest in Mobile, had been "much talked of & read," and "public opinion has come over to me as I was sure it would, *in the South*—the few that hold out admit that it is debateable ground & ought to be investigated."[7]

Hammond agreed. He, too, was concerned about the problem. Nott was on the right track and seemed to have cornered his opponent, for his argument was really more orthodox than that of the "Divines." "They make God the Creator," Hammond explained, "but restrict him to the Creation of a single pair of human beings & in the animal & vegetable Kingdoms to only so many species as Noah could crowd into the Ark. Whence then has come the infinite [number?] of animals & vegetables now known & the very marked varieties of the human species? If there was no other Creation all these things must have been effected by *secondary causes*—the gases fire & fluids of Anaxagoras. But if these natural & secondary causes—without any special interposition of God—acting merely in conformity with the instinct of the Universe according to the . . . Laws of Development, could effect such wonders what becomes of mind—of God? What use have we for him if nature *without his aid* can change the Caucasian into the Malay & the Negro & develop myriads of animals & plants unknown to Noah?" Others had posed these questions in the past. Many more were to pose them in the years ahead.[8]

The first part of Nott's reply to Curtis, written from the oracular heights of the third person, appeared in the July number of the *Southern Quarterly Review*. He complained bitterly that he had been quoted out of context, found Curtis' objections "amusing," humbly asked the reader to peruse with "charity" Curtis' confused review, and generally displayed the impudence he always assumed in controversy. Written in a pose of amused contempt, the reply was heavily flavored with sarcasm and contained little of value to the discussion. Nott did, however, make clear why he insisted on extending the commonly accepted chronology. Scripture gave no evidence that racial distinctions had been miraculously implanted in mankind, and if Nott could "trace these differences up very near to C's date of the deluge, he will have to look out for dry land to stand upon." If physical causes accounted for physical changes, then there must have been sufficient time between the Deluge and the appearance of racial characters for these characters to have developed through dispersion and multiplication. Because it was now common knowledge that the races had not changed in the past three thousand years, these causes must have operated slowly, indeed—over "a series of ages," or a period incomparably longer than any chronology yet formulated provided for. Thus Nott attempted to wedge the reverend naturalist between his theology and his science.[9]

Nott ridiculed the notion that the conditions of domestication produce variations either in man or in animals. "I will not pretend to guess what might be effected by *selections* with a particular view," he wrote. (Making the rounds of English taverns to converse with sheep-raisers and cockpit enthusiasts, Darwin was patiently documenting this very practice.) But left to propagate in the natural state, animals and men would, in Nott's opinion, show no change; the brain of the Negro would not expand, nor his heel contract. If climate effected changes, then we should expect descendants of the early settlers of America to resemble the Indian. But even the Indians were not of the same color in any single region, black or near-white Indians appearing where one would, according to Curtis' theory, least expect to find them.

To Curtis' assertion that hybrids did not reproduce, Nott replied that there were degrees of fecundity in hybrids. Some crosses were prolific, others not. He repeated much of his old article, "The Mulatto a Hybrid," and to show that the Northern Negro was outside his geographical range, cited statistics from the by now disreputable Census of 1840, which indicated that the Negro birth rate was much lower in the North than in the South. Nott admitted that species would not be determined with assurance, and then attempted to throw upon Curtis the burden of proving that man does *not* consist of several species. What evidence did Curtis have that the Negro could exist in the frigid zone? Nott had ceased to deal with observed phenomena and was simply manufacturing hypotheses for Curtis to disprove—an indication that he was neither so amused nor so contemptuous as he pretended.

This was absurd, and in his rebuttal Curtis could do little more than gather up the points at issue. Morton had written Nott that the oldest delineations of Negroes were on monuments dated 1700 B.C., and Curtis explained in the final article in the controversy that this was time enough, that "five hundred or six hundred, at most one thousand years" provided sufficient time for natural causes to have produced racial distinctions after the Deluge. He did not explain whether these causes were still in operation. As for the time necessary for the Egyptians to have developed a great civilization so soon after the Deluge, probably, said Curtis, "the family of Noah brought no little of antedeluvian skill and knowledge into the new world as a foundation at least for the Egyptian perfection." Thus he left the problem resting squarely on the shaky basis of a probable miracle.[10]

Nott's great fault, Curtis suggested, lay in his determination "to go out of his way in an attempt to prove the Biblical scheme wrong anyhow."

After the public exchange, congratulations were in order for both parties. Curtis had heard "from several quarters," he wrote Gray, that his review had done "good service" and rejoiced to learn that Nott was presently attempting to enlighten the world on the subject of mesmerism, a development which amply confirmed his suspicion of Nott's fundamentally unscientific attitude. For his part, Nott concluded that the exchange had served his object of bringing the subject before the "dam'd stupid crowd" and had afforded "amusement for all classes at the parsons expense." Privately, he admitted that he had received "a hell of a rasping."[11]

Upon learning that Nott was involved in controversy with a parson, Gliddon sent him a mass of material on the monuments of Egypt, newspaper reports of his lectures, and a list of books on biblical criticism, against which, he said, an orthodox clergyman stood "no more chance than a stump tailed Bull in fly time." Nott was much impressed, and after examining the material he wrote to Hammond that the Christian religion was "*all* taken from Egypt— the trinity was theirs—the *Cross* was their emblem of eternity—the language of the Bible is in many instances clearly borrowed." There was "a quiet, prudent & sure game going on" which would soon "put Moses in a tight Box." Gliddon reported from Paris that he had found Dr. Jean C. M. Boudin, the French authority on medical geography, "delighted with Dr. Nott's 2 Lectures," and planning to translate them for a French edition. Morton's enthusiasm was considerably more restrained. After reading the first instalment of Nott's reply, he urged caution and noted that some of Nott's conclusions were "in advance of present demonstration."[12]

Undismayed despite the rasping by Curtis, Nott quickly followed up his replies with two articles for the local market. Published in his friend J. D. B. De Bow's *Review*, the first, which appeared in November, 1847, ostensibly dealt with the problem of whether masters should insure their slaves but was actually a vehicle for Nott's opinion on the inferiority of the Negro. Here, apparently for the first time in print, Nott openly excused slavery. Charles Lyell, who had recently paid him a visit in Mobile during his second tour of the United States, had expressed the opinion that through slavery the Negro could be civilized and perhaps even "brought up to the Caucasian standard." Nott, however, disagreed. "I gave him my notions on the subject & he seemed to be much staggered by them—," Nott had written Morton on the day of Lyell's departure from Mobile. The races of men, he said, can, "if docile, be tamed, educated and vastly improved, but there are limits set to each by nature, beyond which no advance can be made," and the Negro in the American South, he added, "*has* reached, his highest degree of civilization." This, he proclaimed in a second article in the same year, was the decision of modern science. "The angry and senseless discussions on negro emancipation, which have agitated Christendom for the last half century, were commenced in ignorance. . . ." The philanthropist must listen to science if he wished to improve the condition of the Negro. Though the distinction appears small today, it should be noted that Nott did not defend slavery as a positive good. He defended it only as the alternative to amalgamation, which, to his mind, meant biological deterioration of two races.[13]

Nott had clearly arrived at the position, which Morton and Gliddon were also nearing, that the races, being permanent and lacking in adaptability, had been created separately in their several environments. Confining his investigations to the natural history of the Negro and Caucasian races, for the ethnology of the Indian was Morton's province, he showed them to have been distinct at an early period. Morton had shown that the Indians were a distinct race and had assumed that they were an ancient race. Thus far, however, their evidence was anatomical and physiological only, and if they were to ground their conclusions of specific distinctions in separate origins, they needed historical evidence comparable to that which Gliddon had brought from Egypt. In short, the problem invited study by a good field man, an archeologist who could solve the question posed by the curious earthworks in the American West— probably the most ancient traces of man in the New World. Who had constructed them? Were their builders—who mysteriously disappeared, leaving behind only the monuments of their civilization— an exotic and now extinct race come to America from the site of the original creation by way of Asia and Alaska? Or were they indeed planted in the "New World" by the hand of the Creator? Morton, Nott, and Gliddon found the man to answer these questions in E. George Squier.

"No Inconsiderable Antiquity"

If Ephraim George Squier is remembered today it is usually because a historian of diplomacy has enshrined him in a footnote. The historian recalls the astonishing success of the young chargé d'affaires in concluding a treaty with Nicaragua, a treaty which brought the United States perilously close to war with England. Or the historian of fashionable society may remember his scandalous marriage, a marriage which gave him a little push along the watery ways of insane delusion and brought to a close a distinguished career.

The first authoritative voice in American archeology, he deserves better of posterity. Younger than Morton, Nott, and Gliddon, Squier was born in 1821 in Bethlehem, New York, the son of the Reverend Joel Squier, a Methodist minister. Largely self-educated, he taught school for a time and studied civil engineering before turning to journalism. After working on various newspapers and magazines, he went to Chillicothe, Ohio, in 1845 to publish the *Scioto Gazette*. He chose Ohio instead of Baltimore, where he had been offered an editorial position, because, he wrote his parents, "I will not live where there are slaves." There he immediately became interested in the large rounded earthworks which rose, incongruous, from the countryside. In the course of his early investigations, he made the acquaintance of Dr. Edwin H. Davis, a prominent young physician of Chillicothe, who had accumulated a large collection of relics from the mounds.[1]

The two decided to conduct a thorough investigation of the mounds and to publish their results. When their study proved to be more costly than they had anticipated, Squier approached several scientific societies in search of financial aid. If assistance were forthcoming, the brash young man wrote his pious father in the spring of 1846, "I will show you some things 'you never dreamed of' in your philosophy." Accordingly, he went east to find backers for the project. Persuasive and likeable, Squier met Dr. John Collins Warren, William H. Prescott, and others: "I met over fifty of the most distinguished gentlemen of Science and learning in Boston," he wrote home proudly. In New York he so interested the venerable Albert Gallatin, president and founder of the American Ethnological Society, in the project that Gallatin offered to publish the results of his researches. In New Haven, at the house of Professor Benjamin Silliman, he met the faculty of Yale College and was elected a member of the Connecticut Academy of Science, and in Worcester he was promised the aid of the American Antiquarian Society. Intensely ambitious and not a little vain, Squier returned much gratified with his reception by the scientific men of the East.[2]

Like everyone else in mid-nineteenth-century America who was interested in anthropology, Squier introduced himself to Dr. Morton in Philadelphia. Confessing that he knew little or nothing of craniology, he wrote to ask if Morton would "have the kindness" to compare whatever Mound Builder skulls he and Davis might turn up, with "the aboriginal remains of Mexico, Central America and Peru." Having devoted so much time and attention to this department of inquiry, he added respectfully, "none are so capable of making such a comparison as yourself." Morton generously promised to aid in any way possible and stated his own conviction, the result of long years of research, that American man was everywhere the same. Professor Montroville W. Dickeson had just returned to Philadelphia from a tour of the mounds, and an examination of the artifacts recovered by Dickeson reaffirmed Morton's belief that the Indian was a distinct race. "Here again," he wrote Squier, "we find the same links of connexion between the demi-civilized & barbarous tribes which everywhere prove a common and indigenous origin for all the American nations." They were not necessarily descended from one pair. "There may have been fifty pairs" for all he knew, but these were "so linked by similarity of conformation, mental endowments, moral traits and archaeological remains, as to constitute a vast homogenous group of mankind," which he believed to have been "*aborigine,* distinct and separate from all others." Thus Morton, privately, mounted to the position Nott had brazenly defended two years before.[3]

When, after many disappointing failures to recover a well-preserved cranium from the mounds, Squier jubilantly announced his success by sending drawings of a cranium to Morton, the latter replied that his examination showed that the skull was "a *perfect type*" of its race, the race which was "indigenous to the American continent, having been planted here by the hand of Omnipotence."[4]

The Smithsonian Institution agreed to publish the work, but its appearance was delayed by a personal dispute between Squier and Davis and by disagreements with Joseph Henry, superintendent of the Smithsonian. Part of the trouble with Henry was due to his desire not to publish a book which might offend the Board of Regents. Henry asked Squier to confine himself "to an accurate account of the facts" of his explorations, and Jared Sparks, professor of history at Harvard, urged Squier to "keep clear of theories & speculations; and in all cases avoid exaggeration." Morton expressed his distaste for controversy. That attempts were made to suppress certain suspected heresies in the manuscripts is indicated by a letter Squier received late in 1847 from his friend George Perkins Marsh, regent of the Smithsonian, member of Congress from Vermont, philologist, and entomologist. Marsh denied that *he* had anything to do with the "suppression" of that portion of the manuscript in which he took great interest. "The age of these monuments is a point second in importance only to their purposes, and every circumstance which throws any light on this point ought to be carefully recorded."[5]

Guided by these admonitions, explicit and implied, Squier was cautious. *Ancient Monuments of the Mississippi Valley* finally appeared in 1848 as the first volume of the Smithsonian "Contributions to Knowledge." It describes the physical conformations of the mounds, details the purposes for which they were presumably erected, and discusses the implements found in them. A definitive study of the remains of what was considered to be America's most ancient populace, *Ancient Monuments* was in every way a work of which the newly formed Smithsonian could be proud. Certainly it created widespread interest, for it was a book to warm the heart of every patriotic American. It was hailed in much the same spirit which had moved Emerson to announce a decade earlier that Americans had "listened too long to the courtly muses of Europe," and then to proclaim: "We will walk on our own feet; we will work with our own hands; we will speak our own minds." America, as well as young E. G. Squier, was feeling its intellectual oats. Undoubtedly many, like the reviewer for the *Literary World,* were pleased to find evidence that Americans—of one variety, anyway,—had been walking on their own feet as long as Europeans. The America discovered by Columbus, the reviewer noted, was an America in "disguise." "It was at first all light skies, tropical fruits, naked savages; a fresh creation of yesterday, a new world. It is now found to have been made at somewhere about the same time as the rest of the round globe . . . and had had its experience, incidents, and an eventful history of its own." Americans need no longer suffer "the reproach" of "the excessive modernness and newness of our country," no longer hear it "described over and over again by foreign and native journals, as being bare of old associations as though it had been made by a journeyman potterer day before yesterday." Squier and Davis had revealed the uniqueness of America: "We find we have here, what no other nation on the known globe can claim: a perfect union of the past and present; the vigor of a nation just born [,] walking over the hallowed ashes of a race whose history is too early for a record, and surrounded by the living forms of a people hovering between the two."[6]

Squier's friend Charles Eliot Norton gave the book a highly commendatory, thirty-page notice in the *North American Review*. Curiously, he praised it on the ground that Squier had "shown no desire to enhance the interest attaching to these works by ascribing to them a very high antiquity," that "his chief object" had been to "present simple truth rather than what might excite attention as extravagant or wonderful."[7]

The restraint to which Norton paid tribute was in reality the result of a decision to subvert, rather than openly attack, orthodox belief. To those who read the book with care it meant something more. Squier and Davis made no attempt to assign a definite date to the mounds, and they carefully eschewed generalization, but the evidence they presented forced the reader to conclude that the Mound Builders were a race of immense antiquity. Of the terraces in Ohio deposited by the subsiding rivers, the authors found mounds on all but the most recent. The terraces upon which no mounds appeared must have been deposited after the close of the mound-building period. The existing structures were therefore very ancient. Further observations revealed an antiquity that staggered the imagination. Applying the rule that the excavating power of "the Western rivers" diminished as the square of the depth increased, Squier concluded that the formation of the latest terrace in the series had required far

more time than the formation of those preceding it. The time necessary for its formation was increased by the dissipation of excavating
power caused by the tendency of the stream to meander. In some
instances a stream had cut a new channel three-fourths of a mile
away from the original bed beside which a mound was constructed.
The "dense forest" standing between the two channels added its testimony to the age of the mound.[8]

Tree-ring dating provided further evidence of age. Squier noted
that on some of the mounds there stood trees of "a positive antiquity
of from six to eight hundred years," surrounded by "the mouldering
remains of others, undoubtedly of equal original dimensions," but
now "almost incorporated with the soil. Allow a reasonable time for
the encroachment of the forest, after the works were abandoned by
their builders, and for a period intervening between that event and
the date of their construction, and we are compelled to assign them
no inconsiderable antiquity." This was, as Squier intended, putting it
mildly.

Two other great questions concerning the builders of the mounds
had long fed the curiosity of American antiquarians. Who were these
people? Where did they come from? Again the authors declined to
give a forthright reply. Instead, Squier stated blandly and without
comment the conclusions which Dr. Morton had reached after examining several crania from the mounds (including the one Squier
had sent), three Peruvian crania, and several from the modern tribes.
Squier reported that Morton had made, with his usual meticulous
care, ten measurements of each of the crania sufficiently intact to permit measurement and had concluded that the skull found by Squier
manifested all the "features characteristic of the American race." In
the opinion of Dr. Morton, then, and Squier offered no other, the
Mound Builder was nothing more nor less than an American Indian.

As to the origin of the Mound Builders, or the Indian, if the reader
chose to accept Dr. Morton's authoritative conclusion, Squier remarked merely that instead of the implements in any given mound
being all of copper, or all of mica, or shell, or obsidian, he had found,
"side by side in the same mounds, native copper from Lake Superior,
mica from the Alleghanies, shells from the Gulf, and obsidian . . .
from Mexico." This evidence seemed "seriously to conflict with the
hypothesis of a migration, either northward or southward." It meant
that the Mound Builders were a large sedentary population with

lines of commerce extending in all directions, and not a horde of migrants slowly shifting to the south. Thus, implicitly but summarily, he dismissed the old hypothesis, basic to scriptural ethnology, which brought the Indian by various routes from Asia to his present abode far to the east of Eden.

Publication of *Ancient Monuments* had been awaited with considerable interest. Francis Lieber, German refugee professor of political science at South Carolina College, asked Squier for prospectuses of the book to distribute during his coming trip to Germany. Nott, whom Squier had doubtless heard of through Morton, was particularly interested. In August, 1848, Squier had written to Nott to introduce himself. Nott replied enthusiastically. (Far from home "at 2 oclock at night, sitting up with a woman in labor!—it is all Science however . . . [for] exploring a woman & a mound are pretty much the same.") He had, he said, "long had my eye upon you & have been awaiting anxiously the results of your labor," for he wanted "very much to see how far back you push the probable antiquity of the Mounds." Chronology was of the first importance, and he looked to Squier "to give the *coup de grace* to that venerable *He brayist,* Moses."[9]

When the work finally appeared, Squier found that his labors had earned him a warm welcome from his predecessors in American ethnology. From Pittsburgh, where he was drawing large audiences, Gliddon wrote to Squier in March, 1847. They had been introduced by a letter from John R. Bartlett of the American Ethnological Society, when Squier had written Bartlett to ask if the much publicized Gliddon would consent to deliver a course of lectures in Chillicothe. Assured of a receptive audience, Gliddon readily agreed. While he was in Chillicothe, Squier let him have a set of the plates of his forthcoming *Ancient Monuments,* which Gliddon then displayed at his lectures as he moved across the nation. In Charleston, South Carolina, he reported, they were "circulated at the Wednesday Evening Literary Club, under the auspices of Judge King, and Dr. Holbrook." They created considerable interest in New Orleans medical circles, and in Mobile, they impressed that "glorious fellow Dr. J. C. Nott." Morton declared that the work was "by far the most important contribution to the Archaeology of the United States" yet submitted to the public. In Europe in the summer Gliddon made Squier's work known to the scholars of the continent. The great naturalist Alexander Humboldt, the most widely revered scientist of his day, linked it with Morton's *Crania Americana* as "the most valuable contribution ever made to the archaeology and ethnology of America." Certainly this dispassionate and scientific survey of the mounds of the West reached a far larger audience than any amount of polemic writing on the subject would have done and commanded a far greater interest because it carried the imprint of the Smithsonian.[10]

Squier had done for the Indian what Gliddon had done for the Negro. Behind them both stood the figure of Dr. Morton. Squier showed that the mounds were extremely ancient, so old that they could be dated only by geological methods, and that their builders were American Indians, a people who had not migrated from abroad. This evidence brought one to the conclusion that the Indian had been in America as long as the Negro had been in Africa. Who was then to say they were descended from a single pair? "Of Irish or Welsh 'Indians,'" Gliddon remarked, "it will be time enough to speak, when their 'coprolites' . . . are found."[11]

The researches of many naturalists had shown that climate, operating within the limited period allotted to man's existence, could not account for racial diversities. True, the accepted chronology was being lengthened by the discoveries of the Egyptologists, but their additions were in small clumps of decades and centuries, and few anthropologists thought in terms of the chiliads which had lately become the chronological units of geology. The new school of anthropologists smugly accepted additions to the chronology of Egypt, for as newly discovered bas-reliefs and inscriptions revealed the early existence of races, the interval backward to the Creation seemed to shorten. They knew that the Negro had not changed in four thousand years, and who was to say that five, or even six, thousand was time enough for climate to have worked the change? Not only were the races ancient, they were widely distributed in ancient times. Craniological and archeological evidence indicated that as far back as chronology retained any accuracy, the Negro had inhabited Africa, and the Indian, America. Nott had indicated that the Caucasian and the Negro were separate species. Although climate was not responsible, it was apparent to all that the races were marvelously adapted to the regions they inhabited. In the general scheme of nature, it seemed entirely appropriate that a black race should inhabit those areas most subject to the direct rays of the sun and that more protected climes should present a race of white skins and sensitive nervous systems. The correlation between the organism and the environment was impressive, and men still marveled at the craftsmanship and economy of the Creator.

Thus the new anthropologists were forced to search anew for the origin of species, and in their quest they were profoundly aware of the appropriateness, the fitness—in the last analysis, the rightness—of the world of nature. Their sense of economy in nature prevented their coming to the revolutionary conclusion for which Darwin even then was doggedly accumulating an impressive mass of evidence. Aside from theological considerations, which they frequently urged against contemporary development theories (regardless of their contempt for orthodoxy), the shocking wastefulness of Darwin's concept of evolution would have repelled them. And the poorly documented evolutionary systems of Lamarck and Robert Chambers were not very persuasive. It is hardly remarkable, then, that the theory of separate creations was the only explanation they could find. Neither was it remarkable that Morton, together with his vociferous publicizers, Nott and Gliddon, was not alone in arriving at this explanation of Nature's manifold aspect.

"Consideration for the
Public Feelings"

Spending the winter of 1845 in Europe, Gliddon found much good news to convey to Dr. Morton. He discovered that his friend's work was "the subject of much conversation" in the scientific circles of Paris. Both the *Americana* and the *Aegyptiaca* had been translated into French, and Dr. Boudin was seeking a publisher. The archeologist Paul Botta sent his compliments, and the poet-orientalist Jean Pierre Pauthier was Morton's "warm advocate." The old geographer and archeologist Edme François Jomard was pleased with the *Aegyptiaca,* and though Letronne, the Egyptologist, had not yet read the work, Gliddon had hinted that it would be greatly to his advantage to do so.[1]

Accompanying his letters, Gliddon sent skulls, books, and minerals, the latter from a cousin living in Australia, whom he had "crammed" with "enthusiasm to serve" Morton. Moreover, the craniologist could expect to augment his collections from still other parts of the world, for Gliddon's younger brother Henry was to enter a situation in Bombay, and his youngest brother was off to Borneo. Now there were "Gliddon's in Australia, India, Borneo, and Paris!" Gliddon had been successful in gathering "a choice armory for Theological polemics" and would return to America with "plenty of stuff to set the Dogmatists at loggerheads!" Even now he was busily translating a manuscript, to be entitled "Chronos," which would probably create something of a stir in theological circles. "Poor Parsons!" he lamented happily, "how the work . . . will demolish all their chronological edifices." He had also gathered up a wife during the stay in Europe, cousin Anne of the Bayswater days. He now sternly hoped, as he wrote his friend John R. Bartlett, that despite his affection for

American women—"as, take them all in all, their virtues far out vie those of sophisticated *Europe*"—he would now, as a husband, "obtain credit for a platonic admiration for American Ladies," a credit hitherto denied by his "d——d good natured friends." All in all, at Paris, "the *centre* of the Earth!" things were looking up: "every door is open, and I shall get all I want."[2]

It was just at such moments as these, when every door was open—experience should have taught him to expect it—that things began to melt away and life slipped out of kilter. There were family quarrels, a sister broke off her engagement "at the 11th hour," and a brother was stranded in Egypt. Too, the crossing in the autumn of forty-six was stormy. But for one small ray of sunshine, the voyage would have been miserable indeed. The "Sea broke into the Second Cabin, & smashed one box" of skulls he was bringing to Morton, "setting the heads floating among the passengers, who were scared to death for a report reached them that the Cook was killed and washed out of the galley," and one of the heads was generally assumed to be the cook's, "as it washed to and fro in the mess!!"[3]

Even back in the Republic the gloom continued, and in the following autumn, Gliddon was hard pressed for cash. The size of his audiences gave no cause for complaint, but he now had an infant son and a brother as well as a wife to maintain. In Charleston during November, however, his lectures were unusually successful, and he was entertained in the best Southern tradition by the scientists of the city and their families. He probably intended to remain there a while longer to profit from both the stimulating intellectual atmosphere and the large audiences, but learning that Professor Louis Agassiz was coming down from Harvard to lecture to Charlestonians, and not wishing, both for his own sake and that of "the cause," to be placed in competition for audiences with Agassiz, he decided to push on to Columbia with news of the latest developments in "Hierological Science." There he was hospitably received by Dr. Robert W. Gibbes and the professors of the College and rejoiced to learn that his host had triumphed in a local skirmish in the public prints with the Reverend Dr. John Bachman of Charleston, a notorious friend of the unity of man. Moving on in January, 1848, to Savannah, where again he found audiences gratifyingly large, he wrote Morton a comprehensive report on his Southern tour. Throughout these states he had found the educated classes much interested in ethnology and particularly in Morton's researches. "Of course," he wrote, "your name and deeds are hourly occurring with those I meet in private; while my public discourses, as you are aware, are based upon your investigations. I can assure you, that you are known, with honor, to an extent often marvellous." In Savannah, for example, he found Dr. Richard D. Arnold, one of the South's really distinguished physicians, "full of enthusiasm about your works."

That something of a stir was being created by certain latecomers who had taken up and publicly preached Morton's doctrine of the "diversity of races" was a puzzle to Gliddon. He was inclined to "smile" when he heard the excited talk; "as if it were a novel doctrine to *you*, and by reverberation, to me! 'How long, O Lord! how long?' have you not asserted the *fact*, and I preached it?"[4]

Gliddon was correct. Morton had long been convinced of the specific diversity of the races, although he had not explicitly stated his conviction in print. Even apart from him the idea was not new; various individuals had surreptitiously examined it where it had long lain in the market place of ideas. Nott was definitely interested, and Morton's close friend Charles Pickering, the botanist, had almost walked off with it only a few years previously. Perhaps it was from Pickering's experience that the craniologist had learned caution.

Pickering had served as naturalist for the United States Exploring Expedition, the government's first venture into overseas exploration and one which was to play an important part in the organization of American science. Between 1838 and 1842 the expedition, under the command of Lieutenant Charles Wilkes, explored the east and west coasts of North and South America and more than two hundred islands in the Atlantic and Pacific, and confirmed the existence of the antarctic region. Pickering had written from the Fiji Islands in the summer of 1840 that his investigations had changed his theories of race. He cautioned Morton not to divulge the contents of the letter, "for various reasons; some of them sufficiently obvious, and among others—because . . . I may find it hereafter convenient to modify my opinions very essentially. I have never yet found any place I have visited, [to] correspond altogether with my preconceived notions." But the notions he had formed by the time he had seen the Fijis altogether corresponded with those Morton was himself conceiving.[5]

Pickering had long thought that man originated in the tropics, and in Tahiti his belief was confirmed. He and some of his fellow scientists had made a journey into the mountains during the rainy season and "could not help remarking that the natives were perfectly *dry*, 10 minutes after a shower of rain, while our clothes once wet continued so the whole day!, and the same thing happens in a minor degree from perspiration.—Was the human skin ever intended to be exposed to a perpetual *Steam-bath*?" He found that it was a common remark among the islanders "that they never 'took colds till they began to wear clothes'!" Pickering concluded from this that man must have originated in a warm climate, that "time has been, when there was no member of the Human family without the Tropicks." His observations had indicated that "among the millions of species, of plants & animals, scattered over this immense Globe," not a single being had ever been "modified or moulded by Climate, but always adapted by nature precisely to that climate in which it is naturally found." If climate were responsible for the character of the organism, northern man would be born with a natural covering, whatever the region of his origin. He was impressed with the precision of adaptation. It was a well-known fact that genera of anmials and plants were restricted to their peculiar countries, but he noted that this rule applied also to much smaller areas—a fact which so impressed Darwin when he studied the birds of the Galapagos Islands. Pickering found "a general consonance among all the productions of a district, independent of affinity, and even some external peculiarity, by means of which a Naturalist, with some practice, may often tell the locality." The rule held even in the undeviating climate of the tropics.

These observations had a direct bearing on the position of man in nature. If the adaptation of plants and animals was so precise, was not man likewise adapted to the districts he inhabited? He had always thought, Pickering wrote Morton, that there were five races of men, but "I have now seen 8! and am not without expectation of meeting with others before reaching home." He did not want to discuss the question of whether these constituted species. Since people generally seemed to desire that there be only one species, he was "content to let them have their way." Their victory, however, was a hollow one, for Pickering left them only the label. He insisted that these races had "different origins, or, were originally placed in different countries."

The scientific world eagerly awaited the return of the expedition and publication of its findings. The anthropologists were particularly interested, referring often in their letters simply to "the U.S. Ex. Ex." Although the squadron returned in 1842, the results of Pickering's researches were not published until 1848. The delay was due to his difficulty in obtaining the consent of a small group of politicians who made up the joint Committee of the Library of Congress. Well aware that his findings were theologically unorthodox, and therefore politically imprudent, Pickering tried to obtain consent for publication without submitting his manuscript to the committee, seeking thereby to spare tender sensibilities delicately attuned to Scripture and congressional elections. He sent his rather unusual request to his friend Morton, who blandly forwarded it to the irascible Wilkes, now promoted to commander, who was supervising preparation of the various reports.[6]

This was unthinkable, the Commander replied with some heat; Pickering had no right to make such a request. Certainly the committee would not grant it, "& the very reason the Dr. assigns, viz. that 'the Public mind is peculiarly sensitive on such subjects' would be the very one that would operate most strongly with them & why they would give no assurance whatever." Wilkes did not believe that the members of the committee themselves had any opinions on the subject—"whether we are derived from a single pair or fifty"—but there were other considerations. Morton should know that the public eye is always upon the politician. A congressional committee, "however freely they may think themselves, on these subjects, may deem that it is extremely necessary to be cautious in publishing any new philosophical inquiries relative to the History of man, wishing to avoid although willing that the subject . . . be treated most fully, anything that may shock the public mind." Political considerations aside, Wilkes saw in this cautious procedure "great propriety as well as consideration for the public feelings." Indeed it would, he felt, "tend greatly to the advantage of the Dr. himself." Pickering doubtless "would avoid any departure from highly moral and correct views." Still, members of Congress, "though not understanding the subject on which he has written at all scientifically," were expert in reading the public mind and might "save him" from "improprieties" by pointing out "where alterations might be made advantageously" —without, of course, "interfering with the proper elucidation of his subject." Wilkes's letter was ungrammatical doubletalk, but it made his point. His advice to Pickering was to share this view of the matter and to submit the manuscript for examination.[7]

Commander Wilkes was undoubtedly right when he stated that committee members would be cautious in publishing "new philosophical inquiries relative to the History of man": the public mind would have been shocked. But when he stated that no member of the committee had "any scruples whatever on the subject," he was only technically correct. While still a judge in Steubenville, Benjamin Tappan, brother of those two staunch angels of the antislavery cause, Arthur and Lewis Tappan, had corresponded with Morton on various scientific matters. Now an antislavery senator from Ohio, he served as agent for the committee from 1843 until his resignation in May, 1846. Evidently Tappan strongly objected to the publication of Pickering's manuscript, for in a letter to Tappan in 1845, Wilkes reported that "Dr. Pickering has lost I think many of the strange notions that you complained of, and his uncle Mr. John Pickering . . . told me the parts of his paper on the races of man that you criticized and objected to, had been rejected and he thought you could have no possible objection to its publication, now." Pickering desired to see his work published. "Although I know your aversion to have anything to do with it," Wilkes wrote, still he hoped that the Senator would soon give consent; otherwise, "the investigation of the races which many look to as the most interesting branch of science to be developed by our researches will be incomplete." At least one critic of Southern institutions had his eye on contemporary developments in science.[8]

The result of submitting Pickering's scientific observations to the test of universal suffrage was The Races of Man and Their Geographical Distribution (Philadelphia, 1848), a large volume, unwieldy both physically and intellectually. None of the book is completely intelligible, and the chapter on "Zoological Deductions" is the most ambiguous and vague of all. Francis Parkman had not yet read the book, but he had heard rumors: it was "obscure" in "method and arrangement," and it derived "the races of mankind from one source." Its informed confusion caused the book to be quoted confidently by all parties to the controversy. An English defender of the unity of man actually wrote a preface for one of the London editions to show from Pickering's findings that all the races were "DESCENDED FROM ONE COMMON PARENT."[9]

By close attention to such phrases as "according to another principle," "the supposition . . . put forth by some writers," "the custom may be noted," one is able painfully to pick out the meaning Pickering so skilfully hid from members of Congress. Before the return of the expedition, he had seen eleven races. He denied that climate or any other environmental circumstance had ever modified "species of organic beings" and rather boldly asserted that "each has been originally fitted in structure and constitution, precisely to the station in which it is naturally found." Thus each of the chief divisions of the earth had "its own natural productions." Certain that man had originated in the tropics, Pickering cautiously offered the observation "that the races of men could all be conveniently derived from the same two centres, the one in the East Indies, and the other in Africa; and if we could suppose separate species, this, agreeably to known laws, would reconcile the geographical portion of the subject."[10]

In short, Pickering could find "no middle ground between the admission of eleven distinct species in the human family, and the reduction to one." Many were to quote this statement as evidence of the unity of mankind on the ground that it was ridiculous to speak of eleven human species, but Pickering had noted that "slight external differences" were sufficient to constitute a specific distinction among animals and plants. He who objected that the races were merely varieties met Pickering's assertion that varieties did not appear among mankind, that despite the mixture of races for two hundred years past, no new race had appeared on the American continent. Whatever the timorous notions of the guardians of the public morals on the Library Committee, Pickering himself clearly believed that eleven races of man had been created in two widely separated centers.

Probably unaware of the author's tribulations with Congress, Dr. Oliver Wendell Holmes exclaimed to Morton in 1849, "Is not Pickering's book the oddest collection of fragments that was ever seen? I have been more puzzled to find the law of association by which many of his observations are brought together than the *savans* ever were by the Rosetta Stone." Frankly, Dr. Holmes thought the book "amorphous as a fog, unstratified as a dumpling and heterogeneous as a low priced sausage," and expressed a preference for "the severe and cautious character" of Morton's researches, "which from their very nature are permanent data for all future students of ethnology."[11]

It was well that Morton's publications never had to pass the scrutiny of Congress. What Pickering was trying to say through the gag imposed by the Library Committee, what honeyed intimidations had urged Squier not to say, what Morton had been hinting at for years, had finally got said in 1846 when Morton sent an account of his collection of crania to the newly formed American Ethnological Society. Emboldened by the work of his colleagues, here for the first time publicly, he clearly set forth his conclusions concerning the origin of races. Although he had already seen enough of the material Squier and Davis had turned up to be convinced that the Mound Builders were of the same race as the modern Indians, he did not believe that the Indians and the Mound Builders were descended from a single pair. On the contrary, he believed "that they have originated from several, perhaps even from many pairs, which were adapted, from the beginning, to the varied localities they were designed to occupy. . . . In other words, I regard the American nations as the true *autochthones*, the primeval inhabitants of this vast continent; and when I speak of their being of one race or of one origin, I allude only to their indigenous relation to each other, as shown in all those attributes of mind and body which have been so amply illustrated by modern ethnography."

He then proceeded to explode another myth. Researches in his collection of Egyptian crania, for which he acknowledged indebtedness to Gliddon, had proved that "the Egyptians had no national affiliation with the Negro races." Further, because they depicted Negroes and Indians separately and distinctly, the Nilotic monuments provided "contrasts" which looked "back to a period of time little short of five thousand years." The Egyptians were not Negroes, but products of the crossing of a race indigenous to the valley of the Nile with a race of conquering invaders from Asia.[12]

John R. Bartlett, corresponding secretary of the American Ethnological Society, read Morton's paper to the members, gathered, as was their custom, at the house of the president, Albert Gallatin. Now ancient and full of honors, Gallatin was distinguished both for his services to the Republic and, as America's most outstanding philologist, for his contributions to anthropological science. The members listened, Bartlett reported, with such interest that at the conclusion a debate took place "between our venerable President and other gentlemen." Although he "expressed a strong desire" to write Morton about this paper, Gallatin was now too old and infirm to hold the pen and urged Bartlett to question Morton regarding his theory of Indian origins. This last of the Jeffersonians, himself a scientist, was a little alarmed at the findings of the new science of craniology. It was Morton's omission of the Eskimo from his discussion of the Indians that disturbed Gallatin. The Eskimo tribes had generally been considered relatives of the Indians, remnants of the great migration from Asia that populated the New World. Resembling both the Indian and the Mongolian, the Eskimo was a testimonial—as Samuel Stanhope Smith had noted—to the Asiatic peopling of America and, therefore, to the specific unity of the human race. Gallatin's own philological researches had provided further evidence of the similarity of Eskimo and Indian and had shown, he asked Bartlett to inform Dr. Morton, "that the inference to be drawn from a comparison of the grammatical structure of the Eskimaux and other American dialects" was that they belonged "to the same family." He had no collection of crania, he had no drawings of skulls, and he would not question Dr. Morton's classification, but "he wished me to ask," Bartlett wrote—and one can almost hear the imperturbable Jefferson asking—"whether climate, habits or local causes might not produce a material change in the physical character of a people rendering them as different as the Eskimaux and the N. American Indians."[13]

Gallatin's queries were of little moment to Morton, for he, together with Nott, Gliddon, and Squier, had no confidence in philology as a means of tracing racial origins and relationships. Anthropology had outgrown philology. Philology was not sufficiently exact, did not lend itself to the precise measurement which the new anthropology demanded. In his reply to Bartlett, Morton pointed out that the island of Madagascar contained three races, Mongols, Hindus, and Negroes, two of them exotic; yet all spoke the same language. Philology was "a broken reed," he wrote rather shortly. Languages were influenced by circumstances; physical characters were permanent.[14]

Morton was not to be deterred from his investigations by such tenuous objections as these, for anthropology was making rapid advances and daily gaining in prestige. Under his direction ethnology had gained eminence among the sciences, until, as Squier announced, it had become "essentially the science of the age; the offspring of that prevailing mental and physical energy which neglects no subject of inquiry" and brings the "most widely separated and diverse nations, with some knowledge of their history, institutions and condition, at once under view, enabling the student to arrive at conclusions under no other circumstances attainable." It was, too, a matter of no little pride that ethnology was "not only the science of the age," it was also pre-eminently "an American science"; for only in America were three of the great families of men living in close proximity. Do we wish to know, Squier asked, in what direction and at what speed civilization developed "among a people separated from the rest of the world, insulated physically and mentally," and totally dependent upon the elements of its own character? "The inquirer," he announced, "must turn to America, where alone he can hope to find the primitive conceptions, beliefs and practices of an entire original people," largely unimpaired by contact with other peoples. "Do we desire to discover the results which must follow from the blending of men of different races and families? Do we inquire in what consists the superiority of certain families over others; to what extent they may assimilate with, to what repel each other, and how their relations may be adjusted so as to produce the greatest attainable advantage to both? The practical solution of these problems can only be found in America. . . ."[15]

Under these circumstances it was hardly surprising that for Squier the greatest of the modern ethnologists was an American—Dr. Morton. Morton had settled two of the basic problems in ethnology. He had proved that the Egyptians were Caucasians and not Negroes, and he had proved that the American Indian was a race distinct from all others and derived from a separate origin. Other scientists had recognized the validity of these conclusions but were too timid to defend them. The doctrine of diversity of origin was still considered a heresy, Squier noted, and had yet "few open advocates," so that "investigators in this, as in many other departments of science, hesitate in pushing their researches to their ultimate results." Squier suggested that discussion of the question could not long be postponed, and added defiantly, "it is not difficult to foresee in what manner it will be finally determined."

As it happened, final determination of the question was not left to American scientists, but public discussion was considerably accelerated with the appearance in America of a new disciple of diversity, Louis Agassiz.

The Geographical Distribution of Race and Grace

While Gliddon was in Savannah, news of Agassiz's Charleston lectures reached him. He remarked wistfully to Morton that the professor had probably "reaped *golden* tokens of his scientific success there." More important, however, was the intelligence that Agassiz had chosen to lecture on anthropology and had, in fact, maintained "the diversity of Races in his public lectures." He had announced to the Charlestonians "that the Mosaic account only mentions *one* race" and that "the brain of the Negro is that of the imperfect brain of a 7 month's infant in the womb of the White." Here was an important acquisition to the cause.[1]

Charles Pickering, unable to persuade Congress to underwrite the unscriptural doctrine of the specific diversity of man, hid his theories under a bushel of confused verbiage. Morton approached the radical doctrine with caution. But, in Louis Agassiz, America gained a new scientist of recognized authority who felt no such compunctions. Long before he appeared in Boston in 1846 with the intention of studying the fossil fishes of the New World, Agassiz had gained prominence in the world's scientific community. He had served as professor of natural history at Neuchâtel since 1832, having declined positions at Heidelberg, Geneva, and Lausanne. A scientist certainly, yet something of a showman as well, he was to dramatize zoology for Americans as Gliddon had dramatized ancient Egypt.

During the weeks before his departure from Switzerland, Agassiz had delivered a final course of twelve lectures on the "Plan de la Création," in the last of which, "Notice sur la géographie des animaux," he emphatically proclaimed his belief in the specific unity of man. "All organized beings, plants as well as animals, are confined to a special area," he announced. "Man alone is spread over the whole surface of the earth." This was all that the staunchest defender of unity could ask. And yet, the professor's defense of unity was not so well documented as his argument for the geographical distribution of the lower animals; indeed, it appeared to be a perfunctory afterthought.[2]

Agassiz admitted that "at first glance" the proposition seemed somewhat paradoxical," but the paradox was not resolved at succeeding glances. Reviewing the localization of various species of animals in their zoological provinces, he pronounced it "a demonstrated fact" that the "natural limits of the different races" coincided "more or less with the distribution of animals." Thus the northern "polar race" which extended over three continents, corresponded "exactly in its distribution" to the polar fauna, which likewise extended over three continents. The same curious fact appeared in the Southern Hemisphere. Although in America the relationship did not appear with the same precision, yet even there, as the animal species ranged widely, so, too, did the red man. If the distribution of animal species was the result of their having been created in the regions they were to inhabit, was then the coincidence between the distribution of human races and the distribution of animal species the result of the same cause? "Evidently not," Agassiz answered, "And here is revealed anew the superiority of the human genre and its greater independence in nature. Whereas the animals are distinct species in the different zoological provinces to which they appertain, man, despite the diversity of his races, constitutes one and the same species over all the surface of the globe." Man was an "exceptional being" in the creation of which he was both "the purpose and the expression."

Agassiz made no attempt to explain the physical divergencies of the human species. He had delivered his opinion and the reader was left to conclude that man, unlike the rest of animate nature, was created, not in several regions, but in one; was descended, not from many stocks, but from one original pair; that his differences were the product, not of the shaping hand of the Creator, but of environmental influences. Thus Agassiz's commitment to unity was tenuous indeed. It was a mere opinion, grounded not on the firm basis of scientific observation, but on the crumbling dogma of scriptural anti-science. He had yet to fix upon man the observant eye with which he had so successfully laid open the secrets of the rest of the animal kingdom. Science abhors exceptions.

Upon his arrival in the United States, Professor Agassiz was given the traditional welcome accorded distinguished visitors. John Amory Lowell, director of the Lowell Institute, had already arranged for Agassiz to deliver the Lowell Institute Lectures for 1846. Having arrived in Boston in October, Agassiz used the weeks before his lectures were to begin to tour the scientific centers of the United States. He journeyed to New Haven where he met "the patriarch of science in America," Benjamin Silliman, with whom he had corresponded for some years past, and young James Dwight Dana, whom Agassiz thought "likely to be the most distinguished naturalist in the United States." Traveling by steamer to New York, he spent one day there before moving on to Princeton where he joined Asa Gray. There he met America's other great botanist, John Torrey, and examined Professor Joseph Henry's famous electrical apparatus. But Philadelphia interested him most of all. In a long letter to his mother in Switzerland he devoted several pages to a description of his experiences there.[3]

Like any visitor who wished to acquaint himself with the progress of science in that city, he went immediately to Dr. Morton at the Academy of Natural Sciences. He was so impressed that he hardly left the building during his stay. "Imagine," he wrote eagerly, "a series of six hundred skulls, mostly Indian, of all the tribes who now inhabit or formerly inhabited America. Nothing else like it exists elsewhere. This collection alone is worth a journey to America." The two scientists were much pleased with each other. Morton presented Agassiz with a copy of his *Crania Americana*, and Agassiz, describing to a friend in Europe the state of science and learning in America mentioned in the company of Emerson, Dana, Bache, Bowditch, and Gray, "Dr. Morton, of Philadelphia, well known as the author of several papers upon fossils, and still better by his great work upon the indigenous races of America." Agassiz's friend, Jules Marcou, who accompanied him on later visits to Morton's home, remembered Agassiz's enthusiasm and remarked that Agassiz "had, at last, found a naturalist to his own liking, without any reserve." "After George Cuvier, Morton was the only zoologist who had any influence on Agassiz's mind and scientific opinions." For his part, Dr. Morton was equally pleased. He was "delighted" with Agassiz's "astonishing memory, quick perceptions, encyclopedical knowledge of Natural History & most pleasing manner. There is no affectation or distrust about him. He has spent most of his time at the Academy, & has already made some very important discoveries in Paleontology." The two remained warm friends for the rest of Morton's career.[4]

Impressive as Morton's anthropological Golgotha was, it was nothing compared to the living anthropological specimens who waited table in Agassiz's hotel in Philadelphia. Never before having been in such proximity to Negroes, Agassiz was shocked. A long and revealing passage described to his mother his first impressions of black men. Their color, he reported, their peculiar limbs and hands, large lips, and black heads topped with wool instead of hair inspired such a fascination of disgust that he must have stared most discourteously, and when his waiter approached, he could hardly refrain from bolting the room. The experience convinced him, he wrote, that, though the Negro was human, he was not of the same species as the white man. The fact that these beings lived in such great numbers in the Southern states would someday, he predicted, cause the downfall of the Republic. Anyone could easily see that the Negro was not the white's equal, and almost everyone did. Even in Boston, where they were free, Negroes were excluded by the force of instinctive repugnance. Even the abolitionists, who were fighting for equal political rights for the Negro, did not allow their daughters to marry them.

This unnerving experience and probably also his conversations with Morton as together they pored over the specimens of the "American Golgotha" produced a marked change in Agassiz's anthropological views. His first contact with the black man was decisive, and as Marcou remarked, "Agassiz was too good a naturalist, too much accustomed to differentiate animals, to accept unity in the genus *Homo*." Thus his reference to the origin of man in his Lowell Lectures contradicted the theory he had expressed in the *Revue suisse* the year before and created somewhat of a stir. The botanist John Torrey, who was hoping to persuade Agassiz to deliver a series of lectures in New York, was alarmed by news brought by John Augustine Smith that Agassiz had voiced opinions "in regard to the origin of human race[s]" that Boston considered "hostile to revealed religion" and had subsequently been "attacked in one of the pulpits of Boston!" Torrey wrote to his old friend Asa Gray for reassurance; if these rumors were true, he did not want to lend his influences "to the diffusion of such sentiments." Besides, it would be difficult to get subscribers to the lectures unless he could assure them that their "religious opinions" would "not be affected."

Gray had not been offended. Indeed, he had found Agassiz's "references to the Creator" so "natural and unconstrained as to show that they were never brought in for effect." Agassiz, he assured Torrey, had simply restated the position which he had long held: that animals and plants were created in large numbers in the regions they now occupy, that there have been several creations of these plants and animals, the last being at the beginning of the "historic era." This "is all we want," Gray wrote pleasantly, "to harmonize Geology with Genesis." Agassiz had merely eliminated from his general view of nature an important exception that did violence to the whole, and the rumor abroad in New York was simply an exaggerated account of a few remarks made at the close of his lectures. He had applied his views on geographical distribution to man by asserting that Negroes and Malays were not descended from the sons of Noah, but from distinct ancestors. Gray did not himself accept the view, "rejecting it," he explained, "on other than scientific grounds, of which he does not feel the force as we do." But Gray did not object to Agassiz stating it, for Agassiz had dealt tenderly with Scripture: "so far from bringing this against the Bible, he brings the Bible to sustain his views,—thus appealing to its authority, instead of endeavoring to overthrow it. . . . We may reject his conclusions, but we cannot find fault with his spirit."[5]

After repeating his Lowell Lectures in Albany, Agassiz delivered another course in Charleston, South Carolina, in November, 1847. There, to his delight, he discovered "new fishes, new turtles, new molluscs." Brought again into contact with the Negro, he reaffirmed his discovery of a new species of man. There, as Gliddon had reported, he stated his views on the origin of races before the Charleston Literary Club.[6]

Gliddon had doubted whether the professor indorsed these views elsewhere than Charleston, but all doubts were laid to rest when in 1850 and 1851 Agassiz wrote three articles for the Unitarian *Christian Examiner*. The first dealt with geographical distribution of animals. Agassiz complained that the greatest obstacle to investigation of the subject was the common notion, wholly without scientific basis, which ascribed "to all living beings upon earth one common centre of origin," from which they supposedly "spread over wider and wider areas, till they finally came into their present state of distribution." Incontrovertible scientific evidence belied this vulgar assumption. "Wherever we trace the animals in their present distributions," he noted, "we find them scattered over the surface of our globe in such a manner, according to such laws, and under such special adaptations, that it would baffle the most fanciful imagination to conceive such . . . arrangement as the mere result of migrations, or the influence of physical causes." The flora and fauna of the Arctic were uniform and those of the temperate zone less so, the differences growing "more and more prominent as we approach the tropical zone, which has its peculiar Fauna and Flora in each continent." This precise "arrangement" was surely "the result of a premeditated plan" unfolding in conformity with "predetermined laws." There were so many evidences of design that Agassiz was convinced that "animals were primarily created all over the world, within those districts which they were naturally to inhabit for a certain time."[7]

The equally popular theory that animals were created in pairs was likewise false. It was merely an assumption resting on no firmer ground than the belief that it showed "a wise economy of means in the established order of things." Its value, therefore, "might fairly be questioned by naturalists." It was natural for some animals to live in pairs. But whoever heard of a "pair of herrings or a pair of buffaloes"? Did beehives ever consist of a "pair of bees"? Among such species as bees, the males outnumbered the females. Was it likely that *they* had been created in pairs? Agassiz himself took a "more natural view" of the matter: "most animals and plants" had originated "over the whole extent of their natural distribution."

He suggested that the differences between the races of men might also be "primitive," but cautiously abstained from "further details upon a subject involving so many difficult problems as the question of unity or plurality of origin of the human family."

Agassiz's first article appeared in March. By July he overcame caution and published a second, "The Diversity of Origin of Human Races." His object now was to prove that racial distinctions were primordial. He disposed of environment as a causal factor by opposing to it the "law" of zoögeography outlined in his first article. The arrangement of species and genera betrayed a design, "a superior order, established from higher and considerate views, by an intelligent Creator." There was no reason why the Creator should have shown less consideration for His own image. The rule held, he found, even in Africa, where, though the inhabitants were all black, still the tribes differed gradually until the Hottentot was reached. The one great exception to the law of human distribution was the American Indian, whom Morton had shown to be of the same race wherever he resided in the hemisphere. But even the exception invalidated the argument that climate created racial distinctions, for the race remained the same despite the greatest possible climatic variations.[8]

Chronology, likewise, suggested that climate did not possess the power to produce variations, for a great period of time would be necessary for the production of such differences as there now were between the races, and sufficient time had not existed. The monuments of Egypt proved that "five thousand years ago the negroes were as different from the white race as they are now, and that, therefore, neither time nor climate nor change of habitation has produced the differences." To assume that they are of the "same order," then, and "to assert their common origin, is to assume and to assert what has no historical or physiological foundation." That is to say, racial differences did not appear in time: they came about at once.

The inefficacy of climate meant that the present distinctions must have preceded migrations "from a supposed common centre." All facts, then, pointed to the conclusion that the races of men, like the animals and plants inhabiting the same regions, must have been created throughout the area of their present habitats. "These conditions," Agassiz pointed out, "are the conditions necessary to their maintenance, and what among organized beings is essential to their temporal existence must be at least one of the conditions under which they were created."

This was of course the old argument of design, but Agassiz's theory of geographical distribution did not rest exclusively upon his conception of the intellectual attributes of the Almighty. It was based also on his own observations of the distribution of fishes. Zoologists had long been puzzled by the phenomenon of animals of the same species inhabiting widely separated localities, and most had believed that migration from a common center was the explanation. Agassiz thought the assumption unwarranted. Simply to assume, he complained, "that perches, pickerels, trouts and so many other species found in every brook and every river in the temperate zone, have been transported from one basin to another, by freshets, or by water-birds" was "to assume very inadequate and accidental causes for general phenomena." Once it was granted that these animals were created in the areas they now occupied, there was "no further difficulty in understanding."

Agassiz had begun his article on the geographical distribution of man with a ringing declaration designed to clear the arena for the purely scientific approach and to remove such objections as those raised by Gray in his refusal to accept Aggasiz's view of racial origins: "We have a right to consider the question growing out of men's physical relations as merely scientific questions, and to investigate them without reference to either politics or religion." This bold assertion, however, was somewhat tempered by his attempt to show that, anyway, his view of man's origin did not conflict with Scripture. Genesis is very unclear on whether there was one creation or many. The creation of Adam is described in some detail, yet Cain married someone's daughter, and surely she was not Adam's. Genesis makes no mention of Indians, Mongolians, or Hottentots: "Hence if we find that these peoples are not descended from Adam and Eve, we shall not have contradicted Genesis."

Moreover, he insisted, his views did not really violate the scriptural doctrine of the specific unity of man. Having burst asunder the unity of man, he neatly put the pieces together again, binding them with a sticky mixture of one part piety, two parts prudishness. Many had thought, he said, seizing the miter from his ecclesiastical opponents, that the unity of man depended upon a common ancestry. This definition of species was "derived from a mere sensual connection." It was a definition which, if it were borne in mind that man was created in the image of his Maker, could not be too strongly reprobated. Agassiz was pained. "We need not search," he said, "for the highest bond of humanity in a mere animal function." His sensibilities offended, Agassiz insisted upon "this distinction," that "unity of species does not involve . . . unity of origin" and that "diversity of origin does not involve . . . plurality of species." The truth of the matter was, there was no general rule in zoology by which one could differentiate species: "what constitutes species in certain types is something very different from what constitutes . . . species in other types" (an observation that was to be made with increasing frequency by twentieth-century taxonomists). Yet he was certain that all men were of the same species because he found "such a community of physical constitution, such a unity of type, such an essential difference from the character of even the highest animals"—even from "those highest monkey tribes which in physical development come nearest to the human frame." The monkey proceeded upon all fours, his upper hands "not yet emancipated from that bondage to the flesh" for "the higher services of the spirit." The erect position and the versatile hand, not to mention "intellectual and moral qualities," were common to all men (in varying degrees) and distinguished equally all men from the lower animals.

There was little to be gained by allowing oneself to be damned as a heretic if one could prevent it. Thus in a third article Agassiz attempted to prove the basic orthodoxy of the doctrine of diverse origins. This took the form of an attack on theories of development—all of which were heretical in the extreme. It was a shrewd tactic, for it allowed him at one stroke both to entrench himself behind the fundamentals of orthodoxy and to shatter the lumbering machinery of development hypotheses which the enemy was bringing to the siege. Impressed by the niceties of geographical distribution, he concluded that the divisions of the animal kingdom were originally thoughts in the mind of the Creator: each animal species was "a manifestation of a special thought," each family "a combination of similar thoughts," and "every great division of the animal kingdom" a "particular train of reflection upon a fundamental idea."

Recognition of this truth excluded "forever" the notion of development and possessed the additional merit of acknowledging "a personal intelligent God." The presence of two or more species in the same area invalidated the notion that mere physical laws had "called into existence any living being." Gradations in the animal kingdom represented, not development of the organisms from one ancestor, but "successive thoughts" in the mind of the Creator. Gradations evident in geology, comparative anatomy, and embryology indicated, not development, but "modifications of the same thoughts." He had condemned those who tried to force nature into a theological mold, into conformity with the idea of a single creation of primordial pairs. He himself found it "much more in harmony with the laws of nature" to admit that in the beginning the Creator "sowed the seeds of animals and plants in large numbers all over the fields they were to occupy."[9]

Agassiz, like the Jeffersonians, was impressed with the general economy of nature, the harmony between man and his environment. Like the Jeffersonians, he looked out upon an orderly universe in which nothing was left to chance. And like the Jeffersonians, he saw the question of equality as one which only science could answer. However, Agassiz chafed under the tyrannical restrictions laid upon science by the Declaration of Independence. Determination of the descent of human races was a question of natural history which ought to be investigated freely by scientists unhampered by the paralyzing tyranny of social or political theories. They should not be deterred by the fear of discovering that men were unequal. The very fact that races do exist "presses upon us," Agassiz asserted, "the obligation to settle their "relative rank." It was an exceedingly difficult problem, but it was the duty of philosophers "to look it in the face." No man could be expected to say what would be the best education, for example, for the various races "in consequences of primitive differences" so long as "the principle itself" was "generally opposed." It was the duty of American scientists "to study these peculiarities, and to do all that is in our power to develop them to the greatest advantage of all parties." Any other course was "mock-philanthropy and mock-philosophy."[10]

There were those who believed that the South had recognized the duty, that its peculiar institution was developing the black man's peculiarities to the advantage of all parties. Nott wrote his friend Squier that Agassiz's article was a "clincher" and warmly welcomed Agassiz to the camp of the new scientists.[11]

Undoubtedly Agassiz's statement caused persons to consider the question who had never before given it much thought. After the appearance of Agassiz's first two articles, Nathan L. Frothingham (1797–1870), minister of the Unitarian First Church of Boston for thirty-five years, anticipated the queries of the orthodox. "Men before Adam! Men even contemporary with that great progenitor! Men of another line . . . and owning no connection with him whom the whole Christian world from the beginning has agreed to recognize as the 'federal head' of our common humanity! What new heresy is this?" He had expected to hear "many exclamations of this kind" when the *Christian Examiner* published Agassiz's views, and he had "not been wholly disappointed." He himself had always "felt inclined" to the belief that all men were descended from a single pair, and Agassiz had not changed his mind, but he vigorously defended freedom of inquiry and insisted that "in no case whatever should the student of physical science be checked or limited in his inquiries by the supposed authority of any ancient writing, however sacred." He then proceeded to make Unitarian hay under the bright sun of science. Unitarians placed no restrictions on science because they were not committed to the doctrine of the divine inspiration of Scripture. Nevertheless, there were others who, "rather than depart from the letter of the Divine writing," would explain any contradicting natural phenomena "by resorting to supernatural interference." Such persons should remember Galileo, Frothingham warned.[12]

He hastened on to show that the new development in science held no terrors for Unitarianism. It contradicted the account of Genesis, but biblical scholarship revealed that "Adam" was there used as a "generic term" and Cain was merely a "mythological, representative man." It contradicted the doctrines of the Fall of Man and Original Sin, which had struck "terror" into "the heart of the world." But the contradictions carried "no danger" to those who rejected these doctrines as "misconceptions of the Gospel." Some feared the new theory might destroy "the doctrine of the brotherhood of mankind," for how can men be "of the same lineage, if they have no common progenitor"? "We are no less men," Frothingham replied, because descended from "several original heads" instead of only two. Although he himself did not agree with Agassiz's theory, he was sufficiently convinced of its probable acceptance that he turned it against the Trinitarians and began to beat a pathway for it through the theological undergrowth.

Moncure Conway (1832–1907), then a youth of nineteen in Warrenton, Virginia, experienced considerably more difficulty in adapting himself to Agassiz's theory, and before succeeding he had undergone political, and indirectly, even religious conversion. Recalling the event from the vantage point of old age, he found that before 1850 he had believed the Negro to be inferior, but was still "searching for principles" to justify his position. Here was a young man who, with the instincts of a reformer, was already devoted to the cause of universal education. He had found, however, that in this cause "slavery barred my way in every direction. Before my radical

Jeffersonianism the negro stood demanding recognition as a man and a brother; else he must be treated as an inferior animal."[13]

"At this moment the new theory of Agassiz appeared—that the races of mankind are not from a single pair." Conway took his problem to Spencer F. Baird, who had been his professor of zoology at Dickinson College and was now at the Smithsonian. Finding that Baird agreed with Agassiz, Conway told the Franklin Lyceum of Warrenton "that the negro was not a man within the meaning of the Declaration of Independence." The reaction was immediate. "All the other members, though not antislavery, exclaimed against the 'infidelity' of the theory, though none answered my argument that Negroes, if human, were entitled to liberty. My eccentric views were talked about, and I found myself the centre of a religious tempest in little Warrenton. If the negro was not descended from Adam he had not like us whites inherited depravity. And wherefore our missions to the many non-Caucasian races?" Conway then sat down and wrote out his beliefs in an "elaborate essay" in which he concluded that "the 'Caucasian' race is the highest species; and that this supreme race has the same right of dominion over the lower species of his genus that he has over quadrupeds."

Something, however, perhaps "the dumb answers of the coloured servants moving about the house, cheerfully yielding . . . unrequited services," soon brought about a reaction which proved to be "the moral crisis" of his life. Conway was shocked by "the ease with which I could consign a whole race to degradation." (One recalls Jefferson's admonition phrased in almost the same words.) The reaction constituted a religious conversion of the eighteenth-century variety, now extinct: "an overwhelming sense of my own inferiority came upon me" and "left me with a determination to devote my life to the elevation and welfare of my fellow-beings, white and black." Thus began Conway's long career in the antislavery movement.

Conway's reaction and that of the good people of Warrenton is revealing. It is a candid picture of the impact that the pronouncement of a noted scientist had upon one man's concept of the Declaration. Agassiz's notion of the "spiritual" unity of mankind was to Conway only an empty phrase, for where Agassiz "feared to tread, my crudity rushed in." The qualitative difference between Caucasian and Negro species which Agassiz had briefly dwelt upon Conway rigorously applied to mean that the Negro was a "lower species." Agassiz had supplied the greatest gift of all, "principles" on which to rest the institution of "dominion."

The new anthropology thrust a dilemma before the Southerner. Genesis, stating that all men are descended from Adam and Eve, certainly implied that all men were of the same species, in the popularly accepted definition of the term. The Southerner was forced either to admit that he was enslaving his fellow men, or, by arguing that the slaves were of a lower species, to reject the scriptural account. He had to accept revelation, equality, and enslavement of his own kind, or Agassiz, inequality, and enslavement of a lower species. To the Southerner—pious, yet the master of slaves, religiously intolerant, yet an enthusiast for science—this was an almost impossible choice. The choice was all the more difficult because of the theological problems involved, problems identical with those Bruno had posed centuries earlier when he boldly argued for the habitability of other planets. If all men were not of the same species and descended from Adam, then which species had inherited original sin? If they had always inhabited distinct provinces, as Agassiz believed, how many Resurrections were there? Of course the pious who accepted the new theory blandly assumed that Adam and Eve were the progenitors of the Caucasian species, but even then they had to face the theological implications of hybridization. Was the mulatto half-saved, half-damned? And the theological problems presented by the quinteroon and octoroon led one into higher mathematics. There was, too, as Conway noted, the practical problem of missions. If Adam and Eve were the first parents of Caucasians, then why send missionaries to carry the blessings of grace to heathen whose own first parents had never fallen from grace? The theory of the specific diversity of man tossed the religious into a theological bramble patch.[14]

"Whoever Heard of a
Cross-Eyed Race?"

The task of completing the argument for the diversity of the human species fell to Morton. His output of anthropological papers increased greatly in the years after 1845. Undoubtedly the entrance, first of Gliddon and Nott, then of Pickering and Squier, into the investigation served to stimulate his writing and to channel interests hitherto spread among geology, paleontology, anatomy, and physiology into the single field of ethnology. His craniological investigations had by this time convinced him beyond a doubt that racial characters were permanent and, consequently, must have appeared in separate creations. It was time, then (Nott had been urging it for years), to launch a full-scale assault on the last remaining obstacle, the rule that species rarely cross and that when such crosses do occur, the offspring is sterile—an assault, in short, against the very foundation of zoological taxonomy, the axiom that fertile reproduction determines specific identity.

Morton collected his materials and at two meetings of the Academy in November, 1846, read a long paper on hybridization, which he then sent to the editors of the *American Journal of Science* at New Haven. Although the ideas presented were scientifically unorthodox and theologically heretical, the Sillimans decided to publish the paper on the ground that "discussion of such questions, not in the spirit of atheism, but in the true line of philosophic enquiry, can do no harm." They did, however, the younger Silliman explained to Morton, "think it proper to add a footnote," stating that they committed themselves to none of the opinions of the author." "Facts," they announced, "are the markings of a Divine hand around and within us, and when studied in all their bearings, they lead in the end to the establishment of truth." Perhaps, but this was neverthe-less an unusual statement for the editors to make, and it jarred against the *Journal's* usual note of hearty good-fellowship in the sci-entific community. It presaged the storm.[1]

"Hybridity in Animals, considered in reference to the question of the Unity of the Human Species" was a survey of the entire ques-tion of hybridization. Since the discovery in 1900 of Mendel's work on heredity there has been a marked revival of interest in hybridiza-tion, and recent zoologists generally accord it an important role in the evolutionary process. Despite the fact that he was concerned primarily with hybridization in animals, which is far less frequent than in plants, Morton's speculations therefore have considerable historical interest. The pioneer in the systematic study of hybridiza-tion was the German botanist Josef Gottlieb Kölreuter (1733–1806), whose experiments were taken up and extended by Karl Friedrich Gärtner (1722–1850). The work of both was well known to the sci-entific community, including Darwin. Their success in producing hybrids, however, did not shake their own or the general conviction, affirmed by John Ray, Buffon (1707–78), and the English surgeon and anatomist John Hunter, that interfertility was a valid test of species.[2]

In taking up the subject of hybridization, Morton assumed that as part of the animal kingdom, man is exposed to the same laws that govern the lower species. All the races of men, he noted, were "capa-ble of producing, with each other, a progeny more or less fertile."

Was it therefore necessary to infer that the races are merely varie-ties of a single species? Aside from the criterion of interfertility, nat-uralists had experienced considerable difficulty in agreeing on a spe-cies concept. Morton himself preferred the criteria given by James Cowles Prichard, "the first Ethnographer of this or any age": "sep-arate origin and distinctness of race, evinced by the constant trans-mission of some characteristic peculiarity of organization." The characteristic peculiarities were so apparent among some groups of animals that anyone would designate them as separate species. No one, for example, would confuse deer and hog, camel and drome-dary, or even sheep and goat. Nevertheless, Morton proceeded to show, even such distinct species as these had on occasion proved in-terfertile. He cited hybrids among species of birds, fishes, insects, and plants. Hybrids had been produced by crossing bull and ewe, buck and sow, deer and sheep, cat and marten.[3]

The infrequency of the phenomenon compelled Morton to conclude that "hybrids, as a general law, are contrary to nature." But infrequency could not serve as a criterion of species for he found "very many exceptions." More hybrids appeared, he believed, in domesticity than in the natural state, and he noted that among many species of quadrupeds and birds, breeders had long been cultivating certain desirable hybrids. He concluded, therefore, that some species were "endowed" with the capacity to produce fertile hybrids and that the greater frequency of hybridization in the domestic state was due to the unnatural proximity of various species and the consequent breakdown of the instinctive repugnance to intermixture which in the feral state was nature's method of preserving species. It appeared to be "a law of nature," he remarked, that "as a species approached the state of domesticity," its "natural repugnance" to intermixture declined, its "latent power of hybridity" came into play, and the probability of its crossing with other species increased.

The optimum conditions provided by domesticity for exercise of the latent power explained why dogs varied so greatly: hounds, terriers, bulldogs, and mastiffs were products of the crossing of domesticated species. Thus it was also with "the most domestic of animals" —man. As the most domestic it should appear "nothing singular if he possessed the power of fertile hybridity."

Having revealed the distinct possibility that man had descended from separate species, Morton added a positive note to the negative evidence he had accumulated. He called attention to "the repugnance of some human races to mix with others," and suggested that this has "only been partially overcome by centuries of proximity, and, above all other means, by a moral degradation consequent to the state of slavery." The repugnance of Europeans toward Negroes was "proverbial" in those parts of Europe where Negroes had appeared. The African showed a repugnance "almost equally natural," for among them "a white skin is not more admired than a black one is with us." Thus the very phenomenon of repugnance that prevented the crossing of feral species became, when applied to man, a test of specificity.[4]

The vast number of species and the curious appearance of variations among them had long puzzled naturalists. Even the great Linnaeus in seeking to account for this phenomenon had been led farther and farther away from his belief in the fixity of species until he came at last to confess bewilderment. Charles Darwin, who in any study of the biological thought of these or any other years is ever present like a Greek chorus in the background, was led to his great discovery by attacking this very problem. To Darwin, who did not know how they appeared, variations were nascent species which were preserved or destroyed by natural selection. To Morton, who did not concern himself with the problem of how variations survived, hybridization explained their appearance. That both men were at work on essentially . the same problem, despite Morton's primary concern with raciology, is evident when one compares their respective authorities. Of the investigators whom Morton cited in regard to hybridization and the species concept, three (the Philadelphia naturalist S. S. Haldeman, the English anatomist Richard Owen, and the English cleric-naturalist William Herbert) were to be listed by Darwin as having in varying degrees anticipated his own hypothesis. Two others, Prichard and Edward Blyth, have since been claimed as Darwin's precursors; while Kölreuter and Lyell supplied Darwin with evidence of crucial importance. In the case of Haldeman and Herbert, Morton noted the identical works of these writers that Darwin was to cite in the "Historical Sketch" which appeared in later editions of the *Origin of Species*. Morton, reviewing in this article the species concepts of other naturalists, called the reader's attention to Haldeman's essay of 1844 on the transmutation of species. He thought it "highly interesting." He noted that Dean Herbert (1778–1847) in his study of bulbous plants had found so many interspecific hybrids that, hoping thereby to retain some element of constancy in nature, he had asserted that "botanical species are only a higher and more permanent class of varieties," and had suggested that not species but genera were immutable. He even noted from results obtained by Herbert and Kölreuter that in some instances fertility of hybrids "exceeds that of the parent plants."[5]

One may well wonder how Morton failed to recognize the survival value inherent in such fertility in the hybrid and, without pushing the comparison to extremes, how it was that Morton was led so far astray from the path zoology was to take—the path first trod by Darwin. The truth is, first, that he was not really so far astray. Morton's approach has since been largely vindicated; for while many of the instances of hybridization which he cited were probably apocryphal, today it is recognized as an important factor operating within the scheme of development that Darwin formulated. Darwin himself, after surveying the problem of hybridization, came to doubt the species criterion of interfertility.[6]

In the second place, it was not Morton but Darwin who was swept by his researches out of the mainstream of contemporary zoology. Like the vast majority of zoologists, Morton could not rid himself completely of the teleological view. Lacking Darwin's commanding powers of imagination, he could not step outside the Christian tradition. Where Darwin needed only one Creation, or by extension of his thought, none at all, Morton needed he himself knew not how many. Finally, it required not only repudiation of the Christian tradition to take the giant stride Darwin was to take; it demanded that one break sharply with the Newtonian view of the cosmos which by this time was so closely intertwined with the Christian tradition: the idea of an orderly, balanced, efficient universe. Yet to Morton God was still the economical Craftsman, if perhaps now a little more generous with miracles than He had been in the Jeffersonian cosmos.

Morton had shown, to his own satisfaction at least, that interfertility was not a valid test of the identity of species and that, consequently, racial interfertility did not prove the unity of the human species. Only structural and phylogenetic relationships remained as species criteria, and on the monuments of Egypt these, in effect, became one. There was plenty of evidence of physical dissimilarities, structural and superficial, and of the existence of these distinctions over what seemed to many people in the nineteenth century enormous periods of time.

Many observers ascribed racial diversity to external influences, others to the appearance of "accidental varieties," but actually, Morton told the Academy in September, 1849, neither of these theories applied to man. It was true, he admitted, that some animals were very pliable and susceptible to climatic influences, but man belonged to a relatively large group of animals which defied the vicissitudes of nature. Like the Bengal tiger, which was "precisely the same in every tint, whether inhabiting the frozen shores of Lake Baikal" or "the jungle of Ceylon," man remained uninfluenced by his habitat. In Guinea, he noted, the wool of sheep became long and hairy, but the hair of the human inhabitants was woolly. There were many instances of two or more distinct races living in the same area. In America, where, as he had shown, all the inhabitants, ancient and modern, from pole to pole, were of the same race, there were no evidences of climatic influence. Neither did "accidental varieties" give rise to races of men, for there was a "contant tendency in nature to restore and preserve a primitive type." This explained why hybrids tended to be infertile, and why, when they did produce, the offspring resembled one or the other of the parent stocks.[7]

Structural differences could readily be explained by separate origins, and historical evidence placed the explanation almost beyond dispute. Lepsius (one sees here the hand of Gliddon) had dated representations of "pure Egyptian forms" on bas-reliefs at the foot of the Great Pyramid as early as 3400 B.C., and Morton could find no difference between these and others which the famous Egyptologist had found in the temples and dated from 1400 B.C. For the immense period of 2,000 years the type had not changed! So much for structural differences.

His theory of the origin of the several human species now complete, Morton was to devote the few years that remained to him to its documentation and defense, assisted unfailingly by the dedicated pen of his friend Nott.

De Bow was so pleased with his new contributor, who had demonstrated his ability to write for readers at large as well as for medical practitioners, that he offered Nott his chair of political economy at the University of Louisiana during the next session of the legislature in order that he might, as Nott interpreted the offer to Squier, "deliver a lecture for him on Niggerology." It would be "a fine opportunity of sowing seed broadcast." He believed that if the scriptural account of the Creation were "blown up" then "the whole field is open to us & if the argument is properly managed the world is ready for it." He determined to "take no ground which will do violence to the Unco Godly," but predicted that he would be abused anyway. At any rate, he promised Squier, "I shall tell them about those heathens Luke Burke, Bunsen, De Wette, Norton, Strauss, Morton . . . and above all that infamous sinner Squier who had had the hardihood to assert that the Indians were making potato hills in [the] *Valley* before Eve was convicted and punished for stealing apples."[8]

In December, Nott delivered two lectures which constituted his most ambitious work to date and which displayed a most welcome improvement in organization and style. He noted in the preface that the warfare which had long raged between science and theology had resulted in victories for astronomy and geology and must soon bring triumph to "the natural history of man." Nott intended to be no idle observer in the conflict, for the avowed purpose of these lectures was "to cut loose the natural history of mankind from the Bible, and to place each upon its own foundation, where it may remain without collision or molestation." Anthropology had made great strides in recent decades and now deserved an honored place beside its sister sciences. It was entitled to "the same liberal construction of the Bible" that had been "conceded to other scientific subjects": unless the Scriptures could be "reconciled with the clearly ascertained facts of science," they would have to be abandoned.[9]

Religious dogmatists, although they held that all men were of one species, were not able to account for the present, much less the past physical diversity of the races. They could present only three theories, none of which could be substantiated: direct action of God in "changing one type into another," gradual action of physical causes, and the appearance of "congenital or accidental varieties." Nott promptly dismissed the first on the ground that there was absolutely no evidence in its support. It was a mere act of faith and as such was not susceptible of scientific investigation. The action of physical causes operated among some species, but because the force of this influence was inversely proportionate to the length of the period of gestation and maturation, man was little affected. Capable above all other animals of protecting himself from external influences, man therefore was, "as we should expect him to be, less influenced by climate than horses, dogs, &c." Acquired characters could not be inherited any more than "a flattened head, mutilated limb, or tatood skin."

Nott had only scorn for the theory that diversities were due to the appearance and propagation of variations. It was a mere "fanciful idea." "Can human credulity go farther, or human ingenuity invent any argument more absurd?" he asked. All kinds of ridiculous examples had been cited—the transmission of a "warty" skin, of crossed eyes, six fingers, deafness, and blindness; but, Nott asked, "did any one ever hear of a club-foot, cross-eyed, or six fingered race, although such individuals are exceedingly common? Are they not, on the contrary, always swallowed up and lost?" These "congenital varieties" appeared frequently but never developed into a race of men. "No one ever saw a Negro, Mongol, or Indian, born from any but his own species." This fact alone should have been sufficient to convince anyone "that the diversity of species now seen" could not be accounted for "on the assumption of congenital or accidental origin." He who still doubted might recall that "the Negro, Mongol and white man" existed "at least one thousand years before Abraham journeyed to Egypt as a supplicant to the mighty Pharaoh."

Calling to his aid Morton on hybridization and craniology, Squier on Mound Builders, and Gliddon on Egypt's chronology, Nott set up the biblical arguments for unity to knock them down with the demonstrated proofs of ethnology. In the second lecture he attempted to show why the Mosaic account of Creation failed to accord with scientific fact. As Nott saw it, the simple explanation was that the Hebrew writers knew no science. Their notions of the universe "were of the rudest kind." Their account of Creation was so "plain, simple, and artless" that Nott found it rather quaint, deserving the understanding smile rather than the "ponderous tomes" written "to reconcile it with advancing science." The biblical writers had been ignorant of many areas of knowledge familiar to the Egyptians and other more sophisticated peoples. They knew no geography and even thought the earth flat. Without geography, they could have no understanding of ethnology. Even the evangelists, who at least did some traveling, "were as ignorant of the north of Europe, north and east of Asia, southern Africa, Australia, America, and Oceanica, as we are of the geography of the Moon." If the Hebrew writers had never seen an Indian, a Mongol, or the Aborigines of Australia, what evidence had they that all were of one species with the Caucasian? And why should we attend them when the facts of science were at hand? Neither did these ancient writers have a true concept of the length of time that men had inhabited the earth. Archeological researches showed that "Egypt, India, and China, and probably America, contained immense populations, with organized governments, and were greatly advanced in civilization, even as far back as the spurious Septuagint date of the deluge." Acceptance of these laughably inaccurate accounts would inevitably fall away before the irresistible advance of science. Already biblical scholars such as

Andrews Norton and Moses Stuart in America, together with De Wette, Strauss, and Eichhorn in Germany, were recognizing the inadequacies of literal interpretation.

Morton read Nott's lectures with "great pleasure and instruction" and was "especially pleased with the triumphant manner" in which Nott "treated the absurd postulate, that one race can be transmuted into another." When he himself had stated in the essay on hybridization that the races stemmed from a plural origin—"and in the Crania Americana my position is the same, though more cautiously worded" —he had done so "with some misgivings," not because he doubted the truth of his opinions, but because he "feared they would lead to some controversy with the clergy." To his surprise, however, nothing of the kind had occurred, and in the light of his experience, Morton believed that if the clergy were not "pressed too hard," they would "finally concede all" on the question of diversity itself, for this doctrine could be "far more readily reconciled to the Mosaic annals than some other points, Astronomy," for example.[10]

Many clergymen had discussed the subject with him, and he had received several "letters from the clergy" and "other piously-disposed persons, but the only one that had any spice of vehemence was from a friend, Dr. Bachman, of Charleston."

"The Great Mooted Question"

Everything considered, Nott was pleased with his performance. In attacking "the authenticity of the Pentateuch directly," he informed Squier, he had quoted "all the parsons this side of Hell" to sustain him and had "knocked their eyes so wide open" that some of the "godly" had "never slept since." The firm of Lea and Blanchard, primly disapproving the author's "notions about the Diversity of the Races, modern origin of the Pentateuch &c," had refused to publish the work, and Nott asked Squier to locate a publisher. Aware that Squier did not share his sentiments on slavery, Nott explained that he "had to mix a little sweet sauce with it in the way of Politics, Sectional feeling &c—religion you know is a funny thing—a man's conscience is always on the side of his interest—" He had recently lost by shipwreck "upwards of $300 worth of rare scientific" works ordered from Europe and hoped the *Lectures* would sell enough copies to make up the loss. He was sure it would be favorably received "*at the South* where the public mind is at present morbidly excited about the nigger business."[1]

The little work did sell remarkably well; indeed, it was taken up "almost with a furor at the South." Although Nott had "had the tact" to put himself "all the way through behind the broad bottomed, big headed German divines" and could, if attacked, say, "gentlemen, the quarrel belongs to the craft, settle it amongst yourselves," he expected that it would "stir up hell in the christians" and result in a certain amount of denunciation. "Some of Gliddons skunks [Gliddon's term for all clergymen] will be at me & I may be compelled to do some skinning." If Nott believed that the counterattack would be led by a Massachusetts abolitionist divine, he was mistaken, for the assault came not from the North but from the South; not from an abolitionist but from a slaveowner. It was based, not upon Scripture, not upon a theory of supernatural interference with the laws of nature, and not upon the direct action of climate, but upon the appearance and propagation of variations, a theory Nott had ridiculed as a "fanciful idea." And it was directed, not at him, but at the true center of the disturbance, at Morton himself.[2]

In the years before the Civil War the three great centers of scientific interest in the United States were Boston–New Haven, Philadelphia, and Charleston. Charleston was proud of its Medical School, its Elliott Society of Natural History, and its Museum, which Agassiz thought the finest in the United States, except for the museum of the Academy of Natural Sciences in Philadelphia. The Charleston scientific community consisted of men of national reputation. There was the mycologist Henry W. Ravenel and his brother Edmund, conchologist and professor of anatomy at the Medical College; Lewis R. Gibbes, primarily a conchologist but contributor to botany and chemistry as well; Francis S. Holmes, professor of natural history at the College of Charleston and curator of the Museum; John Edwards Holbrook, America's outstanding herpetologist; Frederick Peyre Porcher, botanist and professor at the Medical College; the physicians William Middleton Michel, James Moultrie, Samuel Henry Dickson; and John Bachman, naturalist. All kept in close contact with scientific developments in the North, many through correspondence with Morton.[3]

One of the most respected members of the group was John Bachman, minister of St. John's Lutheran Church. Bachman, born in New York State in 1790, was the descendant of early Swiss and German immigrants and the son of a well-to-do farmer of Dutchess County. He became interested in natural history while still a child but was forced to pursue his investigations in secret because of local prejudice against the "trifling pursuits of Natural History." An attack of tuberculosis which interrupted his education at Williams was shortly followed by religious conversion. He taught school for a time, made the acquaintance of the ornithologist Alexander Wilson, and in 1815, still in the grip of consumption, moved to Charleston in the hope of improving his health. Elected minister of St. John's Lutheran Church, a position which he was to hold for over sixty years, he soon established a correspondence with the leading naturalists of the United States and Europe and became known locally as "the Hunting Parson." In 1831 he began a lifelong friendship with John James Audubon, which became a family connection when two of Bachman's many daughters married Audubon's sons. The two naturalists made many journeys together through the South Carolina countryside to study birds of the region, while Bachman struggled to stem the outrageous profanity of his friend and urged him to forego the pleasures, not only of "grog & wine, but snuff," as he himself had recently done. This stocky little man, whose family was plagued with a melancholy round of sickness and death, early gained local renown as a formidable opponent in argument by keeping a wary eye on the Scarlet Lady, fighting nullification during the controversy in the early thirties, advocating numerous improvements in agriculture and education, campaigning for total abstinence, exposing Barnum's "mermaid" as a fraud, and generally fighting small skirmishes for the advancement of Protestantism and science. "There was so much acrimony in his writings," recalled a fellow member of the Literary Club, "that I knew not how to reconcile so much bitterness with the apparent genial disposition of the man."[4]

A national reputation came with Bachman's numerous defenses of the popular Audubon, who was singularly hated by many fellow ornithologists both in the United States and abroad, and with the publication over the years 1845–54 of *The Viviparous Quadrupeds of North America* under the joint authorship of Audubon and Bachman. In 1841 he was offered the presidency of South Carolina College but declined because, among other reasons, "such a step" would "put an end to my amusements in Nat. History."[5]

When Nott's *Lectures* came to the attention of the members of the Literary and Philosophic Club of Charleston, they assigned the task of reviewing it to the Reverend John Bachman, well aware that he had formed definite opinions on the subject.[6] Bachman was an active member of the Charleston Literary Club, which, since the first decade of the century, had been the meeting place for Charlestonians and distinguished visitors interested in natural history and the other sciences. In 1844, Judge Mitchell King had reviewed the *Crania Aegyptiaca* before the club. There Agassiz, during his visit in 1846, had discussed the question of the unity of mankind. In 1847, King and Holbrook had led a discussion of Squier's forthcoming work on the Mound Builders. Thus, when Bachman was assigned the task of reviewing Nott's book, the membership had taken sides and well knew what his position would be. They expected a good show and there is little reason to suppose that he disappointed them, for thereafter "the Unity" became the subject of so many meetings that Bachman decided to go to the source from which he knew the doctrine of multiple origins was emanating—Samuel G. Morton.[7]

Bachman kept in close touch with developments in natural history throughout the nation, and one of his important contacts in the North was Morton himself. For personal reasons, he rarely entered Philadelphia (his father-in-law had deserted wife and children, settled there "with a lewd woman from the North," and sired a new family by the "strumpet"), but for some years past he had corresponded and exchanged specimens with Morton. Little foreseeing "that the collection of human skulls" would enable anyone "to establish the doctrine of plurality in species," Bachman had sent drawings of Indian crania when the *Crania Americana* was in preparation and had been an early subscriber to the book. In response to Morton's request, he had cited numerous examples of hybridization in South Carolina. When he read Morton's articles on hybridization in Silliman's *Journal*, Bachman promptly wrote his Philadelphia friend and expressed his dissent. He attacked Morton's views before the Literary Club but was unable to reply in print because his time was taken up by a controversy with another naturalist over an Eocene whale. However, the appearance of "Notts small affair," which had been "widely disseminated in the South," he wrote Morton, resolved him to take time from writing the last volume of the *Quadrupeds* "to look at this matter." Although "confident" that he could scatter some of Morton's facts "to the wind," Bachman hoped this would not interrupt their friendship, as he regarded Morton in his "many works as a benefactor to [the] country & an honour to science." "Let us battle," he wrote, "for truth and not for victory"—and added, "have you not put yourself in a tight place when you produce the ass, Rat [,] Mouse, peacock & guinea hen as examples . . . where domestication has produced little or no change?"[8]

In keeping with the best traditions of modern warfare, the declaration was announced only after the guns had been primed. Bachman was stealing a march, for, either at the same time he was declaring his intention to Morton or at the most a few days later, he was busily engaged in writing a book, *The Doctrine of the Unity of the Human Race Examined on the Principles of Science,* which was published in 1850.[9]

Simultaneously, Bachman opened a second front with an attack in the pages of the *Charleston Medical Journal*. This was one of the few medical publications of the South of this period that made a serious effort to attain scientific respectability. Bachman's first article, the editors announced happily, was about "the great mooted question of the present day, the Unity or Plurality of the Human Race." It appeared in January, 1850. On the whole, Bachman's articles displayed an even temper. Morton's, although they never reached the stage of bitterness, betrayed a growing exasperation. Humorless, he was stung by Bachman's chiding. Throughout the controversy Bachman played a light fusillade against Morton's authorities, several times, by Morton's own admission, efficiently knocking them over. Morton replied only by setting up other targets in their place. "You hie to Africa," Bachman remarked in one of his sallies, for an account of a hybrid "produced between the ass and the cow"; then off we go to Paraguay to learn that "our common cat, on the plains, performs a double miracle by producing fertile hybrids, with not only one, but two species of the wild cats of South America." Away now to the Bay du Croc "to listen to a recital" about "a wild carabou breaking into a sheepfold, at night, in pursuit of a cow," and "consequent conjectures that she might have been impregnated. My good friend," Bachman concluded patiently, "I confess it is a severe infliction to be obliged to follow you so far out of the track of civilization." Some of Morton's sources "ought long since have been restricted to the toy-shop of the antiquarian." There was, he remarked, "scarcely a vulgar error in existence that could not be supported by an overwhelming mass of testimony . . . witchcraft, for instance."[10]

This was Bachman at his best, and it galled Morton, who, unable to reply in kind, could only restate his position and solemnly collect more authorities in its support. Morton's reply considerably broadened the area of controversy, so that in succeeding articles the entire question of the zoological basis of man's unity or diversity was laid open for examination. When the members of the Literary Club had discussed the question, they had agreed that "should either of the parties, who had any pretensions to a knowledge of natural history, fly the course in this scientific race, they were determined to whip him back into the track by picking at him in the newspapers." Although Bachman struggled manfully to continue this policy in the controversy with Morton, he was not always successful. Thus the exchange between the two American scientists became an exploration of the problem of the origin of species.[11]

Both the opponents and the defenders of the unity of mankind considered species fixed—static, without dimension in time or space. To Morton's way of thinking, they were fixed because they were derived from geographically separate creations. Bachman saw them as fixed because they did not interbreed. He insisted that intersterility was a valid test which for all practical purposes provided a definite line of demarcation between species. Admittedly, there had been instances of closely related species crossing—usually through human intervention—to produce sterile hybrids. There had been instances of the offspring of such an unnatural union proving fertile when crossed with one of the parent stocks. There had even been cases in which these offspring propagated among themselves for several generations. But for every fact there had been a thousand rumors. An unusual animal had appeared in Beaufort and another in Columbia which "whole neighbourhoods" asserted were hybrids of the house cat and the gray rabbit. Accounts had appeared in the public prints all over America and as far away as London. But when Bachman had one of the animals sent to him he found from an examination of the teeth that it was a true cat, of somewhat unusual organization, to be sure—short-tailed with long hind legs—but nonetheless a cat, probably "a second edition of the Isle of Man cat."

He had been assured of mongrels between the deer and goat, between the drake and the common hen, and very recently, between the fox-squirrel and the rat, but they always proved to be deformed or diseased animals. It had not been recorded that "a single new race of animal or bird" had sprung from the crossing of species. "This is at least a credulous world," Bachman observed, "and the student of nature should be on his guard." Unlike Morton, Bachman had conducted experiments in hybridization and had succeeded in producing "a greater number of hybrids than any other individual in our country," but with the exception of the offspring of a cross between the China and the common goose, all had proved sterile. These experiments convinced him that "a union of two species could not produce a new race, and that species were the creation of God."[12]

Differences in physical structure, natural repugnance to mixture, sterility, and oftentimes deformity of the hybrid—all, in Bachman's opinion, prevented the origin of a race from the intermixture of species. Morton had for some time been "laboring to unsettle the public mind" in regard to the origin of domestic animals by asserting that early man had domesticated wild species, interbred them, and so produced horses, sheep, cattle, poultry, and other common domestic animals. But, Bachman objected, many of the supposed ancestors of these animals still existed in the wild state and had proved to be untamable or useless in domestication. He found that of thirty-four species of domestic animals, all but two existed in the wild state; hence they could not be traced to a commingling of species. What Morton regarded as species were nothing more than varieties.[13]

Unlike species, varieties were not always permanent; over periods of time they might display different characters. No one knew why variations appeared, and Bachman did not attempt to explain the phenomenon. He was, he said, content to place himself in company with "the wisest physiologists [who] are obliged to acknowledge their profound ignorance" and suggested that neither party to the present dispute was obliged to provide the answer, "since the facts themselves are self-evident." Nor did he attempt to explain how these new characters were transmitted. It doubtless had to do with "the internal mechanism of those portions of the system where the germs of a new being are to be fashioned into life" and "with the capillaries that convey nourishment," but still it remained a "mysterious process." That the mechanics of this phenomenon could not be explained was, he insisted, no reason to assume that it resulted from the crossing of species. "All the species you have referred to," he told Morton, "are domesticated animals—these are constantly producing new varieties—some of these have originated in our day. . . . You surely would not have the world suppose that every variety that has sprung up in our day, either by admixture of breeds, or from causes which seem accidental, from the fact that we cannot explain them, is a new species."[14]

Whatever the precise mechanics of variation, there seemed to be a decided relationship between variation and environment. This was particularly apparent among domestic animals. Bachman's observations on variation and its causes testify to his careful study and serve to place him in the front ranks of pre-Darwinian naturalists in the United States. With others, he had found that there was little difficulty in differentiating wild genera and species; their differences were so plain "that a naturalist of common sagacity could not fail to fix the species in any country, even from prepared specimens." As his investigations continued, however, he had found that plants and animals introduced from abroad "varied exceedingly from their original forms" in a few generations. Varieties seemed to spring up among domestic animals for no apparent reason. The Englishman Darwin, who some years before had served as naturalist for a British scientific expedition to South America, had noted a peculiar breed of cattle near the Rio Plata. Here was another example, said Bachman,

in evidence of the fact, that without the slightest intermixture of foreign varieties, new breeds of cattle spring up in America. They made their first appearance about eighty years ago . . . , now they have become the only race in an immense region of country where they are nearly wild. What causes have operated to produce this variety? There are no wild animals, not even the buffalo in that country from which any admixture could by any possibility have been derived. Were we not positive of their origin, they would unquestionably be regarded as a new species.

These phenomena convinced Bachman that vertebrates and plants, "when in a state of domestication or of cultivation, were subject to most remarkable changes, and that these variations seldom occurred unless they were removed to other soils, other latitudes."[15]

There was, then, an evident link between environment and variation. But Bachman professed surprise that it should be used to support the argument for plurality in the human species. He had of course read Agassiz's article in the *Christian Examiner* of 1850, and only recently he had heard the same ideas presented by Dr. John P. Barratt in an address to the second anniversary meeting of the South Carolina Medical Association. (This was no coincidence, for upon learning that he had been appointed to deliver the annual address, Barratt promptly wrote to Morton of his predicament. He asked for Morton's views on hybridization and geographical distribution in order "to correct any false notions I may entertain, as truth is my aim." Bachman was evidently unaware of this.) At the conclusion of the address, Bachman told Barratt that geographical distribution offered greater support for unity than for plurality, for he had found a relationship between variation and environment which indicated that the wider the range of a species, the more varieties it presented.

Although some species possessed greater power of variation and adaptation than others, all possessed it in some degree; hence some were widely distributed, others closely restricted. The influence of environment in calling forth variations might be illustrated, Bachman thought, by the blind fish and crayfish of the Kentucky caves. It was "highly probable," he suggested, that further investigation would reveal that these blind specimens "descended from species that were not originally blind." For in the specimens he possessed, he found that despite the absence of an eye, there existed the cavity, rudimentary muscles, and what appeared to be a rudimentary optic nerve. "Could a wise Creator have originally placed all these appendages to the organ of vision without intending them for some use?" A comparison should be instituted between "these singular species" and those in the open streams of the vicinity. Probably, he suggested, "much interesting matter will be furnished us in regard to the effects which peculiar locations, absence of light, chemical formations, waters saturated with lime and other ingredients, are calculated to produce on the forms of animals."[16]

To Bachman, as to the Jeffersonians, the theory of adaptation explained the existence of the races of man. The most domestic and the most widely distributed of animals, man was therefore the most subject to variations. The human constitution possessed the power to adapt and "to produce a succession of strikingly marked varieties." In short, "different climates require different constitutions, and a wise Creator has implanted in the organization of man an adaptation to produce such modifications as are essential to the health, comfort, and future increase of his posterity." Thus the same causes, whatever they were, that produced the blind fish of the caves of Kentucky had produced the races of man. One family in South Carolina, "moving in the highest circles, and justly esteemed on account of their high intellect and worth," provided just such an instance. The grandmother was born toothless, and although her husband was supplied with the usual number, all three of their children and at least one of the third generation were "destitute of teeth." The other descendants Bachman had lost track of. This, he admitted, was a "malformation," and a race of men which possessed it would "finally yield to others, whose structures were more in accordance with nature. But," he added, "the many varieties of animals and men are not malformations; they are equally healthy, fruitful, and long-lived with those of the original species; their constitutions are adapted to the climates in which they reside, and the negro constitution in Africa is as perfectly healthy as is that of the native of Montpellier in his own birthplace."[17]

The conclusion to be drawn from this toothless though well-bred family was that the Indian was simply a Mongolian adapted to a new environment, notwithstanding "the deservedly high authority" of Dr. Morton to the contrary. The other races came into being in the same fashion. He thought the conclusion warranted that human variations, "as well as those of inferior animals, have originated in various parts of the world, some of which have sprung up within the period of authentic history." These transmitted their novel characters and "in the course of time" became "permanent varieties. They multiplied more rapidly than the original inhabitants, and finally, whole regions of country became populated by these new races."

Even while he was formulating his theory of variation, Bachman was insisting on the fixity of species. His theory of variation rested on empirical data, but his belief in the fixity of species did not. It was an incongruous position to take up and one which was imposed upon him from a non-scientific source. He was trying to explain variation while listening attentively to the voice of Scripture denying that nature varies. Because of their theological commitments, all the defenders of the unity of mankind had to assume that species were fixed. Morton and Nott recognized this weakness in the enemy position and made frequent attacks on it, accusing the defenders of unity, to their scandalized indignation, of being disciples of the despised Lamarck. Indeed, in his very first paper on hybridization, Morton had attempted to place the stigma on them. Bachman would have none of it. He hotly denied that his theory accorded with the infidel views of "La Mark." Hurling the epithet back, he admonished Morton to "bear in mind that by our own theory we are only producing varieties from the dog himself—*here* the dog begets a dog; but by [yours] it requires the combined efforts of the several species of d'hole, Jackal, wolf and hyena, to make a dog, and a mixture of four species of wild ass to make 'an improved austral horse.' We are inclined to think that La Mark would reject us as heterodox, and welcome our opponents into his family of true believers." Theories of the development of species were anathema to both parties in this controversy; each was eager to demonstrate that any resemblance

between his own theory and that of Lamarck was purely coincidental. This accusation angered Bachman only a little less than his opponents' infuriating assumption that he was a mere "clerical adversary."[18]

Having rejected the theory of separate creation and established in
Its place his theory of variation and adaptation, Bachman left himself open to the charge that he was doing violence to scriptural chronology. It was doubtful whether the biblical chronology allowed sufficient time for a race of men to develop from a single variation,
however great the advantage this variation of man might enjoy over
his fellows. It was an embarrassing charge, and Bachman's reply was
naturally somewhat confused. At one point he fell back on the explanation Samuel Stanhope Smith had used in the face of the same
accusation: Man was created in a state of semicivilization, possessed
of a knowledge of agriculture and navigation. Hence man did not
have to tarry at the point of his creation. Probably, Bachman suggested, migrations began immediately and distribution early left its
mark. Still, Bachman was not completely satisfied with this solution
and suggested in another place that perhaps "in those early times"
man had produced more varieties than at present. Again, he asserted
that from the scientific point of view chronology was irrelevant, that
even a greatly lengthened chronology "would in no wise affect the
doctrine of the unity of the present human race." The "unbeliever"
might use it as an argument against "the Mosaic record," but the
naturalist could not "make use of it in designating a species." The
naturalist was "governed by the characteristics in nature and not by
historical traditions." Though as a churchman he wished to defend
the biblical chronology, Bachman was too good a naturalist to insist
upon its phylogenetic validity and too shrewd a polemicist to commit himself to its defense.[19]

Thus Bachman was forced to wind a tortuous route between
Lamarck, separate creations, direct influence of climate (which he
regarded as an oversimplification), and the biblical conception of
the Creation. The same theological concepts which led him to reject
Lamarckism forced him also to reject Morton's theory of separate
creations. For if Bachman's "wise Creator" was above all the Creator
of species, He was no less the economical Craftsman who would
not violate without cause His own ordained laws of nature. If Bachman could not admit the "absurd theory of La Mark, who used ar-

guments to show that the human race was derived from the monkey," arguments which obviated the necessity of a geographically separate creation for each species, neither could he swallow the notion of a wasteful Craftsman who created not twice but hundreds of times when once would have sufficed. His concept of the Creator was based on traditional Protestant doctrine: the age of miracles was long passed; God now worked His will through natural law.

In plotting his course among these scientific theories and theological doctrines, Bachman formulated a theory of his own that approached evolution. Much of his argument rings true. He recognized that all kinds of variations are constantly appearing, and even that when "in accordance with nature" these possess survival value, enabling them to multiply "more rapidly" than the original type from which they sprang. He mistakenly believed, as did Darwin, that more variations appeared in domestication than in the feral state and, because adaptation was somehow causally related to environment, more among those species most widely distributed.[20]

If Bachman's theory was not Darwinism, it nevertheless was an advanced one in contemporary zoological thought. His concept of the Deity, which, no less than his observations of nature, propelled him to this position, also prevented his pressing forward to the revolutionary conclusion with which Darwin was wrestling. On the one hand, his sense of the Creator's economy made the doctrine of separate creations anathema and, on the other, prevented his seeing the shocking waste which Darwin recognized in nature—the millions of variations which appear, live out their brief spans, and fall into oblivion. The variations which Bachman saw were all purposeful: they adapted the organism to its environment. He could no more conceive of useless variants than he could useless creations. Despite the similarities of his theory to Darwin's, his concept of a benevolent Nature prevented his seeing the struggle for survival as a factor in preserving favorable variations.

Moreover, like William Charles Wells before him (another American who applied the theory of evolution to varieties) Bachman failed to apply his theory of variation to species. Here he was forestalled by his attempt to show that all varieties of man were conspecific and, again, by the theological concept that species were God's direct and immutable creations. Variation operated only within species. Even here, Bachman did not apply his theory in all its potential rigor. He failed, for example, to explain the blind fish as the descendants of chance variants and, instead, lapsed into Lamarckism, explaining that their ancestors had lost their eyes through atrophy, or through the action of chemicals in the water. Finally, as he did not minutely substantiate, neither did he wholly articulate his theory, for he nowhere presented it with perfect clarity. It was shot through with contradictions which both his theological and his political tenets forced upon him. It is evident, for all his insistence that there could be no conflict between the two, that Bachman was at times torn between his science and his religion, that he suffered, though to a less degree, the rending that a later generation of religious yet intelligent men of science were to suffer. One wishes he had left his congregation to fend for itself and spent more time in the woods and canebrakes with his friend Audubon.[21]

Having formulated his theory, Bachman pointed out the fallacies it revealed in the doctrine of separate creations. The startling variations which many naturalists had noted were now seen to be only variations and not species. The Negro's hair, cranial shape and capacity, color, parasites, and "instincts" were nothing more than useful adaptations of the species Man which had enabled him to live with a greater degree of comfort in the areas to which he had wandered from the site of the Creation. Measurements of the various breeds of cattle, dogs, horses, and sheep would reveal far greater differences than existed between the races of man. Varieties of wolves were as different in color as Negro and white. Compare the instincts of men and dogs, he suggested. Was there a greater similarity between the instincts of the pointer and the poodle than between the Caucasian and the Indian? In order to settle this question of species, naturalists would have to "possess the skulls and examine the physiology of the various races of animals," especially domesticated types. The "praiseworthy labors of Dr. Morton" were only a beginning in a "long series of studies and physiological inquiries" in mammalogy. In short, by the specific test of structural relationships, the races of men were more similar than the varieties of other animals.[22]

Domestication had called forth "striking and often permanent varieties" in every species subjected to its influence, but it had "never evolved a faculty to produce fertile hybrids." Bachman's opponents had set out to prove a hypothesis at any cost. Aware that all human mixtures were equally fertile, they abandoned the untenable notion that mulattoes were not prolific and, brought up short by the natural law of "the infertility of hybrids" which had always been "a stumbling block in the way of their theory," were forced to choose between making man the only exception to the general law of nature and denying the validity of such a law. Choosing the latter course, they "ransacked the almost forgotten tales of ancient travellers, and dragged from obscurity the vulgar errors long hidden beneath the dust of antiquity, and indulged themselves in conjectures and doubts," all "in order to weaken the faith of men in the long established views of naturalists in regard to the sterility of hybrids." Although Nott had first attempted to prove that the mulatto was infertile, Morton had shown that some mixed races, the Egyptians, for example, had multipled for centuries. Opponents of the unity of mankind then "suddenly shifted their sails on the other side" and struggled to "carry their sinking bark to a port of safety under the false colours of fertile hybrids" among the lower species.[23]

Impressed by the differences among the varieties of men and unable to account for them in a scientific manner, they assumed the varieties to have been created separately. This, Bachman complained, was simply an act of faith, an assumption not susceptible to scientific investigation. In order to prove or disprove this concept, naturalists would be forced to rely on "uncertain tradition." Any test of species based on this theory would throw the world of science into the inextricable confusion already evident among the opponents of "the Unity," who could not tell whether there were "five, ten, or an hundred species of men." Surely, he went on, now feigning despair, they could not "fail to perceive" that in departing from "our ancient landmarks" naturalists would be left with "no other guides than those of uncertain conjecture." Driving home his point, Bachman shrewdly reminded Morton, "You, Agassiz, and myself, have described many species, we therefore know what are the characteristics which belong to them."[24]

Bachman was dismayed at the failure of his opponents to see the similarities of the races, amazed at the attack on the unity of the human species, and appalled at the danger to science. Nevertheless, he did not defend equality. His theory of descent from common ancestors and of adaptation through variation should have brought him face to face with the principle of racial equality—or at least to the conclusion that the races, if not now equal, possessed equal potentialities. But a Southerner, indeed a Charlestonian, in the years when the South's peculiar institution was under violent attack, Bachman drew back as if blinded by his approach to political heresy. True, all the races were descended from the same ancestors. True, they were all simply varieties produced with the aid of climate. But some varieties had exhausted their fund of variation and become permanent. Forgetting his admonition to the opposition not to erect barriers to science in the form of imaginative hypotheses, Bachman posited an "original type" which manifested both Negro and Caucasian characters. From this original type, he explained, the Caucasian had "improved" and the Negro "degenerated" through the influence of the regions in which they had chosen to reside. These varieties, improved or degenerate, had become permanent. In still another place, Bachman attempted to explain why Negroes transplanted to America did not become white on the contradictory grounds both that "they belong to a permanent race whose characteristics have become organic," and that no variations were yet observable because they had been in America only a few generations and had largely been confined to a climate similar to that of their homelands.[25]

These confused attempts to escape the consequences of his arguments would serve, Bachman evidently thought, to align him with the defenders of "our domestic institutions," for in the South the flame of liberty was burning low, the dissenter's lot was hard. At any rate, he enjoined his opponents to take care "lest the enemies of our domestic institutions should have room to accuse them of prejudice and selfishness, in desiring to degrade their servants" to the level of the lower animals, "as an excuse for retaining them in servitude." The fact that Negroes were incapable of governing themselves and that "the Scriptures point out the duties both of masters and servants," should be "sufficient," he admonished, "to dispel every improper motive in an unbiased search after truth alone." Bachman's science suffered less from the guiding hands of his theology than from the vicious tentacles of his politics.

"The Parson-Skinning
Goes on Bravely"

When Morton entered upon the investigation of hybridization which led away from the direct experimentation and observation he had so long insisted was the only approach for the truly philosophic investigator—he was motivated by the desire to eliminate chance as an element in the organic world, by an outraged religio-aesthetic sense which clung to the idea that the Creator was above all an economical Craftsman. When he had begun the study of ethnology, he told Bachman,

among the first aphorisms taught me by all the books to which I had access, was this—that all mankind were derived from a single pair; and that the diversities now so remarkable, originated solely from the operations of climate, locality, food and other physical agents. In other words, that man was created a perfect and beautiful being in the first instance, and that chance, *chance* alone has caused all the physical disparity among men, from the noblest Caucasian form to the most degraded Australian and Hottentot.

Thus the same concept of the economical and orderly Creator upon which the Jeffersonians ultimately rested their belief in unity served Morton as an argument for plurality.[1]

He was, of course, impelled too by the desire to fit his craniological discoveries into the system of laws which governed the whole of the animal kingdom. As Agassiz extended his theory of separate creations upward to man, so Morton extended his downward to the animals. He believed as firmly as Bachman that man, in his physical aspects at least, was part of the animal world and subject to its laws. Having satisfied himself that structural differences in human crania were marked and permanent and must therefore constitute specific differences, he had now to show that permanent structural differences indicated specificity in the rest of the animal kingdom. This he could do only by overthrowing the long accepted criterion of reproductive isolation.

His investigations of hybridization had placed him, he remarked, "somewhat in the position of a pioneer in a new field of inquiry." Fortunately, the field had proved fruitful beyond all expectation. His articles on hybridization had provided a solution to the great problem of the origin of species which had so long puzzled the world's naturalists. He had shown them how to account for specific origins without relying on the unphilosophical and unscriptural theory of development. Greatest accomplishment of all, he had eliminated chance as a factor in the creation of man. As Newton had banished chance from astronomy and described the mechanics of the heavens, so Morton had removed chance from zoology and described the mechanics of the organic firmament. Morton was a modest man, but only an exaggerated diffidence could have blinded him to the analogy.[2]

Thus Morton assumed that only professional commitments to the scriptural account prevented Bachman's accepting his solution to the problem of the origin of species. His replies to Bachman's objections were therefore submitted with an air of wearied patience. Although Bachman's stature as a naturalist and the rigor with which he presented his objections forced Morton to take notice and several times even to relinquish some of the more exotic examples of hybridity, Morton never considered his theory in any serious danger of refutation. His replies were often perfunctory and constituted little more than a reaffirmation of his position. Possibly ill health contributed to this lack of interest. An attack of pleurisy late in 1848 had laid him so low that he had written his young friend Squier, "I sometimes think that my 'sands are running out,'" and since then Morton had hardly ventured from his home. Bachman's objections, however, stirred him to the point that, required now to show why the rule which had long served naturalists as a criterion of species should be abandoned, he sent up a barrage of requests to army surgeons in the West asking for skulls of wolves and Indian dogs and for information about the crossing of various animals. He then peppered his replies to Bachman with more instances of the crossing of admittedly distinct species.[3]

He had implied in his earlier articles in Silliman's *Journal* that there were degrees of hybridization which coincided with the close structural relationships between species that all naturalists had observed. It had been difficult indeed to determine whether these "related species" were separate species or merely varieties. Assuming them to be species, Morton asserted that they marked one division in a system of specific crosses which he now formulated. He did not attempt to nullify completely the rule of hybridity, but he had found so many exceptions that he was forced to conclude that it did not operate with the same force among all species, in brief, that there were indeed degrees of hybridization. These he listed as follows: (1) Generic or specific crosses which produced sterile hybrids. These crosses were most common among domestic birds. (2) Crosses which produced hybrids that failed to reproduce among themselves but propagated through union with either of the parent stocks. As examples, Morton cited the hybrid produced by crossing the American buffalo with domestic cattle. (3) Crosses which produced hybrids prolific among themselves. "This phenomenon," he noted, was "characteristic of man, the ox tribe, horses, sheep, goats, dogs," thus including "the head of the zoological series, and those most essential to his wants and his happiness."[4]

This was really, Morton felt, the only explanation which took into account recent discoveries. The old theory that hybridization was a test of species had done yeoman service in the past, but it contradicted the discovery of geographical distribution and the great antiquity of species. Naturalists had found that each species had its allotted region. Since Buffon's time the geographical distribution of animals had been admitted by all naturalists, and many, perhaps most, had adopted the concept of "specific centers" as an explanation of the phenomenon—the hypothesis that each species had been created in its present habitat, unless historical evidence showed that it had been introduced. Both Agassiz and Lyell, Morton noted, agreed on this point, as did many others. Most made an exception of man, however, refusing to apply to him a law which they readily applied to the rest of the animal kingdom. Morton thought their reluctance, though unphilosophical, was understandable, for there had been a time when, unable to find agreement between this doctrine and the teachings of Genesis, he had also been puzzled. But research had convinced him of its validity, and it was now his "matured conviction" that species were created expressly in and for their present habitats, "the kangaroo in New Holland, the sloth in Brazil," and that these species did not appear in pairs only. "A few elephants might serve to stock a continent," he wrote, but when he considered that "hundreds of millions of Polythalmia, (each one as truly organized as an elephant)" existed in "a single cubic inch of the sea mud of our own coast," it struck him as "very absurd to suppose that they are derived from a single pair, or had their origin in Mesopotamia."[5]

The other discovery which any nineteenth-century naturalist worthy of the name had to take into account came from the new science of Egyptology. Students in this field had found that species had been distinct at a period approaching the supposed date of the Creation. As a part of the animal kingdom, the races of men too, it was discovered, had each their geographical limits and were depicted on the monuments of Egypt. Hence, one could not assume, merely because they interbred, that the races constituted a single species. Bachman had asked why, if Morton was determined to show that the races of men were separate species, the various breeds of dogs, which differed even more, were not also elevated to species. Morton had no objection. In fact, he insisted that they were species, for the mummied remains of twelve races of dogs, identical with present breeds, had been found in tombs dated 3500 B.C. And yet, since the Egyptian era, dogs had accompanied man to the ends of the earth and had, consequently, been subjected to every possible climatic influence. Inasmuch, Morton asked in turn, as the structural forms of men and animals had "preserved their identity through such vast periods of time" in the "most diversified climates" and circumstances, was it not "reasonable to believe" that at least some were "essential primeval types"? It remained for those who insisted that these forms were "derived from an aboriginal pair," to present "something more in proof than analogical reasoning, or inferences drawn from arbitrary views of the laws of Nature."[6]

The study of animal distribution showed that many groups of animals, some of which had been thought conspecific, were geographically isolated; archeological researches showed that this isolation had prevailed through great periods of time and that their differences could not be the result of environmental influences. Why then should one conclude, from the mere fact that two rather similar types interbred and produced offspring, that they were of the same species—especially when modern research had demonstrated that many species were able to produce hybrids? Clearly only those smothering in the folds of dead tradition could continue to insist upon hybridization as a test. Thus, after "much observation and reflection," Morton was at last ready with a definition which he hoped would "cover the whole ground better than those which . . . preceded it: SPECIES—a primordial organic form."

"Bravo, my dear Sir,!" wrote Agassiz from Harvard, in his enthusiasm neglecting the complimentary address, "You have at last furnished science with a true philosophical definition of species." Morton realized that determining which forms were primordial would be somewhat of a problem, but he urged recourse to the monuments of Egypt, many of which Lepsius and Bunsen had by now succeeded in dating. "My view," he added, "may be briefly explained by saying, that if a certain existing organic type can be traced back into the 'night of time,' as dissimilar as we see them now, is it not more reasonable to regard them as aboriginal, than to suppose them the mere accidental derivations of an isolated patriarchal stem of which we know nothing?" What Morton termed "species" others might term "primitive varieties," but this was a difference "only in name" and "in no way" influenced "the zoological question."[7]

Reassembling the old test of species as a cog in his own philosophy, Morton insisted that species might be classed in accordance with their propensity to produce hybrids. Species which failed to produce offspring when crossed were "remote species." Interfertile species which produced infertile offspring were "allied species." And interfertile species which produced fertile offspring were "proximate species." The races of men were "proximate species," but even in this group absolute fecundity did not appear in the hybrid. Morton remarked "the singular paucity of half-caste or mulatto children in New Holland." The thirty-one districts contained a native population of 15,000 yet "the whole number of half-castes or mulattoes" did "not exceed 200." This "remarkable fact" was probably to be explained by "the *difference of race*, the disparity of primordial organization," which had resulted in a "limited fertility." Thus the old test of species, now recast in terms of limited fertility, was made again to serve its accustomed function.[8]

Limited fertility served also to explain the curious phenomenon of variation. In some instances the hybrid resembled neither of the parent stocks and constituted, to all appearances, a new species. These "diversified and grotesque varieties" had often been "attributed to the sole operation of external causes," but their origin was actually in the breaking of the "primordial form" by the "crossing of dissimilar species."[9]

Like most innovators, Morton wished to show that he was not one, wished "to prove," as he put it, "that I have committed no heresy in science." He was "strongly disposed to believe, that were Buffon, Linnaeus and Cuvier alive at this time, the accumulated facts of the case might induce them to revise their opinions on this question." Neither did Morton wish to commit heresy in religion, and he was at pains to show that his solution did no real violence to Scripture, for, unlike Nott and Gliddon, he thought a satisfactory rapport could be established between science and religion. He had neither adopted nor announced his conviction, he told Bachman, until he had been "fully satisfied" that it was in harmony with "the sublime teachings of Genesis." That book, he found, gave an "account of the creation of Man" in reference to a particular zoological province. The Garden of Eden was there described as "a paradise for the *Adamic race*" and not a "collective centre for the whole human family." The author of Genesis did not describe the other centers of creation; he simply allowed the one to represent all. Morton hoped his views would not disturb the theological peace, but, peace or war, science must advance. He had no wish "to make startling propositions to ignorant minds," he told Bachman, but as he addressed himself to "educated persons," he did not believe "evil consequences" would "any more result than would follow scientific investigations in astronomy, geology and chronology"—each of which had "in its turn, contended against the inveterate preposs[ess]ions, not only of the ignorant, but of many otherwise learned and enlightened individuals."[10]

Upon the appearance of each of his replies, Morton received the congratulations of his friends. Nott, more experienced in the arts of controversy and denunciation, had been coaching Morton from the sidelines. He was overjoyed. "Well," he remarked, "I feel as if my function was fulfilled—the devil has been pushing me on in spite of myself to, *agitate*, & I have been thumped & pummelled on every side, but . . . I have succeeded in getting some of the rest of you into the fight, & you cant get out now till the field is won." Morton's articles were a real "smash up of old Bachman," and it seemed indeed as if "the parsons" were now "in the way of being well licked." It was as though "a viper had been killed in the fair garden of science." Robert W. Gibbes wrote that Morton's replies had given "general satisfaction" in Charleston, and Gliddon was pleased to note that "the Parson-skinning goes on bravely." One local reader of the *Medical Journal* was so enthusiastic over Morton's first article that he sent the *Courier* an excerpt which filled one full column of small print, added that the *Journal* was "an honor to our city and State," and recommended it to "the father of every family who could afford it." Bachman promptly retorted that the controversy was a scientific discussion and not for the edification of the general reader. As it was now in the open, however, he advised "the teachers of pupils of our Sunday Schools" to read his replies to Morton.[11]

It was generally agreed that Bachman deserved credit for his researches and for his ability as a collector, but no one seemed to doubt that he had come off second best. His generalizations were confused and inconsistent, and, in spite of himself, he had at times lapsed into the discredited theory of appetency—or something very like it—which Lamarck had foisted upon the world of science, thus violating, as it were, the rules of the game. Silliman's *Journal* gave only two brief and noncommital paragraphs to his *Doctrine of the Unity,* and the *Southern Quarterly Review,* though courteous, was restrained. In truth, Bachman's dedication to "domestic institutions" destroyed the force of his arguments. It was thought that Morton, on the other hand, had truly recognized that the doctrine of hybridity was the only alternative to change, chance, and confusion in the animal world.[12]

The controversy might have continued indefinitely. He had learned, Morton wrote Squier, that his "Reverend opponent" had "excommunicated" him "by bell book & candle" in the next number. "Nevertheless," he added, "I am not in the smallest degree discouraged, but shall continue to have an additional 'thorn' for him every No" for months to come, "that is if I have life & health, or even without the latter condition." Aside from sharpening the next thorn for Bachman, Morton was writing a chapter for one of Henry Rowe Schoolcraft's massive volumes on the Indian, working up an article on the races of men for Spencer F. Baird's forthcoming *Iconographic Encyclopaedia of Science, Literature, and Art,* and contemplating a definitive work on the "Elements of Ethnography." These labors exceeded his strength. The attack of pleurisy in 1848 had left him with a collapsed lung and a weakened heart, and after a three-day illness, Morton died in the spring of 1851.[13]

The *New York Tribune* lamented the loss of "one of the brightest ornaments of our age and country," and declared that "probably no scientific man in America enjoyed a higher reputation among scholars throughout the world, than Dr. Morton." One of the religious papers in Philadelphia, though regretting that Morton had "adopted Professor Agassiz's theory of the human race," which the editor regarded "as of infidel tendency," was satisfied that neither his "views of Bible truth" nor his "reverence for the Christian religion" had been impaired by his researches. Gliddon, lecturing to large crowds in Baltimore when the news arrived, was inconsolable, for of all who were associated with Morton in his scientific work, he seems to have been the closest. One cannot help feeling that his friendship with the gentle Morton, bringing as it did a period of relative calm to his stormy career, was the great event of his life. Nott, who had been planning to spend a part of the summer with Morton in Philadelphia, lamented perhaps more truly than he knew: "He was our leader & I look around in vain for one to supply his place—all men of Science knew his talent & learning."[14]

Robert W. Gibbes, who well understood where the Southern loaf was buttered, closed the controversy in the *Charleston Medical Journal* with a brief biographical memoir. "For the present," he concluded, "we can only say that we of the South should consider him as our benefactor, for aiding most materially in giving to the negro his true position as an inferior race. We believe the time is not far distant, when it will be universally admitted that neither can 'the leopard change his spots, nor the Ethiopian his skin.' "[15]

"A Perfect Hair"

Morton's death in 1851 left the scientific attack on equality leader-less at a bad moment. Gliddon was not the man to fill Morton's shoes. His aggressiveness made enemies and his pomposity pro-voked ridicule and laughter. He was forever the butt of somebody's joke. In 1847 he had suffered at the hands of an Anglophobe jour-nalist who published in doggerel verse a long burlesque of the Gliddon platform manner:

> He next produced the chains of brass,
> With which poor Samson, like an ass,
> Was bound, while grinding in the mill
> Of the philistines, on the hill.
> Then, with another gentle vomit,
> With ease he cast up old Mahomet;
> With his old mare, and all his wives,
> Together with his butcher knives. . . .
>
> Of Samson's foxes he'd a tail,
> Wrapped up in fair Delilah's veil.
> And, in some antiquated pan,
> He had some toe-nails from Japan;
> And he declar'd he had a snail
> Fresh from the back of Jonah's whale;
> Together with old Judas' bag,
> Swung o'er the neck of Balaam's nag! . . .
> He had a hencoop of St. Peter,
> And of King Herod a catheter. . . .
> Of Noah's ark he had the rudder
> And Jazebel gave him her udder. . . .[1]

When he turned up in Boston in 1850, Gliddon had, instead of these interesting relics, two newly acquired mummies, said to be the daughters of Egyptian priests. One he planned to save for the edification of the citizens of Philadelphia, his favorite city. The other was to be opened in Boston's Tremont Temple in June at the last of three lectures on the "Art of Mummification among the Ancient Egyptians." The climax of his series of lectures, which he planned with some dramatic acumen, was always the display of a mummy from which Gliddon removed a few of the wrappings at each succeeding lecture, until at the last of the series, the mummy was unrolled before the audience. At this moment, local notables of the scientific and medical professions who had been given seats of honor stepped forward in order "to enlighten" the audience in "their several scientific 'spécialités,'" as Gliddon put it.

The names of those who volunteered to perform this instructive duty before the two thousand in attendance at the final lecture in Boston read like a list of New England's scientific great: Dr. James Jackson, Dr. John Collins Warren, Dr. George Hayward, Dr. Charles T. Jackson, Augustus A. Gould, Henry Ingersoll Bowditch, J. J. Bigelow, Oliver Wendell Holmes, Jeffries Wyman, Charles Pickering, and Louis Agassiz. Among subscribers to the lecture were individuals of hardly less eminence—Edward Everett, Charles Sumner, William H. Prescott, Harvard's President Jared Sparks, and Professors Henry W. Longfellow and Benjamin Peirce. Gliddon had announced in the press that he was to display the mummy of a priestess, and the city responded with enthusiasm. In the popular mind the priestess soon became a princess and "created one of the periodic fevers in Boston," where "enthusiasm amounted even to romance, and poets made anticipatory sonnets to the Theban princess." One who was present recalled that "the company was worthy of the interest in the subject. Scientific men, the erudite Agassiz, and the accomplished Bigelow, with a host of others, were proud to lend their aid in the unfolding of that mystery, which, for the time, was to throw into the shade the lectures of a Hudson [Henry Norman Hudson, popular lecturer on Shakespeare] and the antitheses of a Parker."

Night after night, the "enlightened assemblage" sat in awed silence as Gliddon removed the shroud. At last he withdrew the final remnants and the ancient relic was revealed to the audience. It was the body of a man. "Dr. Bigelow blushed, and Professor Agassiz put his hands in his pockets." A sharp burst of uproarious laughter broke strangely from some two thousand well-bred Boston throats and echoed resoundingly in the local press. Attempting to explain the fiasco, Gliddon sent a serialized five-and-one-half column letter to the editor of the Boston *Transcript* to show that it was all due to the illegibility of the inscription on the mummy case. "All the world," he lamented, had become familiar with the incident; it had provoked "more universal fun than any event since the merry occasion about which Abraham and Sarah laughed."[2]

The progress of science, however, was not to be stayed by ignorant guffaws. All eyes were turned to the next meeting of the newly formed American Association for the Advancement of Science which was to be held in Charleston in March, 1850. More would then be heard on the "great mooted question" of the day, the unity or diversity of the human species. Agassiz was to be there, and Dr. Nott was to prepare a paper. The city of Charleston, proud of its scientists, who were to take a large part in the meeting, assumed the expenses of both the meeting and publication of the *Proceedings*. Its genteel citizenry, entire families of whom attended the sessions, became so enthusiastic that they decided to establish a museum of natural history at the Medical College.[3]

At the Tuesday session, the first day of the meeting, a paper on "Characteristics of the Hindoo Skull" sent by Samuel S. Kneeland, a Boston naturalist who did not believe in the unity of mankind, raised the curtain on the subject of ethnology. Kneeland merely confirmed Morton's measurements of Hindu crania.[4]

Friday was the big day for the ethnologists. Dr. Bachman presided over the morning session and after reading a paper of his own was forced to listen to one sent by Dr. Nott, "An Examination of the Physical History of the Jews, in its bearings on the Question of the Unity of the Races." The Jews, Nott thought, provided a test of the question of unity. It was a well-known fact, as was indicated by the almost interminable series of *begats* in Genesis, that from the time of Abraham the Jews had obeyed the ancient injunction to maintain the purity of their religion, and had refused to marry outside the faith. Nott repeated the biblical genealogy from Noah to Jacob, expressed revulsion at David's relations with Bathsheba, Solomon's penchant for wives and concubines, and Judah's roadside affair with his daughter-in-law—"so far from repenting the sin, he had two children by her"—then, drawing "the veil of oblivion over the depravity of those primitive days," concluded that there had been no real dilution of the Jewish blood. Dr. Morton, he reported, having received from Mr. George R. Gliddon the mummied head of an Israelite from the catacombs of Memphis, had compared it with modern Jewish crania and had found no difference between the two. However, Morton had found a decided contrast between this ancient skull and equally ancient skulls of Egyptians and Negroes from the catacombs. Similarly, Nott pointed out, Jewish figures were displayed on the monuments in distinct contrast to other races. And yet, for four thousand years Jews had existed "in all the climates, and under all forms of government of the earth,— through extremes of prosperity and adversity." The conclusion could only be that environment produced no effect on the physical character of a race. Where then, asked Nott, "is to be found the semblance of an argument to sustain the assumption of a common origin for mankind?"[5]

The same conclusion was to be drawn from the history of other races. Great distinctions were evident even among such broad and imprecise classifications as "Negro" and "Caucasian" and "Indian." The difference in cranial capacity between Negro and white had existed for four thousand years. If the cranial capacity of the Negro had not changed in this immense period, one might safely assume that it never would. There was a moral in all this, and Nott carefully laid it before the assembled scientists for all to ponder: If the races had thus always differed, mentally and physically, how could "any effort of man," however noble the motives, "reverse the law of God, and raise an inferior up to the standard of a superior one"? Nott looked with "painful anxiety to Liberia, as the last hope of the Negro as an independent race." He wished the experiment success but feared it was "a vain struggle against fixed laws of nature." He had heard so many proud descriptions of the colony that he had written to "a scientific correspondent at the North" to inquire "*what blood predominated* in Liberia, and, particularly, what was the pedigree of President Roberts, who has been figuring so much of late in European courts," and had learned that Roberts was "three-fourths *white blood*" and that the secretary of the treasury and the chief justice were also mulattoes.[6]

Nott closed with a few words which he thought due to himself and to "the cause of science." He had been accused of ignorance and infidelity. This he could take in stride, but he had also been accused of making science into "an apology for Negro slavery at the South." This was gross slander. He did not hesitate frankly to state, "even at the risk of shocking Southern feelings," his conviction that "every race, capable of self-government," had "a right to liberty," and no one "the right to withhold it. Nay," he added, "though living at the South, and a slaveowner, we shall not hesitate to avow ourself an *emancipationist* whenever it can be clearly shown that the present condition of our slaves can be changed for the better." But science did not indicate that "sound philanthropy" lay in this course. Nott was saved from emancipation only by the fact that in the South the laws of man and the laws of nature coincided.

Immediately after the reading of Nott's paper, Professor Agassiz rose and stated that he wished "to correct some mis-statements, or at least misapprehensions of his views on the subject of the Unity of the Human Race, or rather with regard to the diversity of the different races of men." There had been misunderstanding. He believed, he had always believed, that the races were one in that all possessed "the attributes of humanity," the "moral and intellectual powers, that raise them above the brutes," and "the hope of eternal life through the means pointed out by revelation," although, to be sure, they exhibited these common characteristics "in very different degrees." Zoologically speaking, however, the races were "well marked and distinct," and as it could be shown by the geographical distribution of animals that they occupied distinct zoological provinces and had not developed from a single pair, so it could be shown by the geographical distribution of the races of men that they occupied equally distinct zoological provinces and that "these races did not originate from a common centre, nor from a single pair." This theory was corroborated by "the permanence of the difference between the Caucasian and the Negro" as manifested in the "ancient records and monuments" of Egypt. He realized that this view was opposed to that traditionally accepted, but it was not at variance with Scripture, which expressly stated that other peoples in other lands existed "as early as the days of CAIN."[7]

This mixture of piety and science must have been an unpalatable dose for the presiding officer, who immediately declared a recess. It was only a brief respite, however, for the next paper, sent by Peter A. Browne of Philadelphia, was an account of an examination of hair from two "black" and two "white" albinos. After determining the length of the hair, its shape, color, luster, direction of growth, its ductility, elasticity, and tenacity at a given temperature, barometric pressure, and dew point; the manner in which it fractured; the characteristics of button, sheath, follicle, cortex, intermediate fibers, apex, and cross-sections, Browne concluded that albinos were not a separate species but merely varieties. To Browne, who was no believer in the unity of the races, this meant that the whitening influence of albinism did not make the Negro a member of the white "species." He remained, though white, a Negro. Browne's paper may well have caused some eminent jaws to drop.[8]

Born in Philadelphia in 1782, Peter A. Browne possessed one of those omnivorous minds which, though now extinct, were not uncommon in the eighteenth and early nineteenth centuries. A Philadelphia lawyer, he took a great interest in civic affairs and busied himself in various branches of science. He was one of the founders of the Franklin Institute and its corresponding secretary for many years. He projected the first geological survey of Pennsylvania, led Philadelphia's "Independent Blues" during the War of 1812, built a Chinese Pagoda and Labyrinth Garden for the entertainment of the populace and an arcade designed by Haviland (both of which were such colossal financial disasters that he came to be called "Pagoda Arcade Browne"), put down the terrible Philadelphia race riots in the summer of 1833, campaigned for public gas lighting, and taught geology at Lafayette College. Aside from these activities, he wrote pamphlets on a large number of subjects—geology, veterinary medicine, the naturalization laws, the Oregon question, international standardization of weights and measures, and the theory and operation of the steam engine, to name a few. Mindful of his accomplishments, Browne was rather pompous. Even after relinquishing the post of deputy attorney general, he continued to use the ponderous technical nomenclature of that office, because, as he remarked in court, "the habit strikes me." Without so much as a nod to Shakespeare, the judge replied, "Yes, yes, you are like the clapper of a bell, that keeps wagging after it has done sounding."[9]

In the 1840's Browne began sounding on the subject of "pile," his term for the hair and wool of men and animals. Probably through hints dropped by his friend Samuel S. Haldeman, Browne had discovered the microscope and had invented a little instrument, which he called the "trichometer," for measuring the various properties of hair and wool. His first efforts were in the examination of bristles and wool used in industry, and his first published work on the subject dealt with the hair of lower animals. By bringing these instruments to bear upon human hair, he made a remarkable discovery. He found that all hair was not alike; that some was oval, some cylindrical, some "eccentrically elliptical." Having examined several hundred, he found that "*these three* are the PREVAILING FORMS OR SHAPES" and that they corresponded to skin color, the hair of the white being oval, that of the Indian cylindrical, and that of the Negro "eccentrically elliptical." Aside from the mere shape of the hair, Browne noted various other differences, which he carefully detailed to the members of the association. He found that the "scales upon the cortex of the pile," which make possible both fulling and felting, were fewer on the Caucasian hair than on the Negro hair. Thus, he noted, "the hair of the white man *will not felt,* but the wool of the Negro *will felt.*" This meant that there was no difference between hair from the head of the Negro and wool from the back of a sheep, except in the "*degree*" of "felting power." Since the white man's covering was hair and the Negro's wool, Browne had "no hesitancy in pronouncing that they *belong to two distinct species.*" Further, he found that the hair of the white was pierced by a canal through which flowed the coloring matter and that the hair of the Negro had "no central canal": when present, the coloring agent was "disseminated through the cortex." "Is not this," he asked, "a specific distinction?"[10]

Browne thought that all these "trichometric" differences constituted specific distinctions which threw light on the problem of racial origin. While some had asserted that varieties of men and animals were the products of climatic influences, Browne pointed out that this view was hardly in agreement with his findings, for it was known from experience that the hair of the white who lived in a hot climate did not become curled or develop felting properties and that the hair of the Negro in a cold climate did not become oval and straight. Herodotus in 413 B.C. had mentioned the woolly hair of the Negro. Thus, the Negro had been "the same black-skinned, wooly-headed animal for the last 2000 years." Browne's certainty was increased when, upon examining hair from the head of one of Gliddon's mummies, a 2,700-year-old female, he found that it was oval, with diameters of 1/416 by 1/364 inches. "The lady belonged to the white race," he concluded. Similarly, measurement of the hair of Mound Builders and Peruvian mummies convinced him that these people were of the same race as the North American Indians.[11]

The discovery that hair-type was a permanent racial character held important implications for the much discussed question of hybridization. Browne found that hair from the heads of "hybrids" formed by the crossing of any two "species" of man consisted of filaments characteristic of each of the parent species. That is, the hair of a mulatto born of a "pure" Negro and a "pure" white was both eccentrically elliptical and oval. By close observation he could determine the "degree of hybridity" of any given individual, and he prepared an elaborate set of tables which gave the nomenclature of human hybridity, of hybrids both "simple" (the offspring of two species only) and "compound" (the offspring of the crossings of all three species). Using the term "mulattin" to denote all crosses of the black and white species (or mixtures of oval and eccentrically elliptical types of hair) he found that the simple crossing of black and white could produce seven degrees of hybridity: "Hepta Mulattin" (fourteen parts white to two parts black, or 14:2), "Hexa Mulattin" (12:4), "Penta Mulattin" (10:6), "Tetra Mulattin" (8:8), "Tria Mulattin" (6:10), "Di Mulattin" (4:12), and "Mono Mulattin" (2:14). Applying the same prefixes to the terms "costin" and "mestisen," he gave the degrees of "simple hybridity" between the black and Indian and white and Indian, respectively. Compound hybrids led to such linguistic feats as "Hepta-hypo-mono-mulattin" and "Penta-hyper-mono-mulattin."[12]

Browne's investigations thus substantiated the conclusions reached by the "American School" of anthropologists. They indicated that the races had separate origins and constituted separate species, and they captured the Egyptians for the white species. A writer in the New York *Evening Post* noted that the theory of "the autochthonous origin of the aborigines of America" which was "held by many on various grounds" seemed to be confirmed by Browne's study of "pile."[13]

Browne's microscopic observations revealed not only quantitative differences: he found a qualitative distinction in the absence of a canal in the Negro hair. "According to the rules of science," he philosophized, the organ which "employs a greater variety of apparatus in the performance of its functions" is to be considered the *more perfect*." In the white man's hair, Browne had found a "canal" for the distribution of "coloring matter" which was *entirely wanting* in hair from the head of the Negro. "The inference," he concluded, "is irresistible. The hair of the white man is more perfect than that of the negro; and, as we know, by experience, that of all pile, that of the head of man is the most completely organized, we will not, perhaps, be wandering astray, in ranking the hair of the head of the white man as *a perfect hair*."[14]

His collection grew rapidly, until Browne attained the interesting distinction of being curator of the world's largest collection of hair. The Secretary of Interior sent out circulars to Indian agents. Missionaries forwarded hair from the heads of people whose souls they were laboring to save. Dr. Nott sent Indian hair. Gliddon and Dr. John K. Mitchell contributed "some Egyptian mummy hair." The collection was also distinguished by specimens from the heads of the world's great. There were hairs from such eminent scalps as those of Napoleon Bonaparte, Professor Benjamin Silliman, "Bartola, the female Aztec dwarf," George Washington, Andrew Jackson, the Chief Justice of the Pennsylvania Supreme Court, Professor Samuel S. Haldeman, John Sergeant, and Bigwater, the Indian chief, together with a small lock of "wool" from the "Bushman Boy," which Professor Charles D. Meigs had presented. The king of Saxony sent a collection of "fine wools collected from the principal sheepfolds of his Kingdom" all "put up in the most elegant manner in port folios."[15]

Yet though his collection was large and his researches meticulous, there was strangely little enthusiasm for "*a perfect hair*." No one seemed to pay much attention. Morton had taken a friendly interest, Browne was asked to Richmond to lecture on pile, and Haldeman was sympathetic, but not even Nott and Gliddon, who searched the scientific world for information on the specific diversity of man, used his discoveries. Worse, the Smithsonian, an institution established specifically for the promotion of knowledge, preferred to publish a volume on algae instead of Browne's work on pile. "What is a work on Algae, with all its merits," he asked disgustedly after a disappointing correspondence with Professor Henry, to a volume "containing more scientific knowledge on hair than has ever before been condensed in one work?" He thought there might be some "political objection" to him and, puzzled, asked Morton, "Can you my dear friend give me a clew to this labyrinth?"[16]

Browne's paper on the hair of albinos brought the meeting of the American Association for the Advancement of Science to a close. Morton had not been able to attend, but his friends gave him a full report. While the "town bell" was "tolling the sad news" of the death of "our great man John C. Calhoun," Robert W. Gibbes wrote that the meeting was "very pleasant" and "passed off very well." He had persuaded Agassiz to spend a week at his home in Columbia, where Gibbes took him on a tour of the neighboring plantations to examine field hands from the various African tribes, "Foulah, Gullah, Guinea, Coromanteé, Mandrigo, and Congo Negroes. He found enough," Gibbes reported, "to satisfy him that they have differences from the other races." In Mobile, Nott rejoiced that his paper on the Jews had "brought out Agassiz," and he was happy to learn that Agassiz intended to write "a book on the races," which would "blow out old Bachmans brains."[17]

Not all were happy, however. Agassiz, attacked by various theologians for his views on diversity, grumbled that there was "no freedom for a scientific man in America!" And Alexander Dallas Bache complained to Lewis Gibbes that "the remarks at the close of the meeting were altogether of too popular a cast to require their printing."[18]

Kicking Up
a "Dam^d Fuss Generally"

By the time of Morton's death, the principal tenets of the doctrine that was coming to be called "polygenism" had been established. If not all American naturalists had been captured, at least none now openly opposed the doctrine, with of course the perennial exception of "old Bachman," half theologian, half scientist, lost and confused between the hemispheres of his own personality.

Ahead lay a struggle. The tenets of the "American School" of anthropology had to be made known to the people generally. The discoveries of modern science had to be presented in a form understandable to the masses. In short, someone had to do for Morton what Voltaire had done for Newton. In order to gain general acceptance for the new anthropology, theological strongholds had to be battered down. Having, as he said, got Morton and Agassiz into the fray, Nott had intended to retire, but that was before the death of the leader. Squier could not be counted on, for he was in Central America trying to make his fortune from a railway across Honduras, and Agassiz was so busy with fishes that he had little time left for races. Thus the task which he had begun in his little essay on the mulatto was left to Nott.

He took it up with an air of weary martyrdom, though privately elated at the prospect of annihilating the parsons and breaking their grip on the popular mind. He was always astonished that his "infidelity" had not destroyed his medical practice but finally concluded that "if a man wants to get on fast, he must kick up a dam^d fuss generally."[1]

Nott had gained influential friends in the editors of the *Southern Quarterly Review* and De Bow's *Review*. William Gilmore Simms, who now edited the *Southern Quarterly*, was a firm believer in separate creations. De Bow's editorials kept the question to the fore. One had noted that "the question of the human race, whether a *unity*, or not, has an important bearing just now, in examining the position occupied by the negro, whom philanthropy is seeking to elevate to the highest status of humanity," and the editor was impressed by the discovery, which appeared to him "to be the better opinion among scientific men," that the Negro was "not of common origin with the Caucasian." There was a time, De Bow noted, when "the unity" had been "almost universally credited," but it had lately been "vigorously" and, he believed, "unanswerably attacked." He quickly saw the political implications of this development in ethnology. If the races of men had a common origin, he reasoned, then a single political system might be applied to all, "and the greatest license" thereby given to "the 'latter day' theorists, who would organize the world upon certain uniform bases, and fit the same institutions and laws to every state and condition of civilization." However, if the races were created separately, these "mad dreamers" would awake to reality and "the world discover that parliament and Congress were "unsuited to the Hottentot and the African, and the ballot-box and trial by jury not altogether the sort of things to flourish . . . among the snows of Russia or by the shores of the Bosphorus. Our faith in political theories," he added for good measure, "has never exceeded a mustard seed." De Bow reviewed the state of controversy over unity as of 1850 and, promising to keep his readers informed, eagerly awaited further developments.[2]

Assured of a welcome by both Simms and De Bow, Nott considerably increased his output. Late in 1850 he published an article in the *Southern Quarterly* attacking the biblical chronology. Ridiculing its absurdities, he asserted that it could not account for archeological facts and predicted its abandonment. Already "in the year 1850, no Egyptologist, of first rate standing" would deny that the "white, black, and other races, as distinct as now, existed at an epoch too remote to be reconciled with any chronology yet drawn" from Scripture. Scientists whose authority it was "presumption in the uninformed to question" had left the short chronologies to the theologians. Such was human frailty that some years would be required "to conduct ethnography safely through the struggles against 'doctrines and polity,'" through which astronomy and geology had had to fight their way, but "the dawn," Nott predicted, was "at hand."[3]

Morton also had strongly questioned the biblical chronology, and Gliddon vehemently denied its validity. It may seem curious that in attempting to show that racial distinctions were not the products of environment, they should have insisted on a longer chronology than was commonly accepted; supposedly the longer time scale would enhance the effect of environment on the organism. Lyell recognized this fact. "The theory," he noted, "that all the races of men have come from one common stock receives support from every investigation which forces us to expand our ideas of the duration of past time." Nonetheless, Morton, Gliddon, and Nott insisted that the biblical chronology was too short, and they confidently asserted that, within the near future, fossilized human skeletons would be found.[4]

Their dissatisfaction with the short chronologies had several explanations. In the first place, as men who kept themselves well posted on the progress of the various branches of science, they knew that the short chronology was doomed. Lyell had destroyed its application to geology with the publication of his *Principles of Geology*, and they never doubted that its application to anthropology would likewise be discredited. Lepsius and Bunsen had already dated some of the Egyptian monuments from an era preceding the so-called Deluge. Further, Nott and Gliddon were glad enough to discredit it as one of the remaining restrictions that theology placed on science. The addition of more decades and centuries which the Egyptologists appended to the old chronology did not provide sufficient time for the creation of varieties through the agency of climate. As for the eagerly awaited discovery of fossil man, it posed to them no more of a problem than the discovery of fossil animals had posed to Cuvier and Agassiz. Such objects were simply part of another creation, another world of nature which had been destroyed by an earth-shaking catastrophe to make way for a new creation. In this way, as Frothingham recognized, they were really reviving the old preadamite heresy, with the expectation that if it could be shown that man had been created in an earlier geological epoch, then their own theory of separate creations would lose much of its objectionable novelty. The acceptance of separate creations in time would smooth the way for acceptance of separate creations in space. They had nothing to fear from the new long chronology—as they interpreted it.

In 1851 De Bow printed Nott's review of Bachman's book as the leading article in the February number. Bachman contended that Negro and white sprang from a single creation and were of the same species, of which the Negro, however, was an inferior variety. Nott was quick to detect the contradiction. Here Bachman "fully admits the *practical fact* for which we have been contending, but denies that this *now* 'permanent inferiority'" is "attributable to a separate origin." Bachman had been forced into contradiction because he would not accept the great scientific discovery of the nineteenth century, the permanence of racial character—a discovery which could "be as clearly demonstrated as the revolution of the earth around the sun, the discoveries in geology, the circulation of the blood." Like those epoch-making disclosures, it would have to fight its way for perhaps a generation before winning general acceptance. Assuming that Bachman spoke for the same forces of bigotry that had forced Galileo to recant, Nott reminded him, "However violent the storm may become, the discussion must be persecuted."[5]

In March, De Bow reprinted in the "Agricultural Department" of his *Review* long extracts from a lecture Nott had delivered the previous December before the Southern Rights Association in Mobile on the "Natural History of Mankind, Viewed in Connection with Negro Slavery." This was an anti-abolition speech in which Nott emphasized the ethnological evidence of Negro inferiority and incapacity for civilization. The Toltecans, he was forced to admit, had achieved a "semicivilization," and the Mongolians had "gone a step farther," but the Negroes had "risen but little above the beasts of the field." In fact, "no pure blooded Negro" had ever "risen above the grade of mediocrity in the whites." The notion that the Negro could expand his brain through education over a series of generations was, he said, a "capital error," and "how it ever got into vogue, with all history, all science and all common sense against it, would be difficult to divine. Absurd religious opinions alone" could explain its currency. One by one Nott explained away the alternatives to slavery. Science showed that abolition could not possibly succeed. Freed Negroes could not be sent to the North, for they would perish in competition with whites. Returned to Africa, they would starve. The idea of amalgamation was not only "insulting and revolting" to all self-respecting Southerners, it was highly impractical as well. Although it would greatly improve the "intellectual grade of the negro," the white race "would be *dragged down* by the adulteration, and their civilization destroyed." It was difficult enough for even the "purest races of the earth to maintain anything like rational governments; and what would become of our institutions in the hands of mullattoes?" This was anthropology's contribution to the legend of the lost Eden of the Old South. The Negro race was a race of children. It was the duty of the South to protect them faithfully from the ravages of a freedom they were not equipped to endure.[6]

Eighteen hundred and fifty-three was a busy year for Josiah Nott. He was at work on a "big scheme" that he and Gliddon had conceived. In addition, his professional labors vastly increased during the great epidemic of yellow fever in Mobile. In this disaster he lost seven relatives, four of them his own children. He was driving away care, he wrote Gliddon with a touch of his peculiar, bitter humor, "by driving 3 horses (professionally) night and day." Too, there was resistance at home in Mobile to his ethnological views. William T. Hamilton, one of the city's leading Presbyterian divines, was taking the position that all racial distinctions had appeared at Babel and that the races were descended from one pair. Hamilton admitted that "the races were distinct at an epoch so near the flood as to have no time for Physical causes to have produced them from one stock," but he went off to Egypt to see for himself whether the races were really as old as Nott and Gliddon said. Nott predicted at the time that Hamilton would "come back acknowledging Lepsius's Chronology & crawling out of the scrape by saying 'it is not given us to understand' the difficulties which surround Genesis." On his return Hamilton published a book, *The "Friend of Moses,"* in which—there it was—he asserted that the question of whether man developed from a single pair lay in the realm of revelation and could not be answered by science. But he could not accept the chronology of Lepsius. He had seen a coffin said to be four thousand years old. This was beyond belief. He found it "utterly incredible that wood, and that the several papyrus rolls, should have existed so many thousands of years." The world could present no "parallel of such durability in materials so frail and perishable."[7]

Despite family tragedy, the pressure of professional duties, and the necessity of cleaning up this pocket of resistance at home, Nott found time to publish a long article on geographical distribution. This was another attack on the "Theological Naturalists," those who looked "to the Book of Genesis, or what they conceive to be the inspired word of God, as a text book, of Natural History, as they formerly did of Astronomy and Geology," as opposed to the "Naturalists proper"—to Nott's mind the *proper naturalists*—who looked to "facts, and the laws of God as revealed in his works," in other words, to science.[8]

This little essay clarified Nott's attitude toward the concept of the pure race. The theory of geographical distribution based upon multiple creations which he, Morton, and Agassiz had formulated left little room for the notion that "pure" races now existed. That a race of men, planted on the same continent with innumerable others, could maintain the purity of its blood would be little short of a miracle, and Nott had long ago ceased to believe in miracles. The superiority of the Caucasian lay precisely in the fact that he was even less pure than other species of man. His conquests throughout the world demonstrated his "pliability," his capacity to survive in a great variety of climates. This quality derived from the fact that he was a blend of many species originally adapted to a particular region and climate. Race mixture conferred enormous benefit. A "small trace of white blood in the Negro improves his intelligence and moral character; and a small trace of negro blood, as in the quartroon, will protect the individual against the deadly influences of climate." The Caucasian was a happy blend of the best qualities of several species, a true "cosmopolite."

This did not mean, however, that the blending process should continue. Nott was neither an apostle of the Pure Race theory nor an an amalgamationist. His concept of the Caucasian was that of a species blended to a nicety, whose outstanding qualities further additions would not augment but only adulterate. Nott had no love for slavery. He did not defend it with any of the numerous arguments then fashionable. Still less did he argue that slavery was ordained by God, as did Samuel Adolphus Cartwright, another prominent Southern physician who searched for proofs of the Negro's supposed inferiority. Nott was simply unable to see any solution other than slavery to the problems presented by two species of men living in the same zoological province.[9]

The Watchman's Response

In 1852 Nott's production came almost to a standstill. He published nothing on the "vexed question" and wrote only one medical paper. (Despite the number of articles on ethnology, there had been no slackening in the number on medical subjects.) The reason was that he and Gliddon, who had come south to lecture in the winter of 1851–52, were plotting a coup. Three years before, Squier had offered to collaborate with Gliddon on a book, but Gliddon had declined on the ground that he was a lecturer, not a writer—an acute subjective insight. Now, however, he needed funds. Although he was "going it strong on niggerology," as Nott observed, the cost of presenting the Panorama greatly reduced the income from his lectures. In March he had persuaded Senator Jefferson Davis of Mississippi to submit a bill providing for the introduction of camels to be used for transport and mail service across the Southwest. Now, in 1853, he awaited official recognition of his contribution, hoping this would take the form of an appointment, accompanied by a handsome stipend, to superintend transport of the animals from Egypt.[1]

In the meantime, Gliddon had hit upon another project that promised to be lucrative. He hoped to persuade Nott to collaborate with him in writing a grand ethnological work. Nott's practice had so increased ("almost beyond endurance & I am an especial favorite with the clergy. . . . I physic them all") that he had decided henceforth to write nothing larger than a "brochure." Still, Gliddon tempted him, he wrote Squier. Unassisted, Gliddon could not manage the facts "on Anatomy & Natural history." Solely out of friendship, therefore, Nott "embarked" upon the venture. They collected a library of works on Egyptology and gratefully accepted Mrs. Morton's offer to lend her late husband's books and manuscripts.[2]

Generally, Nott was pleased with the plan of work. Lepsius had carried the races "up to 3000 B.C.," and Nott felt that he and Gliddon could "take them very comfortably some distance beyond the flood." Their work would be made easier by the admission, "now general among the well informed Skunks" (originally Gliddon's, and now Nott's accustomed term for clergymen) that "time & Climate cannot change one Race into another." His only fear was that Gliddon, who had moved to the outskirts of Mobile and was "living like an Arab in a shanty in the woods," would be "too pugnacious." Gliddon put him in mind "of the Character *Mercure,* in Moliere's Amphytrion, when he tells Sosie that he has not hit any body [for] so long that he feels immensely strong in the arm & is going to hit him a hell of a lick." The parsons had been snapping at Gliddon for years, and only "policy" had "kept him back." Now well aware that he was "generally branded as a dam'd infidel," there was no longer reason for restraint, and he was "keen for taking off gloves & coat & licking the whole crowd." Nott himself, as he modestly informed Squier, wished "simply to post science up to date without condescending to notice the varmonts in any way."[3]

The fruit of their labors was *Types of Mankind,* a ponderous volume of over eight hundred pages, dedicated "to the Memory of Morton." The work is in two main parts. The first, written largely by Nott, deals with the physical types of man, "comparative anatomy of the races," hybridization, and geographical distribution. Defining "type" as a species, or, in Morton's words, "a primordial organic form," Nott discussed Caucasian, African, and Indian types and resurrected his essay on the "Physical History of the Jews." The second part of the book, for which Gliddon was mainly responsible, contains sections on biblical criticism, Egyptology, and chronology, although with courtly graciousness and professional respect, each called upon the other for notes and parenthetical remarks. Gliddon's contribution, written in his inimitable style of pompous didacticism, was mostly in the field of biblical criticism. It was an attack on "the biblical dunces in the United States," which paid off old scores against his clerical detractors, and on the King James Version, the errors of which he meticulously collated with the results of modern investigations in Egyptology.[4]

Agassiz was persuaded, during his visit to Mobile in the spring of 1853, to contribute a chapter on the geographical distribution of animals and men. In this, he charged the defenders of the unity of man with being disciples of Lamarck and accepted publicly Morton's definition of species as "a primordial organic form" as the only one which accounted for all observed facts. In addition, Dr. Henry S. Patterson of Philadelphia furnished a biographical memoir of Morton, and a Mobile physician, Dr. William Usher, added a chapter on geology and paleontology. This, together with "Excerpta from Morton's Inedited Manuscripts," which was made much of, constituted *Types of Mankind*.

The book contained little that was new, for it was designed as a compendium of all anthropological evidence that had been brought forward in support of the specific diversity of mankind. *Types of Mankind* was a fighting book. Nott made this abundantly clear in his introduction. He had searched, he said, through the "annals of Astronomy, Geology, Chronology, [and] Geographical distribution of Animals" and had found that "scientific truth" had "literally fought its way inch by inch through false theology." He concluded that "the last grand battle between science and dogmatism" had now commenced. It was to be fought out on the issue of "the primitive origin of races." There was no question in Nott's mind as to the outcome: ". . . science must again, and finally, triumph." The struggle would not be a battle of tremulous warriors. On former occasions he and Gliddon had trod softly, attempting "to conciliate sectarians, and to reconcile the plain teachings of science with theological prejudices; but to no useful purpose." In return, their opinions and their motives had been "misrepresented and vilified by self-constituted teachers of the Christian religion!" Properly indignant, Nott and Gliddon were "now done with all this." They no longer had "any apologies to offer, nor favors . . . to ask. The broad banner of science," they proclaimed, "is herein nailed to the mast."[5]

In view of the fact that *Types of Mankind* was not an original work and was relatively expensive (five dollars to subscribers, seven-fifty to others), it had a large sale. By the middle of November, 1853, subscriptions were coming in at the rate of six a day, and when the book was issued in April, 1854, the subscription lists stood at 992. The first printing was sold out immediately. It reappeared in at least nine editions before the end of the century.[6]

Squier promptly wrote an unsigned review for the Sunday edition of James Gordon Bennett's *New York Herald*. *Types of Mankind*, he said, was entirely worthy of the tradition established by Morton in the "pre-eminently . . . American science" of ethnology. Its authors, boldly adhering to scientific fact, had written "the most remarkable book" which had "yet appeared in America upon the subject." Refusing to bow to a doctrine either because of its age or its orthodoxy, they had presented the theory of original diversity, not "as a hypothesis to be sustained, but as a result which is demonstrated." The work grappled "with proscriptive dogmas as fearlessly as did geology with the literal acceptance of the so-called Mosaic account of the creation." When the orthodox had seen their chronology destroyed by geology, they sought to compensate the loss "by more vigorous requisitions on human credulity," and, "more imperiously than ever, insisted upon the unity of mankind," but science marched irresistibly forward, not to be "stayed in her path by the lions of bigotry, superstition, and ignorance." The spirit of Galileo could not be laid while "truth" remained "to be discovered, or error to be overthrown." By their restrictions on scientific inquiry, the orthodox had enmeshed themselves in a net of inconsistencies. They insisted on both the "vulgar chronology" and the unity of man. But, Squier assured them, "if the chronology which places the date of the creation of man six thousand years ago, be true, and the existing types of men have been unchanged for five thousand years, then the diversities which men present must have arisen in the four thousand years after the creation, and the causes which produced them have thenceforward ceased to act! Such are the absurdities in which 'orthodoxy' involves its blind followers."[7]

Orthodoxy would surely raise the cry of "infidel!" at this book, but regardless of the menacing gestures of the righteous, *Types of Mankind* carried to their "ultimate results" the facts and conclusions which many scientists had established but had not had "the courage to apply." Altogether, Squier concluded, chafing at the limits of newspaper space, it was the "response of the 'Watchman, what of the night?' of the earnest student," and the "monument" which marked the point of farthest advance of "modern ethnographic science in the first decade of the last half of the nineteenth century." It was destined "to exercise a great influence, and produce a profound and permanent impression on the public mind."[8]

The impression on the public mind is difficult to fathom, but certainly the impression on the Presbyterian mind was profound. While he was nailing the broad banner of science to the mast, Nott had to take care lest fagots were piled below him. The *Presbyterian Magazine*, published in Philadelphia and edited by the staunchly orthodox Cortlandt Van Rensselaer, remarked the excellent binding, format, illustrations, and "unprecedented" sale, but asserted that reviewers, subscribers, the public, and, he hinted, even the publishers, had been duped, all "induced by a cunning device to aid a new effort to overthrow the foundations of revealed religion, to unsettle the faith of the Christian, and to establish a milennium of sceptical science." The absence of an index, "by which to test the book" before "purchase and perusal," was "an exceedingly suspicious omission." By attempting to prove that certain species were peculiar to certain geographical areas and therefore represented separate creations, Agassiz, Nott, and Gliddon, the reviewer asserted, had but one purpose in mind, "that of discrediting revealed religion, and casting contempt on the word of God." Ethnology was "but a secondary object compared with this ignoble design."

Convinced of the subversive purpose of the volume, the reviewer devoted most of his article to attacking the "repulsively affected, and often hopelessly obscure" Gliddon, whose "vulgar ribaldry" and "cool atrocity" he found revolting. He made little criticism of the scientific argument for pluralism. On the contrary, he accepted it. God, he said, created all men of one "genus," and made it "a law of his creation that man and animals should separate into different species" and that each should perpetuate its own type; "hence these types of mankind." He concluded with the devastating witticism that the book was mistitled. "It should have been not 'Types of Mankind,' but 'Types of Infidelity.' "[9]

The reviewer for *Putnam's Monthly,* organ of the new abolitionist-inclined Republican party, was likewise unable to find fault with the scientific argument presented in *Types of Mankind*. He deplored "Mr. Gliddon's flippant and dogmatic" attack on Scripture but was so impressed by the argument for multiple creations that he actually attempted to interpret the scriptural account of creation in such a way that it would conform to the precepts of the "new school of Ethnology." He noted that the researches of Nott, Gliddon, Agassiz, Morton, "and distinguished naturalists in England, France and Germany" absolutely contradicted "every fundamental proposition of the accredited theory" of man's origin which had been generally accepted by theologians. As a consequence, there had sprung up a new controversy between science and religion. With his own method of interpretation the reviewer sought to avert open warfare.[10]

Distinguishing between God's word and His works, by assuming that the former revealed truths that were "above nature" and only to be "spiritually discerned," he asked, "If the primary and exclusive objects of the Word are spiritual, and not at all scientific, can we with any propriety use it as a ground of scientific evidence, without doing violence to its character?" Greatly impressed by Morton's "unrivalled" collection, his "laborious, patient, varied and accurate" investigations, which evinced "a scientific sagacity of the most extraordinary reach and penetration, coupled with a judicial severity of judgment," and fully cognizant of the scientific facts in the controversy, the reviewer found that there were "good grounds for the conclusion that the historical beginnings of man must have been diverse." He would not say that the races were distinct species. Scientists had so "bedeviled" the word by their varied definitions that it was difficult to attach precise meaning to it, and theologians had burdened it with "the most sacred associations, so that to deny the identity of the human species" seemed "like denying the manhood of men." He did not hesitate to state, however, that "so far as scientific and archaeological inquiries go, the preponderance of evidence is on the side of fixed or primordial distinctions among the races, and of a multiple, or nation, rather than an individual or dual origination in history." By interpreting Scripture as the lyrical voice of God, he concluded that "the nations are of one blood, therefore, not genealogically, but spiritually, in their capacities of thought and affection, which the blood only typifies, and which are the very essence and most real grounds of their manhood." Agassiz himself said no more than this.

Upon reading this article, the reviewer of *Types of Mankind* for the *Presbyterian Quarterly Review* expressed "surprise and regret" at the appearance of an article which "shuts up its readers to the miserable alternatives of Infidelity or Swedenborgianism," and accused *Putnam's* of sensationalism and of reading copy with one eye on the circulation lists. Loaded with invective, primed with bitterness, and tamped with the rod of righteousness, this review was the big gun of the orthodox. The reviewer had not wanted to discuss the book. It was mere *"humbug,"* full of weak and ineffectual arguments, a "farrago," undeserving of "respectful notice," and he was induced to review it "only by the fear" that readers might not "understand its utter unsoundness, amidst its immeasurable pretension." Forty pages were required to allay his fear. The reviewer momentarily lost himself in bitter contemplation of Gliddon: "To think of such a man, 'one who has been to a feast of learning and stolen away the scraps,' picking up a little ethnography here, a little craniology there, some superficial Orientalism in wandering about the Levant, some Hebraism from reviews, second-hand books, and an occasional talk over a pipe with a muddy Rabbi, or a mug of beer with a half-infidel German, and with such artillery undertaking to overthrow God's word!" But, quickly recovering himself, he examined the path along which these purveyors of unbelief showed that science was progressing.[11]

This path, he found, would bring "to helpless, remediless degradation many of the races of mankind; and all but the Caucasian to final extinction." It would even "unsettle the faith of men in our holy religion." He suggested an alternative. "It may be a law of nature," he speculated, "that with general uniformity, there shall be occasional deviations, giving a peculiar type to an individual, which, once originated, becomes perpetuated in his lineage." This process had been observed among domesticated animals, a recent instance of which had been "the famous breed of *short, bow-legged* sheep," which were "common in the Green Mountains" and had developed from the same ancestry as the common species. It might be, he continued, that such deviations perpetuated themselves, "unless modified or obliterated by amalgamation with others." Now, as the authors of *Types of Mankind* insisted on a longer chronology than had hitherto been accepted by biblical scholars, the races of men might very well have originated in this manner.[12]

Nevertheless, the reviewer immediately fired four heavy bursts at the authors' chronology, asserting that "before we can adopt the immense periods claimed for Egyptian existence," we must know beyond doubt "that the hieroglyphics are read with perfect accuracy," that the dynasties were successive and not contemporaneous, "that the hieroglyphic-makers were well informed," and "that the Egyptians meant to tell the truth." "When these postulates become certainties," he admonished, "we shall be more disturbed about Scriptural Chronology." These standards were impossible, as he doubtless intended them to be. There was little danger of his being disturbed about scriptural chronology.

He ought, however, to have been somewhat ill at ease on the shaky ground he was defending, for in his indiscriminate flailing about, he had swung at both separate origins and the long chronology and so fallen into contradiction. In repudiating the new Egyptian chronology he was allowing little time between the Deluge and the earliest depiction of the races for "congenital peculiarities" to appear and perpetuate themselves. This review shows clearly the dilemma the orthodox faced. Literal interpreters of Scripture, they were defending theological accretions which had been accumulating for centuries. Nailing *their* banner to the mast, they were caught between chronology and unity and forced to fight on both port and starboard.

Perhaps aware of the fruitlessness of his argument, the reviewer turned to the theological implications of the theory presented by *Types of Mankind*. Complaining that it violated the "great central doctrine of Revelation," Original Sin, and threw into confusion the "great scheme of redeeming grace," he announced that "its relation to revealed religion" was "clearly that of infidelity." Thoughtful Christians should beware of speculation on such subjects. Professor Agassiz had begun "these daring speculations with an earnest endeavor to reconcile them with the Word of God," but Nott and Gliddon, with "that yell of congratulation and triumph," with which "the whole crew of infidel philosophers" applauded the "fanciful deductions of the great naturalist," seized upon his "assumptions," and hurried them "at once" to "their legitimate and startling conclusions." The professor thus found himself a much vaunted contributor to a work which, the reviewer was sure, purchasers would cast away "indignantly" when they learned that its design was "to wrest from them the Word of God, and substantiate in place of its cheerful hopes and consolations, a bleak and frigid infidelity."

One cannot help feeling that this reviewer was not so much disturbed over the scientific doctrine of the book as he was indignant that the authors made "no effort to reconcile their developments with the teaching of Revelation." This was not an isolated sentiment. Bishop Alonzo Potter of the Episcopal Diocese of Pennsylvania suggested that if "the unity of the human race be a delusion, it can be exposed by the appropriate evidence." But the evidence ought not to be accompanied by attacks on Scripture. Never in the whole extent of his reading had he come upon a book "so offensive to good taste."[13]

Not all the reviewers of *Types of Mankind* were professional Presbyterians. A writer in the *Southern Quarterly Review* was offended by the "flippant tone" adopted toward Scripture but thought the work "highly creditable to the learning and talent of the South," and stated his own conclusion succinctly. No one could maintain that the theory of diverse origins was proved beyond doubt "so long as names venerable in the roll of science" still resisted it. But the reviewer believed that "this much, at least," must be conceded: "Either there were separate creations of different types of mankind, or men must have existed on earth for Chiliads of years." Both propositions might be true, "one of them must be."[14]

Calling upon the spirit of Galileo to be their witness, Nott and Gliddon made much of defending science from the tyranny of religious orthodoxy. Not all members of the scientific community, however, wished to have their shackles loosed by Nott and Gliddon. James Dwight Dana spoke for himself. Involved in a controversy with Tayler Lewis, professor of Greek at Union College, in the matter of science versus theology, Dana took care to dissociate himself from the defenders of multiple creations. Lewis had implied throughout his book, *The Six Days of Creation* (1855), that scientists tended to be impelled by a spirit of infidelity. "Who are these infidels?" demanded Dana, calling the names of the Sillimans, Hitchcock, Henry, Gray, Torrey, Bache, and others notoriously pious. He added that Lewis would probably point to a "weak book" which had "recently come forth under the garb of science." But that work, he said, betrayed its "unscientific character" in lacking the "cool argument and well-arranged facts of the philosopher"; its pages abounded "in vituperations, sneers, and expressions of con-temptuous triumph." He thought Agassiz's contribution "wholly different" in spirit, and "altogether out of place."[15]

Dana believed that the unity of the human species would not be disproved, but he would not have its opponents "relax one iota their efforts." "No one but a coward in his religious faith," he added, "should fear the result of the freest discussion." To make doubly sure that he was not to be considered a member of the "American School" of anthropology, Dana quickly followed up his review of

Lewis with another article in the *Bibliotheca Sacra*, "Thoughts on Species," in which he strongly supported the commonly accepted view.[16]

John William Draper (1811–82), the distinguished chemist, physiologist, and president of the medical school at the University of the City of New York, had no less faith in science and no more in orthodox Christianity than Nott and Gliddon. Still, he had no very high opinion of *Types of Mankind*. Draper, as extreme an environmentalist as Samuel Stanhope Smith himself, asserted in his *Human Physiology* (1856) that heat determined complexion, social conditions the form of the brain and, therefore, that of the skull. He insisted that no race was in a "state of absolute equilibrium," or able to maintain its physiognomy, if its environment changed. With "equal facility" all races could "descend to a baser, or rise to a more elevated state," in accordance with circumstances. These developments, however, were gradual. The hypothesis of multiple creations was the result of "mistaking the slow movements of Nature for absolute rest."[17]

Almost every member of the scientific community seemed to have an opinion, and it was not to be expected that old John Bachman should maintain silence. Nott wrote Squier that he did not "care a curse what people say" about *Types of Mankind;* "the devil was in me & as soon as he was out the excitement passed away—." Still, he was interested enough briefly to join in another controversy on the old battleground, the *Charleston Medical Journal*. "Bachman you will see is out upon me strong," he observed to Squier in September.[18]

Disclaiming, as usual, that he derived any enjoyment from controversy and grumbling that he felt "no disposition to waste the remnant of life" that was left "in 'idle disputes,'" Bachman nevertheless wrote a review of *Types of Mankind* so long that the editors had to publish it in four instalments. He was offended by the insulting references to himself in Patterson's memoir of Morton and by the opposition's unwarranted assumption that he was a mere "clerical adversary," and he laid responsibility for both on the "malignity" of Nott and Gliddon. That pair, he wrote, "first awaken public sympathy in behalf of a prominent deceased man and then, either covertly or openly, make false charges against one who met him on the fair field of open argument, who addressed him not as a dead but a living man—his equal and his friend." Their motive was simply "to weaken the influence" of one they feared "likely to give them some trouble in the establishment of their theories." Bachman reviewed the old controversy with Morton, indicating his own unquestionable victory, then, turning to Nott, ridiculed his pretensions as a naturalist. "The moment he leaves the leading strings of Morton and Agassiz he involves himself in inextricable difficulties." Disdaining to discuss scientific matters with one so ill-qualified, Bachman devoted the remainder of his review to answering Agassiz's arguments.[19]

In his contribution to *Types of Mankind*, Agassiz, to Bachman's considerable surprise, had expressed his acceptance of Morton's definition of species as a "primordial organic form" and had asserted that the races of men should be so defined. Bachman did not deny that the species of plants and lower animals were primordial—fixed at the Creation—but he did deny that this fact provided a definition, still less a criterion, of species. If naturalists were to accept this criterion their paths would be rocky indeed. "If the clumsy Egyptian artisan" had given a "representation of a greyhound, whose ears and short turned up tail might be mistaken for a rabbit," a "turnspit that bears some resemblance to the Chinese pig," and "figures of the heads of men and women, whose representatives it would be difficult to find among any of the present known varieties of men," science would be "left without a guide in the examination of species."[20]

As for geographical distribution, Agassiz had oversimplified the whole problem. There were no boundaries applicable to all the species within a province. It was true, Bachman admitted, that each species had its own range, but the range of the human species overlapped them all. He noted that Agassiz himself had exempted man from the confinement of zoological provinces in his article for the *Revue Suisse* in 1845. The notion (which had been paraded before the world as a scientific deduction from the law of geographical distribution) that species must have been created in their several provinces, was no more than unsupported assumption. Consider, for example, Agassiz's Arctic realm. A race of men could hardly have been created there unless the Creator provided His creatures with hooks, lines, sinkers, and bait and the knowledge to use them. The Eskimos ate only meat. If they were created in the Arctic, why did they not possess carnivorous teeth? "If the species of man in a zoological province were moulded in accordance with the structure of the surrounding animal world, we might expect that the Australian man would have been furnished with a corrugated pouch, like the majority of the species that compose his singular realm."[21]

Once again Bachman attempted to dissociate himself from the twin devils of Lamarckism and abolitionism. He indignantly denied that belief in the specific unity of man implied adherence to a theory "best adapted to the views of an atheist." However striking the varieties which appeared, specific differences were "never effaced."[22]

Having, as he thought, cleared himself of Agassiz's charge of scientific heresy, Bachman added "a few remarks on the bearing of the doctrine of the Unity of the Human Race, on the domestic institutions, and vital interest of the South," designed to place him beyond suspicion of political heresy. Because some politicians caught up the argument for specific diversity and brought it to the defense of slavery, those who had supported the "doctrine of the unity," he complained, had "sometimes been stigmatized as abolitionists and the enemies of the South." He had, he said, always lived in a slave state and had always "openly and fearlessly" defended "the institutions of South Carolina." Belief in the unity of mankind was not subversive of Southern institutions. Quite the contrary. He believed that the Negro was "a striking and now permanent variety" of the single species Man and could return to the original specific type only through the "revolting" process of amalgamation. The Negro's intelligence, "although underrated," was so far inferior to that of the Caucasian that he was incapable of governing himself and so was "thrown on our protection."[23]

Bachman explained that it was not the unity of the species, but the doctrine expounded by such works as *Types of Mankind*, that undermined domestic institutions. Proof of the doctrine of diversity would not release Southerners from their "obligations as men and Christians . . . the South would gain nothing." Its acceptance would mark abandonment of the Scriptures, from which "all the strong arguments" for slavery were derived. "Our Southern community" should remember, Bachman warned, that when confronted with the irrefutable arguments from Scripture, the "violent abolitionists of the North" had "openly renounced" the Bible and Christianity. The Unitarians, who had published Agassiz's first articles in support of diversity, had been rendered "more rabid in their curses of slavery and the South" by their abandonment of the Bible as God's revealed word. To attack the veracity of Scripture with the unscientific theory of diversity would be a strategic error "more dangerous," he believed, "than all the ravings of the abolitionists."[24] Bachman concluded with a confident prediction: the time was "not far distant" when "all men of science" would acknowledge the truth that the human family was composed of "one species" and "one blood."

Nott's reply was rather perfunctory and contained no allusion to slavery. He took up his pen, he said, only because a rejoinder was due the memory of Morton, not because Bachman's objections merited reply. After a short but vicious attack on Bachman's book, which he found "tinctured with bigotry and fanaticism," "garbling and special pleading," he restated all the arguments for the doctrine of diversity.[25]

This exchange, in effect, marked the end of the scientific controversy over the unity of the human species, for Bachman, the only scientist who openly attacked the doctrine of diversity, now devoted his time to the duties of his profession. A few months earlier the last clerical opposition to Nott's views in Mobile had disappeared abruptly and under startling circumstances. The friend of Moses, who had journeyed to Egypt to see for himself whether the inscriptions on the monuments confirmed Nott's and Gliddon's theories, had been found guilty of highly irregular sexual activities and hustled out of the city. There was doubtless a portent here. "So dies the last enemy," Nott wrote Gliddon. "It would seem that Providence has taken us under his especial wing."[26]

"The Lord is with us," Gliddon agreed.

"Agitators Often Do Much Good"

Nott blamed unfavorable reviews of *Types of Mankind* on Gliddon's "very impolitic & undignified tone," and expressed the wish that Squier instead of Gliddon had been his collaborator. Yet for all his complaining, he was planning as early as October, 1854, to join Gliddon in another assault on the public mind, and wrote Squier to ask for an article on American archeology.[1]

Gliddon was off again to Europe to collect materials, contributors, and subscribers. There he conferred with Jomard, Maury, Boudin, Prisse d'Avennes, and others interested in anthropology and its allied sciences, studied at the Louvre and the British Museum, and found that *Types of Mankind* was "handsomely welcomed" in the "ethnological and archaeological circle." Once more, all doors were open. Upon his return, however, Gliddon's disappointment knew no bounds when he learned that another had been chosen to conduct the camel experiment in the Southwest. The "whole conception" had been his "from first to last," and he was incensed. "They adopt my every particle," he wrote indignantly to Squier, "except where honor and good-faith dictated the course." He doubted that any of the others who had applied for the position possessed the necessary language qualifications and darkly predicted an inglorious end to the whole project.[2]

In the meantime, Nott was busy with another enterprise. In 1856 he had a new acquaintance, a young Swiss immigrant named Henry Hotz, sometime Mobile newspaperman, secretary to the United States legation at Belgium, and later to be Confederate propagandist extraordinary in England and France. Together they brought out a one-volume American edition of Arthur de Gobineau's four-volume *Essai sur l'inégalité des races humaines*, the Bible of nineteenth-century racists. While Hotz translated, Nott evidently selected those passages which gave most support to his own position. The book was dedicated "to the Statesmen of America," for Hotz thought instruction in ethnology especially important in America, which had long been the abode of three races and was rapidly becoming that of a fourth—the Chinese, who were streaming into California.[3]

Instruction was the more needed because of outmoded thinking in regard to racial equality. Although "most writers" had ceased to insist on the influence of climate on the physical conformation of races, many still defended racial equality, attributing "undeniable" differences solely to "circumstances, education, mode of life." Hotz—and here one sees clearly the manipulating hand of Nott—complained that those who held this view failed to recognize that it was "the first step to gross materialism," for it assumed that man was only a creature of circumstance. Its widespread acceptance was probably due, he thought, to "the favorite belief of our time in the infinite perfectibility of man." History had shown this theory to be absolutely false. The moral and intellectual, as well as the physical diversities of races never changed. Although the Negro and the Indian had possessed every possible advantage of climate, the only noticeable improvement had come through race mixture, which, while it raised those races in the scale of civilization, undermined the civilization that the white race had so laboriously developed. Hotz fully indorsed Gobineau's theory that race was the great historical determinant.

Nott's long appendix to the work was designed to correct certain lapses in Gobineau's theory. He dismissed Gobineau's failure to recognize the specific diversity of human races as merely an accident of the author's Catholicism, an error perpetuated by "want of accurate knowledge" in natural history: having been taught that two distinct species could not produce "perfectly fertile offspring," he had concluded that "all races of men *must* be of one origin." Nott made several snapping passes at Bachman, defended permanence of type as the only valid test of species, and concluded with an appeal for freedom of scientific inquiry. "What we require for our guidance in this world is truth, and the history of science shows how long it has been stifled by bigotry and error."

To rebuke bigotry and correct error, Nott's and Gliddon's new book, *Indigenous Races of the Earth*, appeared early in 1857. Nott was disgusted that "in spite of all sorts of pledges," Gliddon had "pitched into the Bible & Parsons again," and hoped "most devoutly" that he would "never hear the words Mono- & Polygenist" again. "I have no longer any doubt about his insanity on this subject," he wrote Squier. Although hardly more sane on the subject himself, Nott was justified in his criticism of *Indigenous Races*—nearly all of which was written by Gliddon—as all "folly & confusion." The book is a great conglomeration of discourses and diatribes strung out with long and irrelevant digressions and written in Gliddon's style of ponderous ostentation. Agassiz contributed a brief letter on geographical distribution; Joseph Leidy, who had no desire to become embroiled in the controversy, sent a short and noncommittal letter on paleontology; Alfred Maury, librarian of the French Institute, wrote a chapter on the philological evidence for diversity; Francis Pulszky, fellow of the Hungarian Academy and personal secretary to Louis Kossuth, contributed a letter on archeology; Dr. James Aitken Meigs, now curator of Morton's collection, wrote a chapter on craniology; and Nott, complaining that he had exhausted his fund of information in *Types of Mankind,* contributed only one chapter, despite the fact that he was listed as co-author. Gliddon wrote the rest.[4]

Although *Indigenous Races* never attained the sale reached by *Types of Mankind,* it was accorded much the same excited reception by reviewers and even gave rise to another controversy in the medical journals. De Bow, ecstatically contemplating the progress made in ethnology, noted with satisfaction that Gliddon had administered "a proper rebuke upon the want of courtesy and Christian bearing, as well as the intolerance" of a "clergyman of the Dutch Reformed Church of Charleston."[5]

The enthusiastic review of the highly respected Dr. Bennet Dowler (1797–1879) of New Orleans, editor of the *New Orleans Medical and Surgical Journal,* revealed the romantic interest shown by Americans in things Egyptian during the first half of the nineteenth century. From any point of view *Indigenous Races* was an important contribution to anthropology, for its authors had "disinterred significant data from the cinders of long extinguished centuries, the *debris* of former worlds," and gathered "inscriptions, documents and skulls from the dark, dank, and mouldering realm of the dead—from the frontiers of the remote and mysterious past." Dowler predicted, however, that the book would not easily gain public acceptance and suggested that the great "stumbling block" was its chronology, "owing to a seeming antithesis to sacred writings," even though these did "not teach this science any more than physic." Although cautious, Dowler seemed to align himself with those who doubted the unity of mankind, for in conversation with a missionary to the Delaware tribes, he had been told that of the entire congregation, "there was but one man who would not get drunk when an opportunity offered," and concluded that the Delawares presented "altogether a type of mind and manners of low grade."[6]

A new controversy, largely anonymous, opened in the New Jersey *Medical and Surgical Reporter* with an article supporting diversity, written by Dr. William S. Forwood of Maryland. Forwood was answered by "Senex," who, when a young medical student, had received a copy of Dr. Samuel Stanhope Smith's famous *Essay on the Causes of the Variety of Complexion and Figure in the Human Species,* from the hand of its author and now wished devoutly that "a copy of this truly scientific work had a place in every medical library, as an antidote to the poison of infidelity on the variety of the human species." The theory of plurality of species, "Senex" complained, blasphemed against the scriptural account of creation (which he related) and limited the Covenant of Works, the Covenant of Grace, and the Atonement (all of which he carefully described). But "thank God, it is false; His word tells us it is . . . , and this is all, and the best evidence that I want." Lest he be thought a "northern abolitionist," and accused of interfering with "the domestic arrangements of the South," "Senex" felt it necessary to add that while he denied that the Negro was a separate species, "I readily admit his inferiority, and this theory I am prepared to look for from the teachings of God's word. . . . I touch no further on this delicate subject."[7]

Able to accept neither diversity nor equality, neither slavery nor freedom, "Senex" was overcome by the intellectual exertion demanded by the dilemma and reclined in the comforting arms of Scripture. But one Abraham Coles, a Newark physician who combined his reply to Forwood with a review of Nott's and Gliddon's two books, took a stand for unity, equality, and liberty. No less pious than "Senex," Coles asserted that Christianity and unity "stand or fall together" and that both were inconsistent with slavery. *Types of Mankind* and *Indigenous Races,* said Coles, were inspired by their authors' devotion to "Slavery and Infidelity." Nott was impelled by the former, Gliddon by the latter. Gliddon, though not a scientist, "hoped to make himself useful by overthrowing the authority and reliability of the Jewish Scriptures."[8]

With their doctrine of diversity, they had insidiously attempted to undermine the principle of equality embodied both in Scripture and the Declaration of Independence and constituting "the soul and life of our national existence." By denying equality, Americans would destroy their political system and "stand convicted before the world of the greatest hypocrisy and falsehood"; hence men should read *Types of Mankind* and *Indigenous Races* warily, alert both to the writers' fanaticism and to the injury they sought to do the Republic. They had "eaten of the insane root" and were "in so hot and feverish a state of mind," as "to run a muck against all that was "most settled and sacred in our religion, or prized and precious in our civil polity." They had so far succumbed to the power of "exasperated prejudices" that they would willingly "eviscerate" from "our social organism that which constitutes its life" and "pile up against the sun the defunct carcass of a great nation."

Well aware of the danger to republican institutions, Coles was no less concerned with the effect the "infidel" tendencies of the doctrine might have on the souls of men. He indicated its implications for the chief tenets of Christian theology and denounced its "sick, shallow skepticism." But denunciation did not answer the question.

Sooner or later, their critics had to face the scientific facts posed by the authors. Coles could not. After devoting several hundred words to a diatribe against the theory of diversity, he attempted to belittle it as "nothing more than this": there were Negroes "three or four thousand years ago." But inexorably, the dilemma posed by racial divergence within the "accepted chronology" awaited answer. Coles offered a few suggestions, a few speculations. Probably, "the law of variety" began to operate early in the history of mankind. "Believers in the Bible" might say it operated in full force in the days of Babel, at the time of the great confusion of tongues. Or, "for aught we know," varieties of man might have sprung up in accordance with God's original purpose, through, it was "agreeable to experience to suppose," the effects of climate, together with other influences, "inappreciable by the most subtle tests, peculiar to certain localities," which, though operating "powerfully" in that early time, might "now have ceased to act." There might have been "new and special agencies" which the Deity put into operation and which ceased to act "as soon as his design was answered by them." Why not? Is not the Creator all powerful? Or, if these causes be thought insufficient, why, asked Coles, "need any stumble at the supposition of miraculous intervention?" He was aware that anything savoring "of miracle" was "scouted by the infidel," but there was "the miracle of man's original creation," which even the infidel could not ignore, and which "must have happened some time or another." Those who, with Agassiz, believed that men were created in nations, "to escape one miracle, resort to a thousand, and tax credulity in proportion."[9]

This was the best that Coles, or others of the biblical enthusiasts who attacked diversity, could offer in the way of scientific argument. The criticism that the defenders of diverse origins, despite their reluctance to accept those described in Scripture, were forced to multiply the number of miracles necessary to populate the earth, was a shrewd stroke, for by their rejection of development hypotheses, divine intervention became a "fact" from which they could not escape. However, Coles's critique, presenting "new and special agencies," influences "inappreciable by the most subtle tests"—forces not verifiable by science—could satisfy none but literalists.

Perhaps aware of this fact, he ridiculed the efforts of paleontologists to locate fossil human bones, and, turning to address Nott and Gliddon, curled his lip at "your Volneyisms and Voltaireisms; your pedantries and puerilities; your smatterings of science; your contemptible cavillings;" your "decipherings" and "measuring," "as if these were more reliable means of solving the sphinx-riddle and mystery of life than the daylight of Scripture, consciousness, and common sense." Coles resurrected the episode of Gliddon's "Egyptian priestess," ridiculed his literary style, and delivered a paean on Scripture hardly paralleled in the annals of bibliolatry: "The Bible is a venerable book. Most venerable. For four thousand years . . . it has been 'a road through the abyss of time. . . .' It is the only bridge spanning the gulf. . . . Beneath it hell yawns. Faith goes upon it singing. Rainbows of Hope and Promise hover over it. . . . Receiving it as God's Gift-Book, Keepsake, Souvenir, how delightful to turn its pages, odorous with His breath, musical with His voice! . . . How adapted every way to the wants of man! . . . He needs no chemist to tell him that it is sweet, wholesome, beneficient. . . . When the sun shines does he not know it, having eyes to see?" Coles accused Nott and Gliddon of attempting to usher in a second Age of Reason, another "cycle" of "human error," "an age of Downpulling and Disbelief. Once more," he concluded with malice, "is it clever to be a free thinker. The encyclopedists of the eighteenth century are having their imitators in the nineteenth."

In the reviews of Nott's and Gliddon's two books all the elements in the traditional pattern of theological accommodation to science were present: complete denunciation of the new theory and reaffirmation of revelation on the subject, followed by sponsorship of a quasi-scientific hypothesis (that climate determines variation), terminating in acceptance of the new theory—signified by assertions that science must not attack revelation, for Scripture was not intended as a textbook of science.

Whether Nott read Coles's "Critique" is not known. Its anti-intellectualism, its diatribes against the facts of modern science would have confirmed his strong conviction that he spoke for Galileo and Bruno. Gliddon, had the article reached him in the wilds of Central America, would have entered the fray with another "yell of congratulation and triumph." But Gliddon did not live to enjoy the fruits of his "indignant Races," as he called the book. He and Squier had agreed as early as 1854 that he would go to Central America as agent for the latter's great enterprise, the Honduras Inter-Oceanic Railway. After some delays due to financial reverses and the uncertainties of Latin American politics, Gliddon left for his new post in the spring of 1857. Nott was elated at this development, happy to learn that Gliddon had been "transported to a Country where there are no printer types," and he begged Squier, "for God sake make it a part of your bargain that he is never again to afflict suffering humanity with any more books, or even title pages."[10]

A center of controversy even in the jungles of Honduras, Gliddon was unhappy in his new work. In the delirium of tropical fever he inadvertently swallowed an excessive dose of opium and died in November. "What a life,—what a death!" exclaimed a friend in Baltimore. Nott wrote to Squier to rib him about his recent marriage and to inquire about Gliddon's death, and, upon learning the details, remarked that "with all his faults & follies I had a kind feeling for him & am grieved at his death— The poor fellow fought fate with a manly spirit & he did all his nature would allow him to do in making an honourable fame." Hearing that a subscription was being raised for Mrs. Gliddon, he offered to contribute, although otherwise little help could be expected from people in Mobile. Gliddon's books had "made him unpopular, as we all told him they must." Dr. James A. Meigs announced Gliddon's death to the members of the Academy of Natural Sciences, and the cautious Professor Leidy offered a resolution cast in such terms that it could hardly fail of unanimous approval. The members forthwith solemnly resolved to "bear witness to the extraordinary and disinterested zeal manifested by Mr. Gliddon, during the period of his personal connection with this Institution; and to his sincere and ardent pursuit of what appeared to his own judgement as scientific truth."[11]

Mrs. Gliddon packed her few belongings, gathered up her husband's papers, and, together with her young son, returned to England, for the great adventure was at an end. Mourned with modifications, remembered with reluctance, George R. Gliddon left an America far different from the country he had first seen as a young man in 1837, and a little of the change was due to his own indefatigable efforts. He brought a lively bustle, perhaps even some degree of intellectual stimulation, to the somnolent cities of the South. He awakened awe on the frontier. To the country as a whole he introduced ancient Egypt, including ILLUSTRATIONS BRILLIANTLY COLORED, AND COVERING MANY THOUSAND SQUARE FEET OF SURFACE. He contributed information of inestimable value to the founders of the new science of anthropology, and himself helped to establish its "American School." If many Americans were now less committed to what some called the "glittering and sounding generalities" of their Declaration of Independence, they might—but for his impiety—remember Gliddon as their preceptor. And if European respect for American scientists had grown in the last decade, those scientists might—but for his heresies—remember the man who never missed an opportunity to advance the renown of his friends and make them known abroad.

Morton was dead. Gliddon was dead. And Squier was so wrapped up in all sorts of enterprises, financial, diplomatic, and political, that he was lost to ethnology. From Nott's point of view the loss of Squier was perhaps just as well, for Squier, though he wished that the North and South could separate and live side by side in peace, little thought that such a division would lead to anything but "hostility and warfare." He feared that the nation in 1856 was already "trembling on the verge of Civil War," because, he said, "the South is absolutely anti-republican, hostile to the key principles of all liberty, despotic, arrogant, ignorant, and blood-thirsty." Agassiz, though he continued to lecture to his students at Harvard on the diversity of the races, was involved now in other investigations.[12]

With national crisis fast approaching, Nott was almost the sole spokesman for the American School. Since he was busy—writing articles on various medical subjects, teaching a course in anatomy at the University of Louisiana, attempting through the influential James Henry Hammond to secure the reinstatement of a young friend of the family who had been cashiered from the army ("I believe for slapping in the face a superior officer—it was an offense against the law, but as I am informed, the provocation was such, as could not be borne by a high spirited Southern boy"), raising funds for a medical school he and others were establishing in Mobile, and making a tour of Europe to collect books and materials— there was little time left for ethnology. Yet, as he had told Governor Hammond some time previously, the subject must be kept before the public: *"agitators"* often "do much good"; the world would "get on slowly without them, & this may be my principle merit." Consequently, he found time in 1858 to turn out two articles.[13]

In "A Natural History of Dogs," he reviewed the subject of geographical distribution and emphasized its relevance to the races of man. In a second article, "Influence of Anatomy on the March of Civilization," Nott laid down his scientific creed and revealed himself a sensationalist in philosophy as well as in public deportment. Appealing to Locke's *Essay concerning Human Understanding*, he asserted that *all our knowledge is derived from the study of nature*," by means of the senses. All the sciences add to our knowledge, and anatomy provided a particularly rich harvest, for it uncovered, "from the simplest zoophyte up to man," an "immense chain." Thus "while among the mammifers life is maintained by the most complicated apparatus, we find at the other end of the scale, animals, like the hydra, polyps, etc., which have been alternately ranged with animals and vegetables." Anatomically, he found, the races of men differed as widely as did the species within a given genus of animals. In the matter of cranial capacity alone, Morton had found a difference of as much as seventeen cubic inches. Thus there existed a "gradation between the two extremes" of human races, and anatomy assigned to all their "proper position in the scale." No people, he added, could escape its assigned position simply through education, for "until you can fall upon some plan by which seventeen cubic inches of brain can be added to that of the Hottentot, the Bushman, or the Australian, you cannot add to his intellect, or his capacity for civilization," notwithstanding the assertions of "well-meaning philanthropists."[14]

Having forged this new Chain of Being, Nott turned his attention to his new medical school and, despite ill health, sailed for Europe in the spring of 1859. On his return, he recuperated for a time at Sweet Springs, Virginia, and wrote Squier a description of his travels, to which he appended a brief sentence. "I have been well enough," he wrote, "to skim Darwin's book—the man is clearly crazy, but it is a capital dig into the parsons—it stirs up Creation & much good comes out [of] such thorough discussions—."[15]

Political subjects, however, were of more immediate interest. He and Squier had spent some time together when Nott last visited New York, and "over a very good supper" Squier had laughingly ridiculed, Nott recalled, "the 'dam^d grinning bluster, bravado' &c of Southern people—thought they could not be kicked into resistance by black republicans & were incapable of any effort beyond grinning." At the time, however, Nott had thought that by denying the South the right of secession, the North was lighting the fuse for "a terrible upheaval." He had thought then, and now in the spring of 1861 he was sure of it, that "the Southern people would rise up as one man & resist it with the old spirit of '76— The declaration of Independence is the chart by which the Anglo-Saxon race sails—this doctrine is repeated in every one of the State constitutions, & the Southern people will see all the whites & blacks on the globe slaughtered before they will yield this point."[16]

When the cannon on the Charleston Battery boomed out across the harbor, Dr. Nott, with no perception of the rich irony of the situation, was standing firm on the Declaration of Independence.

"The Old Roman"

The war went hard with the scientific community and hardest with its Southern branch. It destroyed for the Southerners the idea that they were engaged in a truly national attempt to wrest knowledge from a reluctant Nature. As early as June, 1861, Edmund Ravenel of Charleston was writing to Lewis Gibbes that he had sent a manuscript to the Academy of Natural Sciences_ and had received no reply. "I suppose," he remarked ruefully, "that from such a 'Rebel' & from such a City, there is little chance of its getting into print."[1]

Old John Bachman, who until the last minute hoped the Union would be preserved, nevertheless offered the opening prayer for the convention which passed the South Carolina Ordinance of Secession. Things grew worse. His collections and library were destroyed in the burning of Columbia, and at the age of seventy-six he was severely beaten by one of General Sherman's hangers-on. Notwithstanding, he preached his fifty-fifth anniversary sermon and lived on to 1874.[2]

Squier, once the fair-haired boy of the American School, kept in the thick of things. He explored Central and South America, toured Europe, was appointed a commissioner to Peru by President Lincoln, wrote books and articles on his explorations, and edited Frank Leslie's publications. Neither he nor his wife was meticulous in observing the marriage vows, but she accused him first (in a spectacular frame-up in which two artists from the Leslie publications performed the function now taken over by the camera) and obtained a divorce in 1873. Shortly afterward he was committed to a mental asylum on Long Island. Slipping easily from this to other spheres and as easily back again, he lived out the days until he died in 1888.[3]

In the spring of 1861 Dr. Nott entertained the distinguished correspondent of the London *Times*, William Howard Russell. After dinner he walked with Russell through the city to show him the "oyster saloons, drinking-houses, lager-beer and wine-shops, and gambling and dancing places." He told Russell that his investigations had caused him "to take a purely materialist view of the question of slavery." "Questions of morals and ethics, pertaining to its consideration," Russell reported him as saying with an ambiguity strikingly appropriate, "ought to be referred to the cubic capacity of the human cranium—the head that can take the largest charge of snipeshot will eventually dominate in some form or other over the head of inferior capacity." Russell gathered that Nott had no affection for the institution of slavery, but, Russell reported, "he does not see what is to be done with the slaves, and how the four millions of Negroes are to be prevented from becoming six, eight, or ten millions."[4]

The war years were bitter, but Nott lived to read three of his own obituaries. After seeing his medical school closed at the end of the second session, he entered the Confederate army as surgeon and served as medical inspector for General Bragg's Second Corps, Army of Mississippi. He lost one of two remaining sons (Morton's son died for the other side), but he himself came out of the struggle still fighting. He found that his property had been destroyed and his medical school turned over to the freedmen. "I confess," he wrote in renewing correspondence with Squier in 1865, "it does not increase my love for the Government when I pass by every day or two & see two or three hundred negroes racing through and tearing every thing to pieces— The chemical laboratory is occupied by negro cobblers."[5]

Nott was likewise reluctant to see the work of a lifetime torn to pieces by the new hypothesis that was racing through all fields of natural science. But even though Darwin had laid bare the machinery of development with a theory strikingly similar to the infidel notions of Lamarck—and similar also to that toward which Bachman had been clumsily groping—Nott was too intelligent to withhold the conviction demanded by a theory so thoroughly documented. Too, as he had remarked before the war, it was a capital dig into the parsons. The truth was, Darwin had beaten him at his own game and outdone even Nott at infidelity.

Although Asa Gray perceived no element of infidelity in Darwinism, he had kept a close watch through the years on the growth of the American School and he detected at once the disastrous impact that Darwinism had on the theory of plural creations of man. As he took up the task of appealing to the religious community to accept Darwinism, he found a persuasive argument immediately at hand. "One good effect is already manifest," he announced. Darwinism rendered irrelevant "the hypothesis of a multiplicity of human species." So far from providing for plural creations of man, Darwin described a process which made it possible to derive all categories of life from an original one and placed the organic kingdom on a self-sustaining basis. Or, as Gray put it, "the very first step backwards" into the Darwinian past "makes the Negro and the Hottentot our blood-relations." Gray also noted that the new theory played havoc with the system of chronology upon which pluralism had rested. "The strongest argument for the original plurality of human species," Gray thought, had been drawn from "the identification of some of the present races of men" upon the "early historical monuments and records" of Egypt. But Darwin assumed that species developed in a magnitude of time vast beyond anything conceived by the combatants of the fifties. Moreover, his theory established a continuity of life through geological epochs and so obviated the necessity for separate creations either in time or space. As he surveyed the ruins, Nott himself recognized the damage done by the Darwinian time scale and told a friend that he "would not have published" *Types of Mankind* "if the pre-historic period of men had been so firmly established" then "as it is at the present day." Gliddon's monuments ceased now to have any relevance to the question of the origins of race.[6]

Still, even if the differences between Negro and white which Nott had been documenting for twenty years had emerged as Darwin suggested, they nevertheless existed. They might not be permanent according to Darwin's way of thinking, but in the framework of that man's thought, nothing was. Nott explained this in a letter to General O. O. Howard, superintendent of the Freedmen's Bureau, in 1866. He solemnly expounded the ethnological reasons why Howard should remove his troops and his Bureau and "leave the relations between the races to regulate themselves." However long man has been on earth, he argued, "we know nothing beyond his modern history, commencing with that of Egypt." In this period, the Negro had created no civilization, had always been a slave. "It is true,"

Nott added, "that Lamarck, Geoffroy Saint Hilaire, Darwin, and other naturalists have contended for the gradual change or development of organic forms from physical causes, yet even this school require *millions* of years for their theory, and would not controvert the facts and deductions I have laid down." He reiterated this position in an article on the "Instincts of Races" in the same year. He pointed out that each race had its own "moral and physical laws" and that "all the power of the Freedmen's Bureau or 'gates of hell' cannot prevail against them," for "forms that have been permanent for several thousand years, must remain so at least during the life time of a nation." Some great names were numbered among those who advocated theories of development and contended "not only that one type may be transformed into another, but that man himself is nothing more than a developed worm." However, the Freedmen's Bureau need not concern itself with "such theories, or refinements of science," for the Bureau would "not have vitality enough to see the negro experiment through many hundred generations, and to direct the imperfect plans of Providence."[7]

Deciding finally that the South was no longer "fit for a gentleman to live in," he determined, he wrote Squier, "to leave the Negroland to you dam^d Yankees," and moved to Baltimore in 1867. But finding Baltimore "the most unintellectual and [un]progressive community I ever saw—no scientific association—no medical society even, no journal, no concert of action," he moved to New York at the invitation of the gynecologist Thomas Addis Emmet. A city "without morals, without political scruples, without religion & without *niggers*," New York was much to his liking. Collaboration with Emmet did not prove successful, and Nott turned to private practice. This became so large that he no longer had time for ethnology, and in the attempt to recoup his lost fortune Nott literally worked himself to death. Suffering a lung hemorrhage in the spring of 1872 which left him unable to speak, he noted that at his age the prognosis was "unpromising," but, he added, "as I have made all out of life worth having, my mind is very calm as regards myself." He took a vacation and returned to work, then, breaking down once more, decided to sell his books, resigned from the Anthropological Institute, and, in the hope of improving his health, moved back to Mobile. Nott had suddenly grown old. Becoming thinner, he looked taller, and people in Mobile called him "the old Roman." There, wracked with pain, but still refusing, as a friend lamented, "to openly confess his belief" in the doctrines of Christianity, Nott died in the spring of 1873.[8]

A founder of the American School of Anthropology, he had helped to execute a revolution in natural science, and, in company with his friends Morton and Gliddon, had overthrown the ancient and honorable doctrine of the unity of man. When their revolution was rendered irrelevant by the Darwinian invasion, he possessed the intellectual courage to relinquish a theory built upon a lifetime of labor and the good grace to accept the new. For, as he had once told Squier, he "never wrote to please the Crowd, but for the advancement of truth." Proud to agitate against the pious defenders of the old order, he followed the light of science to the end. One can ask no more.[9]

The Problem of the Free Hybrid

Dr. Nott capitulated after a brief struggle to the new development hypothesis. Not so Professor Agassiz. Clinging to the old and hitherto respectable theory of catastrophism and to his own theory of plural creations, Agassiz became America's leading opponent of Darwinism. He who long ago had fallen from ecclesiastical grace now found himself the darling of the orthodox, while Asa Gray, pious defender of unity and Scripture, was forced to do battle with him from the ranks of the heretical Darwinians. Gray had received a copy of the *Origin of Species* at Christmastime in 1859, and "struck with the great ability of the book, and charmed with its fairness," he felt "bound to stick up for its philosophy." He was displeased with Agassiz's reaction to the work. "Agassiz," he wrote to the English botanist Francis Boott, "cannot abide it (of course) and so has publicly denounced it as atheism, &c &c." He wanted "to stop Agassiz's mouth with his own words, and to show up his loose way of putting things. He is a sort of demagogue," Gray added, doubtless recalling other days, "and always talks to the rabble."[1]

Although after his contribution to *Indigenous Races*, Agassiz confined his investigation of separate creations largely to the lower animals, he seems never seriously to have doubted the validity of his theory that the races were created separately. In 1863 Dr. Samuel Gridley Howe, formerly a leading abolitionist and accessory of John Brown, was appointed to the American Freedman's Inquiry Commission and visited conquered areas of the South to investigate the Negro's condition. Convinced that "proper treatment" of the problem required "consideration of political, physiological, & ethnological principles," and recognizing, as he said, "my own incompetency," upon his return he wrote to Agassiz. He wished specifically to know whether in freedom Negroes would amalgamate with whites and whether mulattoes could reproduce themselves beyond a few generations. Agassiz's reply was prompt and exhaustive.[2]

He rejoiced "in the prospect of universal emancipation," not only for humanitarian reasons, but also because the scientist could now conduct anthropological investigations without fear of being accused of having proslavery sympathies. However, he realized that emancipation posed certain problems. The recommendations which the commission made would first of all depend upon whether the Negro was to remain a permanent race in America. According to the "theory of the unity of mankind," he informed Howe, "it is assumed that the different races have become what they are in consequence of their settlement in different parts of the world, and that the whole globe is everywhere a fit abode for human beings who adapt themselves to the conditions under which they live. According to the theory of a multiple origin of mankind the different races have first appeared in various parts of the globe, each with the peculiarities best suited to their respective homes." The fact was that some races ranged widely over the earth's surface while others were comparatively restricted. The distribution of the Negro race was such that he had reason to believe that it would flourish indefinitely in the Southern states.[3]

In similar fashion many of the problems, though at first glance seemingly insurmountable, would solve themselves through the operation of natural laws. The same laws which impelled Negroes to congregate in the South impelled the white race gradually to move northward. Unsuited physiologically to the noxious lowlands of the Southern states, the whites would find themselves greatly outnumbered by the blacks and would see it to their advantage to join their fellows in the North, thus bringing about a natural segregation of the races.[4]

So, too, the problem of the mulattoes would solve itself. A degenerate hybrid race, they were weak and infertile and would gradually disappear, their heretofore large numbers being chiefly the result of the overheated passions of younger members of slaveowning families.[5]

Now that slavery was abolished, the first problem to be faced was that of preventing further amalgamation. The races could live side by side in peace so long as racial instincts were not offended by the unholy mixture of white and black. Probably, Agassiz suggested, those men and women whose prolonged agitation against slavery had provoked the war then raging had been impelled by unconscious repugnance at seeing their own racial character manifested in a hybrid race in the South. Not only would amalgamation create social discord, it would lower the level of the white race and have a pernicious effect on civilization. "I beseech you," Agassiz wrote, "while you are in a position to exert a leading influence in the councils of the nation upon this most important subject to allow no preconceived views, no favorite schemes, no immediate object, to bias your judgment and mislead you." Picture the effect upon "republican institutions, and our civilization generally," of a citizenry made up, not of the present "manly population descended from cognate nations," but of "the effeminate progeny of mixed races, half Indian, half negro, sprinkled with white blood. Can you," he pointedly asked, "devise a scheme to rescue the Spaniards of Mexico from their degradation? Beware, then, of any policy which may bring our own race to their level."[6]

Agassiz's advice was not altogether neglected, his theory not entirely forgotten. As it turned out, the solution of the Negro's problem *was* left to nature, although some, like Professor Calvin Stowe and his wife, Harriet Beecher, who attempted to educate white and Negro children in the same classrooms and by the same standards, believed in the equality of Morton's "proximate species." Making the trip up to Hartford after the war, the shrewd Scots Presbyterian David Macrae stopped for a visit with the Stowes to inquire about the future of the Negro race. Mrs. Stowe was hopeful and told Macrae, "The black children get on just as fast as white children. . . . The mixed race is weaker."[7]

"The mixed die out soon," echoed her husband.

"Notwithstanding Mrs. Grundy"

> *The changes in the history of science have a*
> *remarkable, almost comic aspect. . . . Three years ago,*
> *just before Darwin's book appeared, the*
> *theory of the possibility or probability of the*
> *different races of mankind having descended from a*
> *single pair was considered as perfectly antiquated,*
> *and as having lagged behind all scientific progress.*
>
> RUDOLPH WAGNER, 1862

In 1854 irascible old Henry Schoolcraft, his religious sensibilities offended by *Types of Mankind*, thanked Bachman for his blistering criticism of it. He was ashamed that such a doctrine had sprung up in America, and, disgusted, remarked, "Well, if this be all, that America is to send back to Europe, after feasting on her rich stores of learning, science, philosophy & religion for three centuries, it were better that the Aborigines had maintained their dark empire of pow wows & jugglers undisturbed." Schoolcraft had a point. The doctrine of diverse origins was a native growth. But it was not the intellectually contemptible thing he supposed.[1]

That Americans should have been uniquely interested in the "types of mankind" was no wonder. But why did the bulk of scientific opinion in America bear on the side of diverse origins? In the first place the circumstances of the three races in America tended to obscure their common humanity. One section of the nation had a vested interest in concealing it altogether. Inevitably, then, one must ask whether the doctrine of diverse origins was not a deliberate construction of Southerners and Southern sympathizers in the North. The answer to this must be that only Josiah Nott gave evidence of calculatedly furthering political ends. Morton nowhere betrayed interest in the political implications of his researches. Squier, as he wrote his parents when the crisis approached, had a "precious poor opinion of niggers, or any of the darker races," but he had "a still poorer one of slavery." Gliddon vehemently denied that *Types of Mankind* had any political implications whatever and asserted that it was "really, precisely what it professed to be—a memorial of the great anthropologist of Philadelphia." They, and no doubt Nott himself, believed that they were simply reporting objective scientific evidence and documenting indisputable scientific principles.

The conscious extrascientific bond which linked many of these men together was not sympathy for Southern institutions but anticlericalism and antibiblicism. One observer was not far from the truth when he complained that Gliddon could "tolerate a man's believing in the single origin of mankind, provided only he hold the statements of the Holy Bible to be 'myths, fiction, and pretended tradition.'" Although Squier promised to "listen to & reflect on" whatever evidence his friend Charles Eliot Norton brought to the support of the "divine character of the Christian revelation," Norton's five long pages of arguments failed to induce conviction. Here the American School was part of a movement of thought and feeling that comprehended the entire Western world. The peculiarly American cast their work assumed arose not from its motivation but from the subject-matter on which these motives spent themselves— the characteristic American situation of three races in uneasy conjunction.[2]

The significance of this point is well brought out by the general response of educated Americans to the doctrine of diverse origins. The doctrine was soothing to the cultural nationalism of the times, yet the response of the North might have been anticipated. The doctrine lent comfort to slavery and so could not be accepted as a guide to conduct. Northerners rejected in this context the Jeffersonian ideal that science should be the guide of political life and the arbiter of social problems. The Unitarians exhibited a certain sympathy with the forces of science in their common struggle against the trammels of bibliolatry, but their sympathy did not involve affection for slavery. To the abolitionists slavery was not a scientific, but a moral, issue. Howe was impressed with Agassiz's learning and listened respectfully to his advice. But after reading the last of Agassiz's long and earnest letters, he announced his determination "to do the manifest right, regardless of consequences," and regardless, too, of the findings of science. "If you ask me," he added bluntly, "who is to decide what is the manifest right, I answer, that in morals, as well as in mathematics, there are certain truths so simple as to be admitted at sight as axioms, by every one of common intelligence and honesty. The right to life is as clear as that two and two make four, and none dispute it. The right to liberty and to ownership of property fairly earned, is just as clear to the enlightened mind as that $5 \times 6 = 30$." Therefore, "so far as the rights of blacks and the duties of whites are manifest to common & honest minds so far would I admit the first and perform the second, though the heavens fall."[3]

While the North defected, the South had the opportunity to keep faith with the Jeffersonian ideal by grounding the defense of slavery upon a scientific basis. It did nothing of the kind. Southerners discerned in the doctrine of multiple origins an assault upon orthodox religion (a shrewd enough interpretation) and chose to hold fast to the latter. Their devotion to Scripture was not entirely disinterested. They were busily reading about Paul's request for the return of Onesimus, an obvious foreshadowing of the Fugitive Slave Law, and pointing importantly to the curse on Ham in the Book of Genesis. In 1854 the editor of the hotly secessionist Richmond *Enquirer* suspected that many readily accepted the "infidel" doctrine of diversity because it seemed to "favor the system of slavery." But the system could afford no such defenders as Nott and Gliddon if the Bible was to be "the price it must pay for them." The Bible, he pointed out with some acumen, was now "the grand object of attack from Abolitionists, because they know it is the bulwark of Southern principles. . . . Destroy the Bible, and you lay bare the very citadel of our strength to our foes. . . . Let us not then allow this shield of strength to be torn from us until we have something to put in its place." The Bible did lend considerable support to slavery, but so did science. Opting for the Bible was a mark of the South's already profound commitment to religion. Heretofore this had not necessarily been an anti-intellectual position. But when the issue was clearly drawn, the South turned its back on the only intellectually respectable defense of slavery it could have taken up.[4]

By the South's deliberate choice the Amercian School was spared the reproach before history of having effactually furthered the cause of slavery. By so much, its potentialities for directing the course of

American history were frustrated. The lasting significance of the American researches in ethnology before the Civil War must be sought in the history of science. It was of course Darwin who determined the course the biological sciences were to take. But he and the American ethnologists were sifting through the same masses of fact. Both saw organic categories as dynamic entities. The Americans ascribed organic change to hybridization. Darwin ascribed it to variation and natural selection. Today the two are joined. It was not mere facts but a powerful theory to bind the facts together that made Darwin a commanding figure in the history of the world. Yet even in the realm of theory John Augustine Smith was thinking in the same channels. Smith delivered another of his little lectures on anthropology in 1843. He was "thoroughly convinced" of the "mischief of slavery" but was equally certain that the abolitionists were not fully aware of the perils in the course they were pursuing. For "if the negroes should be freed they were as sure to be exterminated as the sun to rise; and upon the principle that as Society advances there must inevitably, in the course of time, be a struggle for the means of subsistence"; and they as the weaker party would be "driven to the wall."[5]

This insight was not so much a credit to Smith as an indication that the American ethnologists were confronting vital problems to good purpose. How good may be seen in the fact that they had already anticipated the most notable weakness in Darwin's thought. Darwin rejected the American School's doctrine of hybridization as a causative factor in evolution and took up variation and natural selection instead. And yet his principal American defender, Asa Gray, who had previously denounced the doctrine of multiple origins as "atheistic," had to acknowledge that some of the further researches incumbent upon Darwin and Darwinians lay in that very direction. There was one thing about the new theory that troubled him. If species derived from varieties, then one should be able to find an instance of two varieties which had diverged enough to produce "some sterility in the crosses." This matter could best be settled by investigating "the best marked human races," for, Gray suggested, "if mulattoes are sterile or tend to sterility, as some naturalists confidently assert, they afford Mr. Darwin a case in point. If, as others think, no such tendency is made out, the required evidence is lacking." The American School had already anticipated the most notable weakness in Darwin's thought. They had long discerned the vacuum at the center of all theories of development—a vacuum that Darwin himself was increasingly inclined to fill with Lamarckism. Where, they asked, did variations come from? Something more, they knew, was needed, something that eluded them but came to birth in the twentieth century as the science of genetics and the rationale of mutations. The American School had been the guardian of a profound insight into nature which if borne in mind would have made the career of Darwinism more uniformly successful.[6]

The career of the American School was an ironical one, for despite their incisive criticism of theories of development they helped to prepare the ground for the coming of Darwinism. It was of course not they but Darwin who appropriated the time scale of the geologists. But by their incessant hammering at the biblical chronology they did help to prepare the public mind for the Darwinian chronology. Their assault on reproductive isolation further prepared the way, for within the context of Darwinism, breaches in the fertility barrier suggested not separate creations but common descent. Small wonder that Nott was taken aback when Darwin took this approach and brought mankind together again—and thereby handed the American School to posterity as a footnote to *The Descent of Man.* The final irony was that for some, like Asa Gray, Darwinism took on added luster for having supplanted the "infidel" doctrine of the American School.

So the American School of ethnology stood for both grave errors and deep insights in science. The power of their mistakes to do social damage by upholding slavery was blunted by the refusal of the South to accept the proffered assistance. Theology would not permit. But our gratitude to theology should be tempered by the reflection that Darwinism also was rejected by the Bible-bound believers in the unity of mankind. Today the theological defenses, unlamented, no longer stand. The only defense against the perpetrators of unsound theory, against future Josiah Notts, is what Nott himself fought so many years to obtain—freedom of inquiry. For, as Gliddon once remarked, science if given free rein advances, "notwithstanding Mrs. Grundy."[7]

Notes

This book rests primarily on original sources: the correspondence among Morton, Gliddon, Nott, and Squier, and their letters to and from other members of the scientific community; the publications of the American School in the scientific and popular journals; and articles and books about their work. All are duly cited in the notes, but a word on the first category is in order.

The most representative sources for the correspondence of the American School are the Samuel George Morton Papers at the Library Company of Philadelphia and the E. G. Squier Papers at the Library of Congress. Although the former collection contains few letters written by Morton, it well illustrates the breadth of his acquaintance in the scientific community. The latter contains many letters from Nott and Gliddon, and a few—evidently the largest group extant—from Morton. Both the Squier Papers at the New-York Historical Society and the Morton Papers at the American Philosophical Society are useful chiefly for their subjects' early years.

Instead of encumbering the text with a multitude of footnote references, citations have been gathered together under one reference for a paragraph or a group of related paragraphs. Except for the abbreviated designations listed below, references are cited with complete titles at first mention in each chapter.

Abbreviations Used in Notes

AAAS American Association for the Advancement of Science
ANSP Academy of Natural Sciences of Philadelphia
APS American Philosophical Society
CPP College of Physicians of Philadelphia
DAB *Dictionary of American Biography*
DAMB Howard A. Kelly and Walter L. Burrage, *Dictionary of American Medical Biography: Lives of Eminent Physicians of the United States and Canada, From the Earliest Times,* New York, 1928.
DNB *Dictionary of National Biography*
JCB John Carter Brown Library
LC Library of Congress
LCP Library Company of Philadelphia

"An Universal Freckle"

1. Samuel G. Morton, [Some observations of the Bushman Hottentot Boy], *Proceedings,* ANSP, IV (1848), 5; see also Joseph Leidy's corroboration of Morton's conclusions in [Joseph] Leidy, [On the Hair of a Hottentot Boy], *Proceedings,* ANSP, IV (1848), 7. Peter A. Browne, *The Classification of Mankind, by the Hair and Wool of Their Heads, with the Nomenclature of Human Hybrids* (Philadelphia, 1852).

2. See the earlier draft of the Declaration in *The Papers of Thomas Jefferson,* ed. Julian P. Boyd (17 vols. to date; Princeton, 1950–59), I, 423–28. Benjamin Rush, *Essays, Literary Moral & Philosophical* (Philadelphia, 1798), p. 8, cited in Daniel Boorstin, *The Lost World of Thomas Jefferson* (New York, 1948), p. 61. John Locke, *Two Treatises of Civil Government* (London, 1690), in the *Works of John Locke* (10 vols.; London, 1801), V, 340. Boorstin's book is a stimulating discussion of the part biology played in Jeffersonian thought and especially its influence on the Jeffersonian idea of equality. I am greatly indebted to it. However, for an opposing view see John C. Greene, "Some Early Speculations on the Origin of Human Races," *American Anthropologist,* LVI (1954), 31–41.

3. "Notes on Virginia," in *The Writings of Thomas Jefferson,* ed. P. L. Ford (10 vols.; New York, 1892–99), III, 249–50.

4. For a concise review of the history of the concept of species see Ernst Mayr, "Species Concepts and Definitions," in Ernst Mayr (ed.), *The Species Problem: A Symposium Presented at the Atlanta Meeting of the American Association for the Advancement of Science, December 28–29, 1955* (American Association for the Advancement of Science Publication No. 50 [Washington, D.C., 1957]), pp. 1–19.

5. For a biographical sketch of Smith see article by John E. Pomfret in DAB.

6. *Essay on the Causes of the Variety of Complexion and Figure . . .* (New Brunswick, N.H., 1810), p. 4; *Essay on the Causes of the Variety of Complexion and Figure . . .* (Philadelphia, 1787), p. 29 n.

7. *Essay* (1787), pp. 1–2, 4, 10–13, 29–36; *Essay* (1810), pp. 16, 29, 55 n.

8. Charles Caldwell, *Autobiography of Charles Caldwell, M.D. . . . ,* ed. Harriot Warner (Philadelphia, 1855), p. 268; Benjamin Rush, "Commonplace Book, 1792–1813," manuscript in APS. Moss was probably suffering from a disorder known as vitiligo. A modern pathologist says that vitiligo "occurs spontaneously and from unknown causes. . . . The disease is intractable to treatment, but some cases are known in which spontaneous improvement has occurred and partial restoration of pigment has followed exposure to actinic rays. Much publicity is often attached to these unfortunate people, and in the newspapers they are referred to as 'Negroes who turn white.' " Julian Herman Lewis, *The Biology of the Negro* (Chicago, 1942), pp. 386–87. Jefferson recorded a similar phenomenon in his "Notes on Virginia" (*Writings,* III, 175).

9. Rush, "Commonplace Book," broadside pasted in with entry for July 27, 1796. Moss seems to have toured several states. See Smith, *Essay* (1810), p. 94.

10. Smith, *Essay* (1810), pp. 83, 92, 95. Moss was also examined by Dr. Benjamin Smith Barton (*Early Proceedings of the American Philosophical Society . . . Compiled . . . from the Manuscript Minutes of Its Meetings from 1744–1838* [Philadelphia, 1844], p. 241) and by Dr. Charles Caldwell (*Autobiography*, pp. 164–65, 268–69). For a similar examination of this nature by Dr. John Morgan see *Early Proceedings*, APS, p. 142, where it is noted that he read "papers on a snake in a horse's eye, and two spotted negro children." See also C[harles] W[illson] Peale, "ACCOUNT of a Person born a NEGRO, or a very DARK MULATTOE who afterwards became WHITE," *Columbian Magazine*, II (1791), 409–10. Hugh H. Brackenridge ridiculed the scientific interest in Moss in his *Modern Chivalry* (1792–1815; New York: American Book Co., 1937), pp. 114–18.

11. Benjamin Rush, "Observations intended to favour a supposition that the black Color (as it is called) of the Negroes is derived from the LEPROSY. Read at a Special Meeting July 14, 1797," *Transactions*, APS, IV (1799), 289–97.

12. *Essay* (1810), pp. 9–10, 315–19.

13. *Ibid.*, pp. 131–36, 278–79, 283–85.

14. *Ibid.*, pp. 16–17, 23–25, 268.

15. *Ibid.*, p. 327.

16. Samuel L. Mitchill, "The Original Inhabitants of America shown to be the same family and lineage with those of Asia, by a process of reasoning not hitherto advanced," *Archaeologia Americana: Transactions and Collections of the American Antiquarian Society*, I (1820), 225–32. This is a letter dated "Newyork, March 31, 1816."

17. *Essay* (1810), pp. 204–5.

18. Rush's interest is indicated in J[ames] H[aines] M'Culloh, *Researches, Philosophical and Antiquarian, concerning the Aboriginal History of America* (Baltimore, 1829), p. v. The early pages of this work contain some biographical information; see also *Appleton's Cyclopaedia of American Biography* and *Complete Army and Navy Register of the United States of America, from 1776 to 1887 . . .* (New York, 1888), p. 617. M'Culloh's theory of Indian origins is taken from his *Researches on America: Being an Attempt to Settle Some Points Relative to the Aborigines of America &c.* (2d ed.; Baltimore, 1817), pp. xi–xii, 24, 97. I have used the 1817 edition because of the scarcity of the 1816 edition. Richard Harlan, "Remarks on the Variety of Complexion, and National Peculiarity of Feature (Lecture delivered before the Academy of Natural Sciences, A.D. 1822)," in R[ichard] Harlan, *Medical and Physical Researches; or, Original Memoirs in Medicine, Surgery, Physiology, Geology, Zoology, and Comparative Anat-*

omy (Philadelphia, 1835), pp. 521–89. On Harlan's place in the history of science see George Gaylord Simpson, "The Beginnings of Vertebrate Palae-ontology in North America," Symposium on the Early History of Science and Learning in America, *Proceedings,* APS, LXXXVI (1943), 130–88.

19. M'Culloh, *Researches on America,* p. 217; Samuel L. Mitchill, "The Orig-inal Inhabitants of America consisted of the same Races with the Malays of Australia, and the Tartars of the North," *Archaeologia Americana,* I (1820), 321–25; Caleb Atwater, "Description of the Antiquities Discovered in the State of Ohio and Other Western States . . . ," *Archaeologia Americana,* I (1820), 105–267; C[onstantine] S. Rafinesque, *Ancient History, or Annals of Kentucky; with a Survey of the ancient monuments of North America . . .* (Frankfort, Ky., 1824), p. 13; Josiah Priest, *American Antiquities and Discoveries in the West . . .* (5th ed.; Albany, 1837), pp. 18, 44–58, 114–29, 229–42; John Delafield, Jr., *An Inquiry into the Origin of the Antiq-uities of America* (Cincinnati, 1829), pp. 102–3; Alexander W. Bradford, *American Antiquities and Researches into the Origin and History of the Red Race* (New York, 1843), p. 434.

That America was originally peopled by Tartars or Jews was not a novel doctrine. See, on the former, Edward Brerewood, *Enquiries Touching the Diversity of Languages, and Religions, through the Chief Parts of the World* (London, 1622), pp. 94–102; on the latter, Thomas Thorowgood, *Iewes in America, or Probabilities That the Americans Are of That Race* (London, 1650). On the whole subject of early theories respecting the early peopling of America see Don Cameron Allen, *The Legend of Noah: Renaissance Rationalism in Art, Science, and Letters* (Urbana, Ill., 1949), pp. 113–37.

20. *Essay* (1810), p. 240 n.

21. *Ibid.,* p. 171 n.

22. *Ibid.,* pp. 267, 275.

23. Rush, "Observations intended to favor a supposition"; C[onstantine] S. Rafinesque, *The American Nations; or, Outlines of Their General History, Ancient and Modern . . .* (2 vols.; Philadelphia, 1836), II, 110.

24. George H. Moore, *Notes on the History of Slavery in Massachusetts* (New York, 1866), pp. 118, 124, 133, 149–50.

"Either a Philosopher or an Infidel"

1. An exception was the English writer, Edward Long. In 1788 the *Columbian Magazine* reprinted two chapters from his *History of Jamaica* (London, 1774) including "some Curious Particulars respecting Negroes." He listed the usual distinctions between the Negro and the white and concluded that the two races were "different species of the same GENUS." He suggested that the Negro held a place in the scale of being between the white man and the orangutan. With this arrangement, he pointed out, "the system will seem more consistent, and the measure of it more complete, and analogous to the harmony and order that are visible in every other line of the world's

stupendous fabric." Long thus turned the Great Chain of Being against the equalitarians. [Edward Long], "Observations on the Gradation in the Scale of Being between the Human and the Brute Creation. Including some Curious Particulars respecting Negroes. (From a late History of Jamaica.)," *Columbian Magazine*, II (1788), pp. 14–22, 70–75. This was brought to my attention by John C. Greene's article, "The American Debate on the Negro's Place in Nature, 1780–1815," *Journal of the History of Ideas*, XV (1954), 384–96.

2. Jefferson had attempted to correct this fallacy in his "Notes on Virginia," in P. L. Ford (ed.), *The Writings of Thomas Jefferson* (10 vols.; New York, 1892–99), III, 154–55.

3. Henry Home [Lord Kames], *Six Sketches on the History of Man, Containing, the Progress of Men as Individuals* (Philadelphia, 1776), pp. 13–14, 29–30, 45–47. This was originally published as *Sketches of the History of Man* (2 vols.; Edinburgh, 1774). I have used the Philadelphia edition because it was evidently the one Smith read. Kames's book passed through nine editions by 1825. In a later edition (4 vols.; Edinburgh, 1788) Kames stated flatly that the different races had been created for their respective regions (III, 147, 182).

4. Charles White, *An Account of the Regular Gradation in Man, and in Different Animals and Vegetables; and from the Former to the Latter* (London, 1799), pp. 55–57, 65, 125, 127, 133. For biographical information see article on White by Charles W. Sutton in DNB.

5. *Account of the Regular Gradation*, pp. 1, 134.

6. *Ibid.*, p. 135.

7. *Ibid.*, pp. 136–38.

8. John Augustine Smith, "A Lecture introductory to the second Course of Anatomical Instruction in the College of Physicians and Surgeons for the State of New-York; delivered in that Institution, on Friday, the 11th of November, 1808 . . . ," *New-York Medical and Philosophical Journal and Review*, I (1809), 32–48. For biographical information on Smith see article by Wyndam B. Blanton in DAB and John H. Redfield, "Personal Reminiscences," in Herman L. Fairchild, *A History of the New York Academy of Sciences, Formerly the Lyceum of Natural History* (New York, 1887), pp. 84–96.

9. However, he did find an objective standard in the fact that "the white complexion has certainly one advantage over all other, as by means of its varying tints, some of the more exquisite and delicate emotions of the female mind are expressed, whereas a blushing African would be a phenomenon indeed."

10. Caldwell, *Autobiography of Charles Caldwell, M.D.*, ed. Harriot Warner (Philadelphia, 1855), p. 349. See also the article on Caldwell by Edgar Erskine Hume in DAB. His first assault on Smith was [Charles Caldwell], "An Essay on the Causes of the Variety of Complexion and Figure in the Human Species, &c. &c. . . . ," *American Review of History and Politics*, II

(1811), 128–66. This was continued in [Charles] C[aldwell], "An essay on the causes of the Variety of Complexion, and figure in the human species, &c. &c. . . . ," *Port-Folio,* 3d ser., IV (1814), 8–33, 148–63, 252–71, 362–82, 447–57. These reviews were enlarged in Charles Caldwell, *Thoughts on the Original Unity of the Human Race* (New York, 1830), which was later reissued, with an introduction (Cincinnati, 1852).

11. Samuel D. Gross, *Autobiography of Samuel D. Gross, M.D. . . . , with Sketches of His Contemporaries* (2 vols. Philadelphia, 1887), II, 287.

12. "An Essay on the Causes," *American Review;* "An essay on the causes," *Port-Folio.*

13. "An Essay on the Causes," *American Review.*

14. The quotation in this and the paragraph following are from "An essay on the causes," *Port-Folio.*

15. Years later, Caldwell remarked in his *Autobiography,* "By his family and immediate acquaintances . . . I was charged with being essentially instrumental in his death. And . . . strenuous and unprincipled efforts were made to render me unpopular, and injure me in my profession. . . ." But since Caldwell added, with perhaps pardonable pride, that "his death is not the only one that was maliciously attributed to the severity of my pen," it may be that Caldwell was more concerned for its severity than for its veracity. *Autobiography,* pp. 272–73.

16. Jefferson to Roger O. Weightman, June 24, 1826, *Writings,* X, 390–92.

"White Pepper Seed"

1. For a good survey of these developments in anthropology, see Walter Scheidt, "The Concept of Race in Anthropology and the Division into Human Races from Linneus [*sic*] to Deniker," in *This Is Race: An Anthology Selected from the International Literature on the Races of Man,* ed. Earl W. Count (New York, 1950), pp. 354–91; Earl W. Count, "The Evolution of the Race Idea in Modern Western Culture during the Period of the Pre-Darwinian Nineteenth Century," *Transactions of the New York Academy of Sciences,* XXIV (1946), 139–65. An excellent account of the general attitude toward evolution in the pre-Darwinian period is Loren Eiseley, "Charles Darwin, Edward Blyth, and the Theory of Natural Selection," *Proceedings, APS,* CIII (1959), 94–158.

2. Morton later became an Episcopalian. For biographical information see William R. Grant, *Sketch of the Life and Character of Samuel George Morton, M.D.: Lecture Introductory to a Course on Anatomy and Physiology in the Medical Department of Pennsylvania College, Delivered, October 13, 1851* (Philadelphia, 1852); Sanford B. Hunt, "Samuel George Morton," in Samuel D. Gross (ed.), *Lives of Eminent American Physicians and Surgeons of the Nineteenth Century* (Philadelphia, 1861), pp. 582–604; Daniel Moore Fisk, "Samuel George Morton," DAB; George B. Wood, "A Biographical Memoir of Samuel George Morton, M.D., prepared by appointment of the College of Physicians of Philadelphia, and read before

that body, November 3, 1852" (Philadelphia, 1853); Charles D. Meigs, "A Memoir of Samuel George Morton, M.D., Late President of the Academy of Natural Sciences of Philadelphia" (Philadelphia, 1851); Henry S. Patterson, "Memoir of the Life and Scientific Labors of Samuel George Morton," in J[osiah] C. Nott and George R. Gliddon, *Types of Mankind; or, Ethnological Researches . . .* (Philadelphia, 1854), pp. xvii–lvii; "Death of Dr. Samuel George Morton," *New York Daily Tribune,* May 20, 1851.

3. Silliman to Morton, Oct. 11, 1832; Mantell to Morton, Sept. 16, 1836; various letters from Hitchcock and Eaton to Morton, Morton Papers, APS. Holmes to Morton, May 8, 1850; Atlee to Morton, Apr. 15, 1845, Morton Papers, LCP. For bibliography see Wood, "A Biographical Memoir of Samuel George Morton."

   Jules Marcou considered Morton's *Synopsis* "the starting point of all palaeontological and systematic work on American fossils." Jules Marcou, *Life, Letters, and Works of Louis Agassiz* (2 vols. New York, 1896), II, 28.

4. Wood, "A Biographical Memoir of Samuel George Morton."

5. Samuel George Morton, "Letter to the Rev. John Bachman, D.D., on the question of Hybridity in Animals considered in reference to the Unity of the Human Species," *Charleston Medical Journal,* V, (1850), 328–44; "Account of a Craniological Collection; with Remarks on the Classification of some Families of the Human Race," *Transactions of the American Ethnological Society,* II (1848), 215–22; Wood, "A Biographical Memoir of Samuel George Morton"; Morton to Ravenel, Sept. 21, 1832, Ravenel Papers, Charleston Museum; Z[ina] Pitcher to Morton, Sept. 11, 1832, Morton Papers, APS; Morton to Hildreth, Jan. 3, Aug. 2, 1833, May 27, 1835, Hildreth Papers, Marietta College. See also the following letters to Morton: Douglass Houghton, Nov. 21, 1837; J[oseph] Sullivant, Aug. 29, 1839; H[enry] Piddington, Feb. 18, 1837; Alex[ander] Nasmyth, Mar. 27, 1838, Morton Papers, APS. Tho[ma]s J. Page, May 7, 1845, Morton Papers, LCP. There are letters from Ruschenberger and Strain in both collections.

   Pitcher (1797–1872), geologist, botanist, physician, and devoted citizen of Detroit, was at this time in the army. For biographical information on Pitcher, see article by James M. Phalen in DAB; on Hildreth see article by Henry E. Handerson in DAMB.

6. Zina Pitcher to Morton, Mar. 4, 1837, Morton Papers, APS. Henry Galeiotti, a botanist connected with the *Éstablissement géographique de Bruxelles,* having just returned from Mexico, admitted, "as to Indian Skulls I never could obtain one in spite of all my efforts; there is great danger attending to such an enterprise." Henri Galeiotti [?] to Morton, Dec. 27, 1841, Morton Papers, LCP.

7. Morton to Hildreth, July 10, 1833; May 27, 1835; July 18, 1838, Hildreth Papers, Marietta College, Pitcher to Morton, Mar. 4, 1834, Morton Papers, APS.

8. Morton, [Prospectus to the *Crania Americana*], sent in a letter to Hildreth, Jan. 25, 1837, Hildreth Papers, Marietta College.

The copy of Morton's *Catalogue of Skulls* from which the above extract is taken is in the ANSP.

Aleš Hrdlička believed that Morton was primarily interested in phrenology. "The teachings of Gall . . . gave rise to various craniological collections, and were the main incentive to Morton's ultimate and remarkable work, the 'Crania Americana.'" Hrdlička, *Physical Anthropology: Its Scope and Aims; Its History and Present Status in the United States* (Philadelphia, 1919), p. 10. See also Hrdlička to Edward J. Nolan, May 2, 1911, Morton Papers, APS.

9. Samuel George Morton, *Crania Americana; or, A Comparative View of the Skulls of Various Aboriginal Nations of North and South America, to which is Prefixed an Essay on The Varieties of the Human Species* (Philadelphia, 1839). Published in London in the same year, the English edition was dedicated to the eminent ethnologist James Cowles Prichard. The American edition was dedicated to W. S. W. Ruschenberger. John Collins, "Circular," inserted in end-papers of *Crania Americana*.

10. *Crania Americana*, pp. 1–3, 88 n. The popularly accepted chronology was that propounded by Archbishop Usher, who placed the date of the Creation at Wednesday, October 26, 4004 B.C.

11. *Ibid.*, pp. 1–3.

12. *Ibid.*, p. 260. "White pepper seed was selected on account of its spherical form, its hardness, and the equal size of the grains. It was also sifted to render the equality still greater." Morton later changed to lead shot when he found that it gave a greater accuracy; i.e., successive measurements of a skull were found to be the same, whereas with the pepper seed there was some variation. See S. G. Morton, [Some observations on a mode of ascertaining the internal capacity of the human cranium], *Proceedings*, ANSP, I (1841), 7.

13. Smith, *An Essay on the Causes of the Variety of Complexion and Figure . . .* (New Brunswick, N.J., 1810), p. 240 n.; *Crania Americana*, pp. 3–7, 8–9, 40.

14. *Crania Americana*, pp. 71, 75, 81. There were many English as well as French, German, and Greek editions of Robertson's work.

15. *Ibid.*, pp. 275–76.

16. George Combe, *Notes on the United States of North America* (3 vols.; Philadelphia, 1841), I, 254; II, 63–64, 77–79, 112. See also II, 79–80.

17. *Ibid.*, II, 215, 373–75, III, 171–72, 307; Combe to Morton, May 2, 1839, Morton Papers, APS; and see Combe to Charles F. Mayer, Jan. 26, 1839, Etting Papers, American Scientists, Historical Society of Pennsylvania. For biographical information on Combe see the article by Leslie Stephen in DNB. On the career of phrenology in the United States see John D. Davies, *Phrenology, Fad and Science: A 19th-Century American Crusade* (New Haven, 1955).

One of those who signed a similar testimonial at the end of the second course was Dr. Samuel George Morton (*Notes on the United States*, II, 375). Bache wrote Morton that he was "eager to do something to call attention to his [Combe's] lectures," for he considered them to be "in an educational point of view . . . of high importance" (Bache to Morton, Nov. 2, 1838, Morton Papers, APS). For Silliman's address see [Benjamin Silliman], "Phrenology," *American Journal of Science*, XXXIX (1840), 65–88.

18. *Notes on the United States*, III, 439 n. Much of the criticism of phrenology in this period rested on objections to its "materialism." It may be, as Sir Leslie Stephen remarked in his biographical article on Combe, that phrenology, despite the fact that it long fell into discredit, served "to excite an interest in science and a belief in the importance of applying scientific method in moral questions." Despite its naïve and oversimplified concept of enormously complex problems, phrenology leveled an early blow, in the name of science, at religious dogmatism on questions of science. Hrdlička thought that Gall's teachings were important in the growth of anthropology, for "however erroneous in application . . . , they stimulated research into the variations of the head, skull, and brain, gave rise of various craniological collections . . ." (Hrdlička, *Physical Anthropology*, p. 10).

19. *Crania Americana*, p. i; Combe to A. D. Bache, Oct. 28, 1838, Morton Papers, APS; *Notes on the United States*, II, 301–2; Combe to Morton, Mar. 19, 1839, Morton Papers, APS.

20. *Crania Americana*, pp. i, 99; Combe to Morton, Feb. 28, 1840, Morton Papers, APS (later, as a matter of fact, Morton did discover that these crania had been artificially compressed); [George Combe and Benjamin Horner Coates], "Crania Americana . . . ," *American Journal of Science*, XXXVIII (1840), 341–75. This review was reprinted in the *Edinburgh New Philosophical Journal*, XXIX (1840), 111–39, no copy of the *Crania Americana* having yet reached Britain. On the attribution of this review to Combe and Coates, a prominent Philadelphia physician, see Benjamin Silliman to Morton, Mar. 27, 1840; Combe to Morton, Feb. 19, 28, 1840, Morton Papers, APS. Combe explained about the postscript in letters to Morton on Feb. 28, Mar. 6, 13, 1840, Morton Papers, APS. I have been unable to locate any letters from Morton to Combe and do not know what his explanation was.

21. *Crania Americana*, p. i. In 1840 Morton warned his class in anatomy against "adopting too hastily these minute details of the localities and functions of supposed organs, which have of late found so many and such zealous advocates. For while it is difficult to suppose that the brain, with all its varied and beautiful parts, acts throughout with equal impulse on every moral and intellectual emotion, let us be cautious how we attempt to localize organs which are beyond our sight and reach, and of which the exact position can only be ascertained by numberless comparisons, and these made without reference to the preconceived opinions of other men, no matter how highly we may respect their love of truth and accuracy" (Samuel George Morton, *Brief Remarks on the Diversities of the Human Species, and on some Kindred Subjects* . . . [Philadelphia, 1842], pp. 15–16).

22. [Jeffries Wyman], "Crania Americana . . . ," *North American Review,* LI (1840), 173–86. Combe was interested in seeing that the *Crania Americana* was given a good press and was much displeased when anti-phrenologists praised Morton's work but looked down upon his own contribution or failed to see its relevance. See "Crania Americana . . . ," *British and Foreign Medical Review,* X (1840), 475–85; and Combe's reaction in Combe to Morton, Aug. 20, 1840, Morton Papers, APS. This letter indicates Combe's concern and his attempts, several times successful, to get the work reviewed by friends of phrenology. For other reviews, see [James Kennedy?], "Crania Americana . . . ," *Medico-Chirurgical Review,* XXXIII (1840), 435–64; "Crania Americana . . . ," *Edinburgh Medical and Surgical Journal,* LIV (1840), 443–69; "Crania Americana . . . ," *The Eclectic Journal of Medicine* (Philadelphia), IV (1840), 97–99.

23. C[harles] C[aldwell], "Crania Americana . . . ," *Western Journal of Medicine and Surgery,* II (1840), 35–56, 105–30.

24. Samuel Forry, "The Mosaic Account of the Unity of the Human Race, Confirmed by the Natural History of the American Aborigines," *American Biblical Repository,* 2d ser., X (1843), 29–80. See also his "On the Position of Man in the Scale of Organic Creation," *ibid.,* XI (1844), 274–301. In his review Combe stated, "The Unity of the human race is assumed by Dr. Morton" ("Crania Americana").

   For scattered biographical information on Forry see "Samuel Forrey [*sic*]," *Appleton's Cyclopaedia of American Biography;* "Obituary Record," *American Journal of the Medical Sciences,* IX (1845), 264; Stephen D. Williams, "A Brief Notice of some of the Physicians of the United States who have died within a few years," *Transactions of the American Medical Association,* III (1850), 429–70; and "J. S.," "The Late Samuel Forry, M.D.," *New York Journal of Medicine,* IV (1845), 7–9.

25. Morton, [Some observations on a mode of ascertaining the internal capacity of the human cranium]; [Results of the measurements of forty-five adult negro crania], *Proceedings,* ANSP, I (1841), 135; *Brief Remarks,* pp. 14–15, 21–22.

26. *Brief Remarks,* pp. 14–15, 21–22.

27. *Ibid.,* p. 8.

28. Augustus A. Gould, Charles K. Dilloway, and W. I. Bowditch to Morton, June 1, 1841, Morton Papers, APS; Samuel George Morton, *An Inquiry into the Distinctive Characteristics of the Aboriginal Race of America* (2d ed.; Philadelphia, 1844). Read April 27, 1842, this appeared originally in the *Boston Journal of Natural History,* IV (1842), 191–223, and was widely reprinted. The separately printed edition is somewhat more complete.

29. Of course it did no harm to point out that one's findings conformed to Scripture or, indeed, to add one's bit in glorifying the power of the Creator. Morton told the Boston scientists that his conclusion was not "incompatible with the history of man, as recorded in the Sacred Writings," for "where others see nothing but chance, we can perceive a wise and obvious design,

displayed in the original adaptation of the several races of men to whose varied circumstances of climate and locality which, while congenial to the one, are destructive to the other." *Inquiry into the Distinctive Characteristics*, p. 26.

"A Grand Theme of Conversation"

1. Morton to Gliddon, Nov. 7, 1837, in Henry S. Patterson, "Memoir of the Life and Scientific Labors of Samuel George Morton," in J. C. Nott and George R. Gliddon, *Types of Mankind; or, Ethnological Researches . . .* (Philadelphia, 1854), pp. xvii–lvii; Gliddon to Morton, Mar. 31, 1839, Morton Papers, APS.

2. Gliddon to Morton, Mar. 31, 1839, Morton Papers, APS. For evidence that Gliddon was the first to lecture on Egyptology in the United States see Luke Burke's introduction to Gliddon's *Otia Aegpytiaca: Discourses on Egyptian Archaeology and Hieroglyphical Discoveries* (London, 1849); Francis L. Hawks, *The Monuments of Egypt; or, Egypt a Witness for the Bible* (New York, 1850); "G. W. S.," "The Progress of Ethnology," *Mercersburg Review*, I (1849), 127–39; *Journal of a Voyage up the Nile, Made between the Months of November, 1848, and April, 1849* (New York, 1850), p. 10.

    The best biographical sketch of Gliddon is an unidentified manuscript obituary in the APS. Most complete of the published sources is the obituary in the New York *Herald*, Nov. 30, 1857. Others are: Austin Allibone, *A Critical Dictionary of English Literature and British and American Authors* (Philadelphia, 1870); *Appleton's Cyclopaedia of American Biography* (1887 ed.); Caroline Ransom Williams, "The Place of the New-York Historical Society in the Growth of American Interest in Egyptology," *New-York Historical Society Quarterly Bulletin*, IV (1920), 3–20; and various of Gliddon's own works, especially his *Appendix to the American in Egypt* (Philadelphia, 1842) and J[osiah] C. Nott and George R. Gliddon, *Indigenous Races of the Earth . . .* (Philadelphia, 1857), p. 531 n.

3. *Otia Aegyptiaca*, pp. 4–5 n.

4. William B. Dinsmoor, "Early American Studies of Mediterranean Archaeology," *Proceedings*, APS, LXXXVII (1944), 70–104, contains an excellent account of the romantic interest Americans of the period were taking in things Egyptian; "Americans in Egypt," *New York Observer*, Mar. 16, 1854; William C. Prime, *Boat Life in Egypt and Nubia* (New York, 1857), p. 359; [John Lloyd Stephens], *Incidents of Travel in Egypt, Arabia Petraea, and the Holy Land . . .* (New York), 1841.

    American interest in Egypt was somewhat belated, for Bonaparte's great expedition to Egypt had taken place in 1798, Young and Champollion had begun deciphering the hieroglyphics in 1821, the French and Tuscan governments had sent out an expedition under Champollion and Rosellini in 1827, Wilkinson had made knowledge of Egypt accessible in his great *Manners and Customs of the Ancient Egyptians* in 1837, and Lepsius had led the famous Prussian expedition in 1842. For a concise description of the growth of Egyptian studies see Harry Reginald Holland Hall, "Egypt," *Encyclopaedia Britannica* (1948 ed.).

5. Anna Theresa Kitchel, *George Lewes and George Eliot: A Review of Records* (New York, 1933), pp. 15–16, Appendix III; Eliza Lynn Linton, "George Henry Lewes and Thornton Hunt," *The Bookman*, III (1896), 520–23; Lawrence and Elizabeth Hanson, *Marian Evans & George Eliot: A Biography* (London, 1952), p. 155; Thornton Hunt, "A View of Leigh Hunt's Intimate Circle (from an unpublished work by Thornton Hunt entitled 'Proserpina')," in Edmund Blunden, *Leigh Hunt and His Circle* (New York, 1930), pp. 358–67; E. Irving Carlyle, "Frank Stone," DNB; G. C. Boase, "Thomas Milner Gibson," DNB. When his wife deserted him for Thornton Hunt, Lewes lost interest in the semi-Fourierist phalanstery—although his friendship with Hunt was not disturbed—and wandered into the arms of Mary Ann Evans, thus providing English literary circles with a subject to whisper about for a quarter-century.

6. The quotations in this paragraph are from Luke Burke, Introduction to Gliddon, *Otia Aegyptiaca*, pp. 5–6. See also Gliddon's advertisement, "Lands, Sacred & Classical," *Baltimore Sun*, Apr. 30, 1851; "An Evening in Egypt with Gliddon," *Literary World*, V (1849), 492–93, 543–44, VI (1850), 25–28, 169–71. Gliddon sometimes displayed specimens from the collection of Col. Mendes I. Cohen, perhaps the first collection of Egyptian antiquities in the United States. Williams, "The Place of the New-York Historical Society in the Growth of American Interest in Egyptology."

The full title of Gliddon's book was *Ancient Egypt: A Series of Chapters on Early Egyptian History, Archaeology, and Other Subjects Connected with Hieroglyphical Literature* (New York, 1844). On his surrender of the copyright to Benjamin see "A Sketch of the Progress of Archaeological Science in America," *Southern Literary Messenger*, XI (1845), 420–33.

7. Ferris Greenslet, *The Lowells and Their Seven Worlds* (Boston, 1946), pp. 210–11, 233–34; Boston *Daily Evening Transcript*, Dec. 4, 1843.

8. Boston *Daily Evening Transcript*, Nov. 4, 8, 11, 15, 18, 1843. In a letter to Morton in 1841 concerning the projected *Crania Aegyptiaca*, Gliddon had stated that he was "hostile to the opinions of the African origin of the Egyptians. . . . The idea that the monuments support such theory, or the conclusion that they came down the Nile" was "untenable," and he had suggested that Morton refute it, "unless," he added, "you are convinced from Comparative Anatomy, with which science I am totally unacquainted" (Gliddon to Morton, Oct. 21, 1841, quoted in Patterson, "Memoir"). For a very commendatory report on Gliddon's Lowell Lectures see "Egyptian Antiquities—Mr. Gliddon," *New World*, VI (1843), 241–43.

9. Samuel G. Morton, "Summary of His Series of Observations on Egyptian Ethnography," *Proceedings*, APS, III (1843), 115–18.

10. Samuel G. Morton, *Crania Aegyptiaca; or Observations on Egyptian Ethnography, Derived from Anatomy, History and the Monuments* (Philadel-

phia, 1844), p. 1. This was read before the APS in December, 1842, and in January and April, 1843. It was published in the *Transactions*, APS, N.S., IX (1844), 93–159, under the title "Observations on Egyptian Ethnography, Derived from Anatomy, History, and the Monuments." Later in the year it was published separately in Philadelphia and London.

11. *Crania Aegyptiaca*, p. 59. Morton added that Negroes were not the only slaves in Egypt, that, indeed, slavery "was imposed on all conquered nations, white as well as black."

12. Retzius to Morton, Apr. 3, 1847, in Patterson, "Memoir"; James Cowles Prichard, *The Natural History of Man: Comprising Inquiries into the Modifying Influence of Physical and Moral Agencies on the Different Tribes of the Human Family* (2 vols.; London, 1855), II, 148. Prichard devoted an entire chapter to excerpts from *Crania Aegyptiaca*.

13. Gliddon to Morton, Mar. 29, Apr. 6, 1844; Hodgson to Morton, Mar. 29, 1844; Hodgson to Morton, Apr. 2 [i.e., May 2?], 1844, Morton Papers, LCP. Hodgson seems to have erred in dating this last letter, for it is postmarked May 2. On March 29 he was in Charleston on his way north to a meeting of the National Institute and could hardly have made this trip, attended the meeting, and returned by April 2. Gliddon in his letter to Morton of April 6 said, "Hodgson had just passed through on his way back to Savannah." I have been unable to find Morton's letter to Hodgson and have relied on this letter for the statement that Morton wished Calhoun to have the volume.

A citizen of Savannah, Hodgson (1801–71) was a plantation owner, diplomat, and authority on the Berber language of West Africa. He maintained a correspondence with Morton for several years. He was active in the National Institute of Science, a short-lived museum and scientific society which in 1846 was superseded by the Smithsonian Institution, and was one of the original members of the American Oriental Society. Hodgson was strongly proslavery. He made something of a showplace of his home by dressing domestic slaves in oriental livery and once was haled into a Georgia court on a charge of "cruel treatment of my fat, lazy, rollicking Sambos" (William H. Russell, *My Diary North and South* [Boston, 1863], p. 157; Hodgson to James Henry Hammond, June 19, 1859, James Henry Hammond Papers, LC). For biographical information see Cyrus Adler, *Christopher Columbus in Oriental Literature ... Note on William B. Hodgson ...* (New Haven, 1892); Leonard L. Mackall, *William Brown Hodgson* (Savannah, 1931).

14. James H. Hammond, "Two Letters on the Subject of Slavery in the United States, addressed to Thomas Clarkson, Esq., January 28, 1845," in *Selections from the Letters and Speeches of the Hon. James H. Hammond of South Carolina* (New York, 1866), pp. 114–98; Hodgson to Morton, Dec. 4, 1845, Morton Papers, LCP.

Hammond (1807–64), a nullificationist in the early 1830's and one of the earliest of the Southern defenders of slavery, in these letters was replying to petitions from abolitionists both in the North and in England which asked the release of one John L. Brown, of Fairfield, South Carolina, who had been convicted of aiding a slave to escape and was to be hanged. Hammond's letters were a defense of slavery. Widely read, they were circulated in manuscript form, appeared in the Charleston newspapers, and then were printed separately in four separate editions. For an account of the circumstances and the popularity of these letters, see Elizabeth Merritt, *James Henry Hammond, 1807–64* ("Johns Hopkins University Studies in History and Political Science," Series XLI, No. 4 [Baltimore, 1923]), pp. 73–77.

15. Gliddon to Morton, Apr. 6, 1844, Morton Papers, LCP. The book also met a ready reception in Baltimore. Gliddon to Morton, Apr. 28, 1844, Morton Papers, LCP. Mitchell King (1783–1867) founded the Literary Club of Charleston, was president of the trustees of the Medical College of Charleston, and a strong Unionist during the nullification controversy in South Carolina. For biographical information, see Francis S. Drake, *Dictionary of American Biography* (Boston, 1879), *Lamb's Biographical Dictionary,* and *Appleton's Cyclopaedia of American Biography.*

Holbrook (1794–1871) was America's outstanding student of reptiles in this period. Born in South Carolina, he received his bachelor's degree from Brown University, and, like so many other Southern medical students, a medical degree from the University of Pennsylvania. After four years of study in Europe, he began practice in Charleston in 1822. Two years later he helped to establish the Medical College of South Carolina and lectured on anatomy there for thirty years. For biographical information see Robert Wilson, Jr., "John Edwards Holbrook," DAMB.

"Less in Love with Freedom"

1. [Thomas Hamilton], *Men and Manners in America* (Philadelphia, 1833), pp. 321–22.

2. William Aikman, *The Future of the Colored Race in America: Being an Article in the Presbyterian Quarterly Review, of July, 1862* (New York, 1862). Aikman added, "He, then, who does not take slavery into account in his thinking on this war, has not begun to get a glimpse of what it means. . . . Its origin was in slavery. . . ."

3. *Annals of Congress,* 1 Cong., 3 sess. (1790), II, 1455–56.

4. *Address to the Citizens of South Carolina on the Approaching Election of a President and Vice-President of the United States, By a Federal Republican* (Charleston, 1800); [William Linn?], *Considerations on the Election of a President: Addressed to the Citizens of the United States* (New York, 1800), p. 13; Jefferson to Benjamin Banneker, Aug. 30, 1791, P. L. Ford (ed.), *The Writings of Thomas Jefferson* (10 vols.; New York, 1892–99), V, 377–78, as quoted in [William L. Smith and Oliver Wolcott], *The Pretensions of Thomas Jefferson to the Presidency Examined; and the Charges against John Adams Refuted, Addressed to the Citizens of America in general; and particularly to the Electors of the President* ("United States,

1796"). The italics are the authors'. See also Thomas Moore, "To Thomas Hume, Esq. M.D. from the City of Washington," *The Poetical Works of Thomas Moore* (Boston, 1835), p. 149; Hamilton W. Pierson, *Jefferson at Monticello: The Private Life of Thomas Jefferson* (New York, 1862), p. 110; Coley Taylor and Samuel Middlebrook, *The Eagle Screams* (New York, 1936), pp. 72–76, 85; Charles O. Lerche, Jr., "Jefferson and the Election of 1800: A Case Study in the Political Smear," *William and Mary Quarterly*, V (1848), 467–91; Maude H. Woodfin, "Contemporary Opinion in Virginia of Thomas Jefferson," in *Essays in Honor of William E. Dodd*, ed. Avery Craven (Chicago, 1935), pp. 30–85.

5. [Hamilton], *Men and Manners in America*, p. 174; David Francis Bacon, *Wanderings on the Seas and Shores of Africa* (New York, 1843), p. 111. Dr. James M'Cune Smith (1813–65), probably the most scholarly Negro writer of his day and a prominent abolitionist, cited this testimony of Bacon in his refutation of Jefferson's Fourteenth Query in the *Notes on Virginia* (James M'Cune Smith, "On the Fourteenth Query of Thomas Jefferson's Notes on Virginia," *Anglo-African Magazine*, I [1859], 225–37).

6. Speech of Representative William Smith of Maryland, *Annals of Congress*, 16 Cong., 1 sess. (1820), col. 269, quoted in William Sumner Jenkins, *Pro-Slavery Thought in the Old South* (Chapel Hill, 1935), p. 63; "Amor Patriae," *The Blasphemy of Abolitionism Exposed: Servitude and the Rights of the South, Vindicated, A Bible Argument, etc.* (New York, 1850), 17–18; "The Black Race in North America; Why was Their Introduction Permitted?" De Bow's *Review* XX (1856), 1–21, 190–214, 290–315, 447–68. For a few examples of the many proslavery attempts to explain away the Declaration see Albert T. Bledsoe, *An Essay on Liberty and Slavery* (Philadelphia, 1856); Thomas R. R. Cobb, *An Inquiry into the Law of Negro Slavery in the United States of America* (Philadelphia, 1858); Thomas R. Dew, *An Essay on Slavery* (Richmond, Va., 1849); William Harper, *Memoir on Slavery* . . . (Charleston, 1836); James P. Holcombe, "Is Slavery Consistent with Natural Law?" *Southern Literary Messenger*, XXVII (1858), 401–21.

7. Charles Francis Adams, *An Oration Delivered before the Municipal Authorities of the City of Fall River, July 4, 1860* (Fall River, Mass., 1860); *The Collected Works of Abraham Lincoln*, ed. Roy P. Basler (8 vols.; New Brunswick, N.J., 1953–55), II, 298–410. On the subject of the collapse of the doctrines of the Declaration of Independence in the United States see Carl Becker's classic *The Declaration of Independence: A Study in the History of Political Ideas* (New York, 1922), pp. 224–79.

8. Edward Jarvis, "Statistics of Insanity in the United States," *Boston Medical and Surgical Journal*, XXVII (1842), 116–21, 281–82.

Jarvis (1803–84) was born in Concord, Massachusetts, and received his medical degree from Harvard in 1826. While practicing in Concord, he came under the influence of Lemuel Shattuck and became interested in vital statistics. In the period 1837–43 he practiced in Louisville, but, hating slavery, he returned to Massachusetts and settled in Dorchester. For biographical information see Robert W. Wood, *Memorial of Edward Jarvis, Read at the Annual Meeting of the American Statistical Association, January 16, 1885* (Boston, 1885); William R. Leonard, "Edward Jarvis," DAB; and "Edward Jarvis," DAMB. On the Census of 1840 see Albert Deutsch, "The First U.S. Census of the Insane (1840), and Its Use as Pro-Slavery Propaganda," *Bulletin of the History of Medicine*, XV (1944), 469–82.

9. "Statistics of Insanity in the United States." His first notice of the census appears on pages 116–21 and his embarrassed correction on pages 281–82. Curiously, neither Deutsch, in his study of Jarvis' efforts to correct the census, nor Wood, in his biographical sketch, mentions the first conclusions that Jarvis drew from the census.

10. Edward Jarvis, "Insanity among the Colored Population of the Free States," *American Journal of the Medical Sciences*, N.S., VII (1844), 71–83.

11. "An Inquirer," "Table of Lunacy in the United States," *Hunt's Merchants' Magazine*, VIII (1843), 460–61; "Reflections on the Census of 1840," *Southern Literary Messenger*, IX (1843), 340–52. That slavery had a stabilizing effect on the Negro mentality was suggested also in "Statistics of Population: Table of Lunacy in the United States," *Hunt's Merchants' Magazine*, VIII (1843), 290.

12. "Insanity among the Colored Population of the Free States."

13. John Quincy Adams, *Memoirs of John Quincy Adams, Comprising Portions of His Diary from 1795 to 1848*, ed. Charles Francis Adams (12 vols.; Philadelphia, 1874–77), XII, 61–62 (entry for June 21, 1844). Adams called on Upshur on February 19, 1844.

14. John C. Calhoun, *The Works of John C. Calhoun*, ed. Richard K. Crallé (6 vols.; New York, 1853–55), V, 330–33. Aberdeen's dispatch was dated Dec. 26, 1843.

15. Calhoun to Pakenham, Apr. 18, 27, 1844, *Works*, V, 333–39, 343–47. The treaty of annexation was concluded on April 12, but it failed of Senate ratification on June 8.

On hearing of this exchange, George Bancroft remarked, "What can be more sad than for a man to serve under John Tyler? What: unless it be to found an argument in defence of slavery on fictitious statistics, and address it to a British minister!" (Bancroft to Van Buren, May 2, 1844 [A series of letters between George Bancroft and Martin Van Buren], *Massachusetts Historical Society Proceedings*, XLII [1909], 381–442).

16. Nott, introduction to J. C. Nott and George R. Gliddon, *Types of Mankind* ... (Philadelphia, 1854); Gliddon, May 9, May 17, Aug. 2, 1844, to Calhoun, Calhoun Papers, Clemson College. Gliddon sent Calhoun his *Memoir on the Cotton of Egypt* (London, 1841), *Appeal to the Antiquaries of Europe* (London, 1841), and *Ancient Egypt* (New York, 1843). Besides Morton, Gliddon referred Calhoun to Holbrook of Charleston, Hodgson of Savannah, and Richard K. Haight of New York. Hodgson sent a copy of his *Notes on Northern Africa* (New York, 1844) to Calhoun, adding, "In the

natural history of Man I shall continue to assert the existence of an Organic law, by which the white and black races, when in contact, must ever stand in relation of supremacy and subjection. If from any cause, this relation should cease, I should . . . maintain, that this . . . law would require the removal of one race. . . .

"I am largely interested in this question, as one of property. And I have much anxiety for the fate of the great National Measure [i.e., the annexation of Texas] now pending, which I believe, will give greater security to that property, as well as larger guarantees for this Union" (Hodgson to Calhoun, Jan. 24, 1845, Calhoun Papers, Clemson College).

17. Calhoun to King, Aug. 12, 1844, *Works*, V, 379–92. See also his second letter to King on this subject, Dec. 13, 1845 ("Strictly Confidential"), Calhoun, "Correspondence of John C. Calhoun," ed. J. Franklin Jameson, in *American Historical Association Report*, II (1899), 631–33.

18. Calhoun to Francis Wharton, Nov. 20, 1844, "Correspondence," pp. 629–30.

19. Gliddon to Calhoun, Dec. 26, 1844, Calhoun Papers, Clemson College; Hammond to Calhoun, May 10, 1844, "Correspondence," pp. 953–55; Adams, *Memoirs*, XII, 36 (entry for May 27, 1844).

20. Adams, *Memoirs*, XII, 22–23 (entry for May 6, 1844).

21. John Homans, [Report of the Committee appointed to investigate the subject of insanity among the colored population of the State of Massachusetts], *Medical Communications of the Massachusetts Medical Society*, VII (1845), 83–84; John Homans, John Ware, Ephraim Buck, O. W. Holmes, E. Jarvis, [Final Report of the Committee appointed to investigate the subject of insanity among the colored population in the State of Massachusetts], *Medical Communications of the Massachusetts Medical Society*, VII (1845), 90–95; Edward Jarvis, William Brigham, J. Wingate Thornton, "Memorial of the American Statistical Association, Praying the adoption of measures for the correction of errors in the sixth census," *Senate Document* No. 5, 28 Cong., 2 sess. (1844); Adams, *Memoirs*, XII, 28–29, 36, 61–62 (entries for May 17, 18, 27, June 21, 1844). The Joint Committee on the Library, which received the petition, though it agreed in its report to the Senate that "in nearly every department of the late census errors have crept in, which go very far to destroy confidence in the accuracy of its results," did not recommend either that the census be corrected (because of the "great expense") or that Congress withdraw its "sanction" to the "authenticity and correctness" of the document, for "its near approximation to the truth is all that can be hoped for." The committee contented itself with recommending legislation to prevent like errors in the Census of 1850 (*Senate Document* No. 146, 28 Cong., 2 sess. [1845]).

22. *Journal of the House of Representatives*, 28 Cong., 1 sess. (1844), p. 471. Quoted in Deutsch, "The First U.S. Census of the Insane."

23. Deutsch, "The First U.S. Census of the Insane"; Calhoun to J. W. Jones (Speaker of the House), Feb. 8, 1845, *Works*, V, 458–61.

24. "Startling Facts from the Census," *American Journal of Insanity*, VIII (1851), 153–54. Jarvis replied with still another refutation of the census and the absurd conclusions which had been drawn from it (E[dward] Jarvis, "Insanity among the Colored Population of the Free States," *American Journal of Insanity*, VIII [1852], 268–82).

25. Walter Reed, "The Propagation of Yellow Fever—Observations Based on Recent Researches," *Yellow Fever (Sen. Doc.* No. 822, 61 Cong., 3 sess. [1911]). Reed also gave Nott credit for having mentioned the mosquito as the possible agent—an excess of generosity on Reed's part, for Nott merely had noted the coincidence of the death of mosquitoes and other insects from the first frost with the conclusion of yellow fever epidemics. See Nott's "Sketch of the Epidemic of Yellow Fever of 1847 in Mobile," *Charleston Medical Journal*, III (1848), 1–21, which attracted the attention of Oliver Wendell Holmes, G. C. Shattuck, Daniel Drake, Austin Flint, and others of the American Medical Association's Committee on Medical Literature. Oliver Wendell Holmes, *et al.*, "Report of the Committee on Medical Literature," *Transactions of the American Medical Association*, I (1848), 249–88. For a recent appraisal, see Palmer Howard Futcher, "Notes on Insect Contagion," *Bulletin of the History of Medicine*, IV (1936), 536–58.

26. Nott, Sept. 19, 1835, Nov. 5, 1836, to James M. Gage, James M. Gage Papers, Southern Historical Collection, University of North Carolina. The best contemporary biographical sketch of Nott is the obituary by W[illiam] H[enry] Anderson, *Biographical Sketch of Dr. J. C. Nott* (Mobile, 1877). Other biographies by Nott's contemporaries are: William M. Polk, "Josiah C. Nott," *American Journal of Obstetrics*, LXVII (1913), 957–58; Thomas M. Owen, *History of Alabama and Dictionary of Alabama Biography* (4 vols.; Chicago, 1921); Kenneth R. H. Mackenzie "The Life and Anthropological Labours of Dr. Nott of Mobile, Hon. F.A.S.L.," *Anthropological Review*, VI (1868), lxxix–lxxxiii. See also George H. Ramsey, "Josiah Clark Nott," DAB. For a recent account of Nott's life and for a good, though not entirely complete, bibliography—to which, I should add, I am much indebted—see Emmett B. Carmichael, "Josiah Clark Nott," *Bulletin of the History of Medicine*, XXII (1948), 249–62.

Nott did not study under Morton, as is suggested in Jenkins, *Pro-Slavery Thought in the Old South*, p. 256.

27. "Philanthropist," "Vital Statistics of Negroes and Mulattoes," *Boston Medical and Surgical Journal*, XVII (1842), 168–70. This was reprinted as "Interesting Facts in Physiology" in the *African Repository*, organ of the American Colonization Society, an organization ever ready to support any argument which would promote their object in exporting free Negroes to Africa.

28. *American Journal of the Medical Sciences*, VI (1843), 252–56. On the mixed ancestry of American Negroes see Melville J. Herskovits, *The Anthropometry of the American Negro* (New York, 1930). The genetic benefits of race mixture to a population are today generally recognized—by geneticists.

29. [Josiah C. Nott], "Dr. Nott's Reply to 'C' . . . ," *Southern Quarterly Review*, VIII (1845), 148–90 (Nott here quotes from Morton's letter); Nott to Morton, Oct. 15, 1844, Morton Papers, LCP.

30. The quotations in this and remaining paragraphs of the chapter are from *Two Lectures on the Natural History of the Caucasian and Negro Races* (Mobile, 1844), pp. 1, 6–8, 10–11, 16–19, 29–34, 40–41.

31. Traveling in Egypt in 1851–52, Bayard Taylor recorded that he was "greatly interested in a procession of men, representing the different nations of the earth. The physical peculiarities of the Persian, the Jew and the Ethiopian are therein as distinctly marked as at the present day. The blacks are perfect counterparts of those I saw daily upon the Nile, and the noses of the Jews seem newly painted from originals in New York. So little diversity in the distinguishing features of the race, after the lapse of more than three thousand years, is a strong argument in favor of the new ethnological theory of the separate origin of different races." Nevertheless, Taylor believed that the races were one species, descended from a single pair, and therefore concluded that "the date of the first appearance of Man on the earth, must have been nearer fifty thousand than five thousand years ago" (Bayard Taylor, *A Journey to Central Africa; or, Life and Landscapes from Egypt to the Negro Kingdom of the White Nile* [New York, 1854; "Household Edition," 1889], pp. 118, 494).

"A Hell of a Rasping"

1. Orville Dewey, "On American Morals and Manners," *Christian Examiner*, XXXVI (1844), 250–80. Dewey restated this position in *A Discourse on Slavery and the Annexation of Texas* (New York, 1844). See also James M'Cune Smith, "On the Fourteenth Query of Thomas Jefferson's Notes on Virginia," *Anglo African Magazine*, I (1859), 225–37.

2. W[illiam] B[enjamin] Carpenter, "Letter from W. B. Carpenter, M.D.," *Christian Examiner*, XXXVII (1844), 139–44. See his article "Varieties of Mankind," *The Cyclopaedia of Anatomy and Physiology* (1852). For biography of Carpenter see article by G. T. Bettany in DNB.

3. S[amuel] H[enry] Dickson, "Letter from S. H. Dickson, M.D.," *Christian Examiner*, XXXVII (1844), 427–32. This was printed separately in S[amuel] Henry Dickson, *Remarks on Certain Topics Connected with the General Subject of Slavery* (Charleston, [S.C.], 1845). I have used the latter edition because Dickson claimed that the editors had severely pruned the *Examiner* version. This pamphlet was in Morton's library and is now in the LCP.

Dickson (1798–1872) was a prominent physician. A graduate of Yale and the University of Pennsylvania Medical School, he founded two medical schools in South Carolina, was professor for three years at the medical school of the University of the City of New York, and in 1858 accepted the chair recently vacated by his friend Dr. John K. Mitchell at Jefferson Medical College in Philadelphia. He was a close friend of William Gilmore Simms, who dedicated *The Yemassee* to him. For biography see Edgar Erskine Hume, "Samuel Henry Dickson," DAB; and Samuel D. Gross, *Autobiography of Samuel D. Gross, M.D., with Sketches of His Contemporaries* (2 vols.; Philadelphia, 1887), II, 369.

4. See J[ohn] Augustine Smith, "Sketch of a Lecture on the Different Races of Men . . . , Reported for the New-York Tribune," issued with Charles Lyell, *Lectures on Geology, Delivered at the Broadway Tabernacle, by Charles Lyell, F.R.S. Second Edition, with a General Introduction* (New York, 1843).

5. Curtis to Gray, Jan. 6, 1845, Historic Letter File, Harvard University Herbarium; "Two Lectures on the Natural History of the Caucasian and Negro Races, by Josiah C. Nott . . . ," *Southern Quarterly Review*, VI (1844), 525. For biography of Curtis and a bibliography of his botanical writings see Thomas F. Wood, "A Sketch of the Botanical Work of the Rev. Moses Ashley Curtis, D.D., Read before the Mitchell Society at the University of North Carolina, May 22d, 1885," *Journal of the Elisha Mitchell Scientific Society, for the Year 1884–85*, pp. 9–31; C. L. Shear and Neil E. Stevens, "The Mycological Work of Moses Ashley Curtis," *Mycologia*, (1919), 181–201.

6. This and the following two paragraphs are based on [Moses Ashley] C[urtis], "Unity of the Races," *Southern Quarterly Review*, VII (1845), 372–448.

7. Nott to Morton, Feb. 20, 1845, Morton Papers, LCP; Nott to Hammond, July 10, 25, 1845, Hammond Papers, LC. The lack of books was a constant complaint with Nott, and it illustrates the extent to which the South was isolated from contemporary cultures. In 1851 he explained to a friend in the North, "I have no kindred spirit here—no public library—no body to talk to, & have sent abroad for all my books—I have to buy a great many & my foreign correspondents are very kind in donation" (Nott to [E. G. Squier], Mar. 26, 1851, Squier Papers, LC).

8. J[ames] H[enry] H[ammond] to Nott, Aug. 3, 1845, Hammond Papers, LC. Hammond promised "to do anything in furtherance of yr. speculations on the Unity of the Races or Negro intellect."

9. [Josiah C. Nott], "Dr. Nott's Reply to 'C.' . . . ," *Southern Quarterly Review*, VIII (1845), 148–90; "Unity of the Human Race.—A letter addressed to the Editor on the Unity of the Human Race," *Southern Quarterly Review*, IX (1846), 1–57. This and the two paragraphs following are based on these articles.

10. Nott, "Unity of the Human Race.—A Letter addressed to the Editor"; [Moses Ashley] C[urtis], "The Unity of the Human Race.—Rejoinder to the Reply of Dr. Nott," *Southern Quarterly Review*, IX (1846), 372–91. This and the paragraph following are based on this rejoinder.

11. Curtis to Gray, June 10, 1846, Historic Letter File, Harvard University

Herbarium; Nott to Hammond, Aug. 12, 1845, Hammond Papers, LC; Nott to E. G. Squier, Sept. 30, 1845, Squier Papers, LC.

Nott became interested in hypnosis through his friend Dr. Robert W. Gibbes of Columbia, South Carolina. He recognized its value as an anesthetic, suggesting that it be used for the extraction of teeth, in treating neuralgia and "the nervous headaches of females." Mesmerism belonged, he asserted, to the medical profession, and he complained that it had fallen into the hands "of ignorant and dishonest charlatans" (J. C. Nott, "A Lecture on Animal Magnetism, delivered by request before the Mobile Franklin Society, 18th Feb., 1846," *Southern Journal of Medicine and Pharmacy*, I [1846], 261–89).

12. Nott to Hammond, Aug. 12, 1845, Hammond Papers, LC; Gliddon to Morton, Oct. 31, 1845; Nott to Morton, July 15, 1845, Morton Papers, LCP (quotes Morton). So far as I have been able to determine, no French edition of Nott's book appeared. Boudin, however, in his *Traité de géographie et de statistique médicales et des maladies endémiques* (2 vols.; Paris, 1857) several times cited "un médicin américain distingué, le docteur Nott, de Mobile," and listed (II, 220) the eight conclusions from Nott's "The Mulatto a Hybrid."

13. Josiah C. Nott, "Statistics of Southern Slave Population, with Especial Reference to Life Insurance," De Bow's *Review*, IV (1847), 275–89; Nott to Morton, Feb. 23, 1846, Morton Papers, LCP; Josiah C. Nott, "The Slave Question," De Bow's *Review*, IV (1847), 287–89. Somewhat irrelevantly, Nott concluded that the slave should not be insured, for "that 'Almighty Dollar' would soon silence the soft, small voice of humanity." Coming from Josiah Nott, the recommendation jars against the Southern tradition of the benevolent master. Here again Nott quoted much of "Philanthropist's" article and reprinted a portion of his own "The Mulatto a Hybrid," without making any reference to the source of his statistics, the Census of 1840.

For Lyell's opinion on Negro inferiority see Sir Charles Lyell, *A Second Visit to the United States of North America* (2 vols.; New York, 1849), II, 80.

"No Inconsiderable Antiquity"

1. Squier to parents, Jan. 1, Feb. 24, July 20, 1845, Squier Papers, New-York Historical Society. For an unfriendly account of Squier's arrival in Ohio see J[ames] E. Wharton to J[ohn] P[atterson] MacLean, in MacLean, *The Mound Builders; Being an Account of a Remarkable People. . . .* (Cincinnati, 1879), pp. 96–97.

Edwin Hamilton Davis (1811–1888) was a native of the mound country of Ohio. He graduated from Kenyon College in 1833, received the medical degree from Cincinnati Medical College in 1837 or 1838, and practiced in Chillicothe until 1850, when he became professor of materia medica and therapeutics at New York Medical College and one of the editors of the *American Medical Monthly*. His collection of objects from the mounds was the largest in the United States and in 1864 was sold to Blackmore's Museum in Salisbury, England. A second collection of duplicates went to the American Museum of Natural History. For biography see article by Walter Hough in DAB.

2. Squier to parents, Mar. 10, June 29, 1846; to father, July 9, 1846, Squier Papers, New-York Historical Society. See his correspondence with Samuel F. Haven of the American Antiquarian Society in the library of that institution. Because of shortage of funds, the Antiquarian Society and the Boston Academy of Arts and Sciences decided against financing Squier's researches (Squier to John Russell Bartlett, Sept. 21, 1846, Bartlett Papers, JCB). On Albert Gallatin's interest see especially John R. Bartlett's manuscript "Autobiography," Bartlett Papers, JCB.

3. Squier to Morton, June 10, 1846, Morton Papers, LCP; Morton to Squier, June 11, Dec. 8, 1846, Squier Papers, LC. See also Squier to Samuel F. Haven, Aug. 14, 1847, American Antiquarian Society.

4. Squier to Morton, Apr. 6, 1847, Morton Papers, LCP; Morton to Squier, Apr. 10, 1847, Squier Papers, LC.

5. Henry to Squier, Dec. 17, 1847; Sparks to Squier, Feb. 19, 1847; Marsh to Squier, Dec. 31, 1847, Squier Papers, LC. Henry was also disturbed that Davis had not been listed as co-author of the article based on their joint researches, "Observations on the Aboriginal Monuments of the Mississippi . . . ," *Transactions of the American Ethnological Society*, II (1848), 131–207.

6. E. G. Squier and E. H. Davis, *Ancient Monuments of the Mississippi Valley; comprising the results of Extensive Original Surveys and Explorations* (Washington, 1848); Emerson, "The American Scholar: An Oration Delivered before the Phi Beta Kappa Society, at Cambridge, August 31, 1847," in *Complete Works* (12 vols.; Riverside Edition, Boston, 1883–93), I, 71–97; "The Western Mound Builders," *Literary World*, III (1848), 767–68.

7. [Charles Eliot Norton], "Ancient Monuments of the Mississippi Valley . . . ," *North American Review*, LXVIII (1849), 466–96. On attribution of this review to Norton see Squier to Norton, Jan. 10, 1865, Charles Eliot Norton Papers, Houghton Library, in which Squier addresses Norton as "my old & valued friend, the first reviewer of my first book, & that too in the old N.A." They had been introduced in 1849 by their mutual friend Francis Parkman and remained close friends.

8. This and the three paragraphs following are based on *Ancient Monuments*, pp. 289, 291 (Table A), 304–6.

9. Lieber to Squier, May 26, 1848; Nott to Squier, Aug. 19, 1848, Squier Papers, LC. Lieber's son, Oscar Montgomery Lieber, was then a student of mineralogy at the University of Berlin and helped to introduce the works of Morton and Squier in Germany (Lieber to Squier, Feb. 20, 1848, Squier Papers, LC).

Francis Lieber, although he disliked slavery, was uncertain of the

Negro's equality. See his article, "Negro," in his *Encyclopaedia Americana* (1832 ed.).

10. Squier to Bartlett, Feb. 20, 1847, Bartlett Papers, JCB; Gliddon to Squier, Mar. 15, Nov. 22, 1847, Apr. 29, Aug. 18, 1848, Mar. 12, 1849, Squier Papers, LC; "Great American Work" (advertisement of *Ancient Monuments*), *Literary World*, III (1848), 658; Don C. Seitz (ed.), *Letters from Francis Parkman to E. G. Squier, with Biographical Notes and a Bibliography of E. G. Squier* (Cedar Rapids, Iowa, 1911), p. 12.

11. Nott and Gliddon, *Types of Mankind* . . . (Philadelphia, 1855), p. 651.

"Consideration for the Public Feelings"

1. Gliddon to Morton, Nov. 30, 1845, Morton Papers, LCP. On all these individuals see Pierre Larousse, *Grand dictionnaire du XIXᵉ siècle*.

2. Gliddon to Morton, Oct. 16, Oct. 31, Nov. 30, Dec. 30, 1845; Apr. 24, 1846, Morton Papers, LCP; Gliddon to Bartlett, Mar. 9, 1847, Bartlett Papers, JCB.

3. Gliddon to Morton, Nov. 30, 1845, Oct. 6, 1846, Morton Papers, LCP.

4. This and the preceding paragraph are based on Gliddon to Morton, Jan. 9, 1848, Morton Papers, LCP. See also [James Wynne], "Louis Agassiz," *Harper's Magazine*, XXV (1862), 194–201, who also said that Agassiz first gave his views on multiple creations of man while he was in Charleston.

5. This and the two paragraphs following are based on Pickering to Morton, Aug. 7, 1840, Morton Papers, APS.

   The National Institute, the United States National Museum, and the United States Botanical Garden were all outgrowths of collections made by the Exploring Expedition. See Daniel C. Haskell, *The United States Exploring Expedition, 1838–1842, and Its Publications, 1844–1874* (New York, 1942).

6. A man singularly difficult to work with, Wilkes had been subjected to court-martial proceedings on his return and retaliated by filing charges of his own. He was involved in many personal difficulties in supervising publication of the reports. On the trouble between Wilkes and Asa Gray see Jane Loring Gray to Charles G. Loring, Apr. 4, 1857, Harvard University Archives.

7. Wilkes to Morton, Nov. 6, 1846, Morton Papers, LCP.

8. Wilkes to Tappan, May 28, 1845, Benjamin Tappan Papers, LC, Vol. XX. This letter was brought to my attention by Haskell, *The United States Exploring Expedition*, p. 64. John Pickering, in a letter to Wilkes, praised the latter's *Narrative of the United States Exploring Expedition* (Philadelphia, 1845) as "a *general* Narrative," but added that "the most important part of the great national work still remains to be brought before the public"— the results of investigations in the various branches of science. European savants awaited these "with the most intense eagerness." To satisfy the European scientific community, these reports must be published "under the personal direction of their respective authors." To do otherwise, he

correctly noted, would not only be an "injustice to the authors," it would "diminish the *authority* of this national work." "Even the most learned Societies of Europe," he added, "expressly disclaim all responsibility for the Memoirs they publish, and hold the author alone responsible." So should the federal government (John Pickering to Charles Wilkes, May 20, 1845, Benjamin Tappan Papers, LC).

John Pickering (1777–1846), eminent Boston lawyer, writer on law, and linguist, was one of the founders of the American Oriental Society, incorporated in 1843, and maintained a long correspondence with Alexander von Humboldt. Both he and Charles were friends of Gliddon and Morton. John Pickering tried to establish an Egyptian museum in Boston, probably with the idea of placing Gliddon in charge (John Pickering to Morton, Apr. 21, 1845, Morton Papers, LCP).

9. Parkman to Squier, Apr. 2, 1850, in Don C. Seitz (ed.), *Letters from Francis Parkman to E. G. Squier* . . . (Cedar Rapids, Iowa, 1911), pp. 28–30; John Charles Hall, "An Analytical Synopsis of the Natural History of Man," *The Races of Man; and Their Geographical Distribution* (London, 1863), pp. vii–lxxii. For a recent appraisal of Pickering's work see Harley Harris Bartlett, "The Reports of the Wilkes Expedition, and the Work of the Specialists in Science," *Proceedings*, APS, LXXXII (1940), 601–705.

10. This and the following paragraph are based on *The Races of Man* (London, 1863), pp. 2, 311–15. I have used this edition because it is easily obtainable.

Unlike Morton, Pickering did not believe that any race had been created in America. See Pickering to Morton, Aug. 7, 1840, Morton Papers, APS; *The Races of Man*, p. 313.

11. Holmes to Morton, Nov. 27, 1849, Morton Papers, LCP.

12. Morton, "Account of a Craniological Collection with Remarks on the Classification of Some Families of the Human Race," *Transactions of the American Ethnological Society*, II (1848), 215–22. This appears in the form of a letter to John R. Bartlett, dated Dec. 1, 1846.

13. Bartlett to Morton, Dec. 21, 1846, Morton Papers, LCP.

14. Morton to Bartlett, Jan. 28, 1847, Bartlett Papers, JCB. Those who attacked the unity of the human species, with the sometime exception of Squier, generally took this view in regard to what is now considered cultural anthropology. As Nott suggested (*Two Lectures on the Natural History of the Caucasian and Negro Races* [Mobile, 1844], p. 39), philologists tended to uphold the unity of the human species.

15. This and the following paragraph are based on E. G. Squier, "American Ethnology," *American Review*, IX (1849), 385–98.

The Geographical Distribution of Race and Grace

1. Gliddon to Morton, Jan. 9, 1848, Morton Papers, LCP.

2. L[ouis] Agassiz, *Notice sur la géographie des animaux* (Neuchâtel, 1845). See also Marcou, *Life, Letters, and Works of Louis Agassiz* (2 vols.; New

York, 1896), I, 247. On the whole subject of Agassiz's anthropological views see Edward Lurie, "Louis Agassiz and the Races of Man," *Isis*, XLV (1954), 227–42, and Lurie's forthcoming biography of Agassiz, to be published by the University of Chicago Press in 1960.

3. Agassiz to Prince of Canino, Apr., 1843, Jan. 7, 1845, Elizabeth Cary Agassiz, *Louis Agassiz: His Life and Correspondence* (2 vols.; Boston, 1886), I, 363, 379; Agassiz to his mother (Rose Mayor Agassiz), Dec. 2, 1846, Agassiz Papers, Houghton Library. Part of Agassiz's letter to his mother is included in Louis Agassiz, II, 409–29. This and the two paragraphs following are based on this letter, except where otherwise noted.

4. Morton to Samuel S. Haldeman, Oct. 26, 1846, Joseph Leidy Papers, ANSP; Agassiz to [Henri] Milne-Edwards, May, 1847, in E. C. Agassiz, *Louis Agassiz*, II, 434–42; Marcou, *Life, Letters, and Works*, II, 28–29 (see also I, 284–85).

5. Marcou, *Life, Letters, and Works*, I, 248; Torrey to Gray, Jan. 11, 1847, Historic Letter File, Harvard University Herbarium (I am indebted to Mr. Edward Lurie for calling this letter to my attention); Gray to Torrey, Jan. 24, 1847, typescript in Asa Gray Letters, Harvard University Herbarium. Agassiz lectured before the College of Physicians and Surgeons in New York in October and November, 1847.

For a similar reaction on the part of an Englishman who arrived in Charleston about 1830 see John P. Barratt, M.D., "An Address Delivered before the South Carolina Medical Association, on their Second Anniversary, February, 1850," *Minutes of the Proceedings of the South-Carolina Medical Association, at its Annual Meetings, February, 1849–50, together with . . . the Anniversary Oration . . .* (Charleston, 1850).

6. Marcou, *Life, Letters, and Works*, I, 292–93.

7. L[ouis] A[gassiz], "Geographical Distribution of Animals," *Christian Examiner*, XLVIII (1850), 181–204. This and the two paragraphs following are based on this article.

8. Louis Agassiz, "The Diversity of Origin of Human Races," *Christian Examiner*, XLIX (1850), 110–45 (and see Agassiz to Adam Sedgwick, June, 1845, in E. C. Agassiz, *Louis Agassiz*, I, 387–95). This and the five paragraphs following are based on this article.

9. L[ouis] A[gassiz], "Contemplations of God in the Kosmos," *Christian Examiner*, L (1851), 1–17.

10. "The Diversity of Origin of Human Races."

11. Nott to Squier, May 4, 1850, Squier Papers, LC.

12. N[athan] L[angdon] F[rothingham], "Men before Adam," *Christian Examiner*, L (1851), 79–96. This and the paragraph following are based on this article. For biography of Frothingham see sketch by George Harvey Genzmer, DAB.

13. Moncure D. Conway, *Autobiography, Memories and Experiences of Moncure Daniel Conway* (2 vols.; New York, 1904), I, 87–90. This and the three paragraphs following are based on this work.

14. For a Southern Presbyterian's appreciation of the theological implications of the theory of diversity see William T. Hamilton, *The 'Friend of Moses'; or, A Defense of the Pentateuch as the Production of Moses and an Inspired Document, against the Objections of Modern Skepticism* (New York, 1852), pp. 453–54.

"Whoever Heard of a Cross-Eyed Race?"

1. Silliman, Jr., to Morton, Nov. 11, 1846, Morton Papers, LCP; S. G. Morton, "Hybridity in Animals, considered in reference to the question of the Unity of the Human Species," *American Journal of Science*, 2d ser., III (1847), 39–50, 203–12 (also published separately: New Haven, 1847). The presentation of Morton's thoughts in this and the six paragraphs following is based on this article.

2. For a brief survey of the history of thought on hybridization and a good discussion of recent findings, see G. Ledyard Stebbins, "The Role of Hybridization in Evolution," *Proceedings*, APS, CIII (1959), 231–51.

3. For an authoritative statement of authenticated crosses between the species of mammals, see Annie P. Gray, *Mammalian Hybrids: A Check-List with Bibliography* (Commonwealth Bureau of Animal Breeding and Genetics, Technical Communication No. 10 [Edinburgh, Farnham Royal, Bucks, England, 1954]); on flora, see Stebbins, "The Role of Hybridization in Evolution."

4. This sharp reference to slavery is, strangely, the only hint I have found of Morton's awareness of contemporary social or political problems.

5. For a brief but moving account of Linnaeus's growing bewilderment, see Loren Eiseley, *Darwin's Century: Evolution and the Men Who Discovered It* (Garden City, N.Y., 1958), pp. 24–26. The "Historical Sketch" appeared first in the sixth edition of *The Origin of Species* (London, 1866). On Prichard's relation to evolution, see Edward B. Poulton, "A Remarkable Anticipation of Modern Views on Evolution," in his *Essays on Evolution: 1889–1907* (Oxford, 1908), pp. 173–92; Philip G. Fothergill, *Historical Aspects of Organic Evolution* (London, 1952), pp. 83–86; C. D. Darlington, "The Origin of Darwinism," *Scientific American*, CC May, 1959), 60–66. On Blyth, see Loren C. Eiseley, "Charles Darwin, Edward Blyth, and the Theory of Natural Selection," *Proceedings*, APS, CIII (1959), 94–158. S[amuel] S. Haldeman, "Enumeration of the Recent Freshwater Mollusca Which Are Common to North America and Europe; with Observations on Species and Their Distribution," *Journal of the Boston Society of Natural History*, IV (1844), 468–84. William Herbert, *Amaryllidaceae* (London, 1837), p. 19. Darwin quotes this passage from Herbert in his "Historical Sketch."

6. For two among many expressions of Darwin's doubt of the reliability of interfertility as a species criterion, see Charles Darwin, *The Foundations of the Origin of Species: Two Essays Written in 1842 and 1844,* ed. Francis Darwin (Cambridge, 1909); *The Origin of Species* (6th ed.; London,

1872), chap. ix. For a recent criticism see Ernst Mayr, "Isolation as an Evolutionary Factor," *Proceedings*, APS, CIII (1959), 221–30. Both Darwin and Morton mistakenly concluded that more variations appeared in domesticity than in the feral state. Morton attributed them to hybridization only. Darwin saw them both as hybrids and as inexplicable variations. Thus both were especially impressed by the great number of breeds of dogs and were inclined to ascribe them to descent from and crossing of separate species (Darwin, *Foundations*, pp. 10 n., 11–12, 71–74). For recent opinion, see Arne Müntzing, "Darwin's Views on Variation under Domestication in the Light of Present-Day Knowledge," *Proceedings*, APS, CIII (1959), 190–220.

7. Samuel George Morton, "Observations on the Size of the Brain in various races and Families of Man," *Proceedings*, ANSP, IV (1849), 221–24; V (1850), 1–3, 4, 30–32, 33. Quotations in this and the paragraph following are from this work.

8. Nott to Squier, Sept. 7, 30, 1848, Squier Papers, LC. Wilhelm Martin Leberecht de Wette (1780–1849), German theologian and one of the founders of biblical criticism. Andrews Norton (1786–1853), American biblical scholar, one of the earliest critical students of biblical literature in America. David Friedrich Strauss (1808–74), German theologian and man of letters, whose critical *Leben Jesu* (1835) produced a sensation in the religious community.

9. Josiah C. Nott, *Two Lectures on the Connection between the Biblical and Physical History of Man. Delivered by Invitation, from the Chair of Political Economy, Etc., of the Louisiana University, in December, 1848* (New York, 1849), pp. 7, 14, 24–31, 57, 86. This and the three paragraphs following are based on this work.

10. Morton to Nott, Jan. 29, 1850, as quoted in Henry S. Patterson, "Memoir of the Life and Scientific Labors of Samuel George Morton," in J. C. Nott and George R. Gliddon, *Types of Mankind . . .* (Philadelphia, 1854), pp. xvii–lvii.

"The Great Mooted Question"

1. Nott to Squier, Sept. 7, 1848, Feb. 14, Aug. 6, 1849, Squier Papers, LC. The publisher Squier found was Bartlett and Welford, which consisted of John R. Bartlett, corresponding secretary of the Ethnological Society, and Charles Welford, a member.

2. Nott to Morton, Sept. 1, 1849, Morton Papers, LCP; Nott to Squier, Aug. 6, 1849, Squier Papers, LC.

3. J. H. Easterby, *A History of the College of Charleston, Founded 1770* ([Charleston, S.C.], 1935), p. 110.

4. [Catherine L. Bachman], *John Bachman . . . , the Pastor of St. John's Lutheran Church, Charleston* (Charleston, 1888), p. 17; Jennie Haskell Rose, "John Bachman at Home," unpublished manuscript in possession of the Charleston Museum; Alexander Sprunt, Jr., "Audubon and Bachman—

Naturalist and Clergyman," *Audubon Magazine,* LIII (1951), 76–83 ff.; Bachman to Audubon, Nov. 29, 1843, Bachman Papers, Charleston Museum; Samuel Gaillard Stoney (ed.), "Memoirs of Frederick Adolphus Porcher," *South Carolina Historical and Genealogical Magazine,* XLIV (1943), 65–80, 135–47, 212–19, and continued in quarterly instalments through XLVIII (1947), 20–25.

For biographical information see [Bachman], *John Bachman;* John F. Ficken, *A Sketch of the Life and Labors of John Bachman . . .* (Charleston, 1924); Donald C. Peattie, "John Bachman," DAB.

5. Bachman to J. J. Audubon, Dec. 7, 1841, Bachman Papers, Charleston Museum. Examples of Bachman's defenses of Audubon are: John Bachman, "Retrospective Criticism. Remarks in defense of the Author of the Birds of America," *Loudon's Magazine of Natural History,* VII (1834), 164–75; "An Account of some experiments made on the habits of the Vultures inhabiting Carolina . . . ," *Journal of the Boston Society of Natural History,* I (1834), 15–31. And see Francis H. Herrick, *Audubon the Naturalist: A History of His Life and Time* (2 vols.; Philadelphia, 1917), II, 54, 81–84.

6. Bachman to Morton, Oct. 15, 1849, Morton Papers, LCP.

7. Thomas Smyth, *The Unity of the Human Race Proved to be the Doctrine of Scripture, Reason and Science . . .* (1850), *Complete Works of Rev. Thomas Smyth . . .* , ed. J. W. Flinn (8 vols.; Columbia, S.C., 1910), VIII, 31. For a description of the club and a list of its members see "Memoirs of Frederick Adolphus Porcher." Members of the club who defended unity were much in the minority. Drs. D. J. Cain and F. P. Porcher, editors of the *Charleston Medical Journal,* reported to Morton that opinion "appears to be pretty well divided in this City—most if not very nearly all of the *Medical men* leaning towards the side occupied by Mr. Agassiz and yourself" (Cain and Porcher to Morton, July 10, 1850, Morton Papers, LCP). Nott mentioned to Morton that the medical men in Charleston "are all with us [specifically Dickson, Holbrook, and Eli Geddings] but I presume are afraid of injuring their [Charleston Medical] school" (Nott to Morton, May 4, 1850, Morton Papers, LCP).

8. Bachman to Richard Harlan, June 29, 1835, Gilbert Collection of Manuscript Letters, I, 67, CPP; John Bachman, "A Reply to the Letter of Samuel George Morton, M.D., on the question of Hybridity in Animals considered in reference to the Unity of the Human Species," *Charleston Medical Journal,* V (1850), 466–508; Bachman to Morton, Mar. 17, 1837, Morton Papers, APS; Bachman to Morton, Oct. 15, 1849, Morton Papers, LCP.

9. Published in Charleston, S.C. In his preface, Bachman stated that the work was written in November, 1849. Nott had learned of the coming publication of Bachman's book and urged Morton to reply, for "there is evidently a strong attempt to kill you off, & if the facts are not very fully met, the progress of truth will be much retarded" (Nott to Morton, Mar. 1, 1850, Morton Papers, LCP). In presenting Bachman's arguments for the unity of man, I have relied largely on his book, where they are presented with

a fulness which contrasts to the fragmentary nature of the articles written in reply to Morton's objections.

10. "To Readers, Correspondents, &c.," *Charleston Medical Journal*, V (1850), 274; Bachman, "Reply to the Letter of Samuel George Morton. . . ."

11. J[ohn] B[achman], "Correspondence of the Courier," *Charleston Courier*, May 28, 1850. See also Bachman to Morton, Oct. 15, 1849, Morton Papers, LCP.

12. Bachman, "An Investigation of the Cases of Hybridity in Animals on Record, considered in reference to the Unity of the Human Species," *Charleston Medical Journal*, V (1850), 168–97; *Doctrine of the Unity*, pp. 14–15, 80–81.

13. Bachman, "An Investigation of the Cases of Hybridity." Generally speaking, a viable hybrid is uncommon, although crosses do occur between some species. Between the dog and the wolf reciprocal crosses are possible and the hybrid of either sex is viable and fertile. Sometimes structural differences prevent hybridization: "The conception rate of the asses served by stallions is low, probably because the penis of the horse is shorter than that of the ass." That reproductive isolation is in some measure due to repugnance to intermixture is evident from the fact that though hybrids are rare in the feral state, they are less rare in the laboratory. Often the hybrid is, as Bachman noted, abnormal to the extent that it is unable to reproduce; spermatozoa are not formed in the mule, for example (Annie P. Gray, *Mammalian Hybrids: A Check-List with Bibliography* [Commonwealth Bureau of Animal Breeding and Genetics, Technical Communication No. 10 (Edinburgh, Farnham Royal, Bucks, England, 1954)], pp. 21, 46). See also chap. ix, "Hybrid Sterility," in Theodosius Dobzhansky, *Genetics and the Origin of Species* (New York, 1941).

14. Bachman, *Doctrine of the Unity*, p. 154; "Second Letter to Samuel G. Morton . . . , on the Question of Hybridity in Animals, considered in reference to the Unity of the Human Species," *Charleston Medical Journal*, V (1850), 621–60.

15. Bachman, *Doctrine of the Unity*, pp. 7, 10–11, 13, 305–6. For Darwin's observations see Charles Darwin, *Journal of Researches into the Natural History and Geology of the Countries Visited during the Voyage of H.M.S. Beagle Round the World* (London, 1840; New York, 1846), I, 185–86.

16. Barratt, "An Address Delivered before the South Carolina Medical Association"; Barratt to Morton, Sept. 24, 1849, Morton Papers, LCP (see also Barratt to Morton, Sept. 2, 1846, Morton Papers, LCP); Bachman, "Second Letter to Samuel George Morton"; *Doctrine of the Unity*, pp. 184–85. Forgetting his objections to Lamarckism, Bachman remarked that their sight "gradually became extinguished, in the darkness of the cavern from want of use." He failed to apply his theory of variation here, failed to note that a blind fish simply appeared and bequeathed its peculiar character. For twentieth-century theories see, for example, M. T. Hents, "Regressive Evo-

lution in Cave Animals," *Evolution* (Symposia of the Society for Experimental Biology, Vol. VIII [Cambridge, 1953]), pp. 290–309.

17. This and the paragraph following are based on Bachman, *Doctrine of the Unity*, pp. 179, 185–86, 268.

18. Bachman, "An Investigation of the Cases of Hybridity."

19. This and the paragraph following are based on Bachman, *Doctrine of the Unity*, pp. 36, 276, 286.

20. Others recognized a connection between wide distribution and frequent variation. See, for example, Alexander Humboldt, *Cosmos* (6th ed.; 2 vols.; London, 1849), I, 352. For twentieth-century opinion see Dobzhansky, *Genetics and the Origin of Species*, p. 62; Arne Müntzing, "Darwin's Views on Variation under Domestication in the Light of Present-Day Knowledge," *Proceedings*, APS, CIII (1959), 190–220.

21. See William Charles Wells, *Two Essays: One upon Single Vision with Two Eyes; the other on Dew. A Letter to the Right Hon. Lloyd, Lord Kenyon, and, An Account of a Female of the White Race of Mankind, Part of Whose Skin Resembles that of a Negro; with Some Observations on the Causes of the Differences in Colour and Form Between the White and Negro Races of Men . . . with a Memoir of His Life . . .* (London, 1818).

22. This and the paragraph following are based on Bachman, *Doctrine of the Unity*, pp. 29–34, 36, 42–46, 117–18, 127, 136, 138, 146, 149, 199.

23. Bachman failed to note, in the framework of his theory, that viable and fertile hybrids would be likely *not* to survive because they would be less well adapted to their environment than the parent stocks. For a discussion of hybridization among birds and its effect on survival see David Lack, *Darwin's Finches* (Cambridge, 1947), pp. 95–96, 100.

24. Bachman, *Doctrine of the Unity*, pp. 127, 136, 146; "Second Letter to Samuel George Morton." For a like objection by another defender of the unity of man see James L. Cabell, *The Testimony of Modern Science to the Unity of Mankind . . .* (New York, 1859), pp. 20–24. Cabell was professor of anatomy and physiology at the University of Virginia.

In 1860 Agassiz told the American Academy of Arts and Sciences that he had "discarded the sterility or fertility of crosses from the tests of the validity of species" ([Professor Agassiz's opinion that what are called varieties by naturalists do not in reality exist as such], *Proceedings of the American Academy of Arts and Sciences*, V [1860–62], 72).

25. This and the paragraph following are based on Bachman, *Doctrine of the Unity*, pp. 8, 158, 209. Cabell, like Bachman, did not object to theories of Negro inferiority; he objected merely to the theory of multiple creations.

"The Parson-Skinning Goes on Bravely"

1. Morton, "Letter to the Rev. John Bachman . . . , on the question of Hybridity in Animals considered in reference to the Unity of the Human Species," *Charleston Medical Journal*, V (1850), 328–44.

2. Morton, "Additional Observations on Hybridity in Animals, and on some

collateral subjects; being a Reply to the Objections of the Rev. John Bachman . . . ," *Charleston Medical Journal,* V (1850), 755–805.

3. Morton to Squier, Dec. 23, 1848, Squier Papers, LC. Many of the replies from army surgeons are in the Morton Papers, LCP.

4. Morton, "Letter to the Rev. John Bachman." Morton actually listed four degrees of hybridity in his article. The third was "That in which animals of unquestionably distinct species, unite and produce a progeny that is prolific *inter se.*" Citing the dog and wolf, fox and jackal as examples, he did not list man in this group of "unquestionably distinct species," but in a paper read before the Academy of Natural Sciences in September, 1850, he reduced the number of degrees of hybridization to three and implied that man belonged to the third group, as I have given it here ([Some remarks on the value of the word *species* in zoology], *Proceedings,* ANSP, V [1850], 81–82, 84). For recent opinion see Annie P. Gray, *Mammalian Hybrids: A Check-List with Bibliography* (Commonwealth Bureau of Animal Breeding and Genetics, Technical Communication No. 10 [Edinburgh, Farnham Royal, Bucks, England, 1954]).

By 1844 Darwin had come to the conclusion that there were degrees of hybridization. ". . . I think we must admit that there exists a perfect gradation in fertility between species which when crossed are quite fertile (as in Rhododendron, Calceolaria, &c.), and indeed in an extraordinary degree fertile (as in Crinum), and those species which never produce offspring, but which by certain effects (as in the exsertion of the pollen-tube) evince their alliance. Hence, I conceive, we must give up sterility, although undoubtedly in a lesser or greater degree of very frequent occurrence, as an unfailing mark by which *species* can be distinguished from *races, i.e.* from those forms which have descended from a common stock" (Charles Darwin, *The Foundations of the Origin of Species: Two Essays Written in 1842 and 1844,* ed. Francis Darwin [Cambridge, 1909], p. 99).

5. Morton, "Letter to the Rev. John Bachman"; "Additional Observations." For Lyell's opinion as to whether man, too, was separately created see Sir Charles Lyell, *Principles of Geology . . .* (9th ed.; New York, 1853), pp. 630, 660.

6. [Samuel G.] Morton, [Observations on the antiquity of some races of dogs], *Proceedings,* ANSP, V (1850), 85–89. For recent opinion on the dog question, see the fallible but interesting work by Konrad Lorenz, *Man Meets Dog* (Boston, 1955).

7. Morton, "Notes on Hybridity, designed as a supplement to the memoir on that subject in the last number of this Journal," *Charleston Medical Journal,* VI (1851), 145–52; "Additional Observations" (Morton had given this definition at the September 10 meeting of the Academy [Some remarks on the value of the word *species* in zoology]); Agassiz to Morton, Dec. 21, 1850, John Torrey Papers, ANSP.

8. Morton, "Additional Observations"; "Notes on Hybridity, designed as a Supplement"; [Some remarks on the infrequency of mixed offspring be-

tween the European and Australian races], *Proceedings,* ANSP, V (1851), 173–75 (appears in manuscript in Morton Papers, APS).

9. Morton, "Notes on Hybridity in Animals, and on some collateral subjects . . . Being a Third Letter to the Editors of the Charleston Medical Journal and Review," *Charleston Medical Journal,* VI (1851), 373–83.

10. Morton, "Notes on Hybridity, designed as a Supplement"; "Letter to the Rev. John Bachman"; "Additional Observations."

11. Nott to Morton, May 4, 27, 1850, Apr. 6, 1851; Gibbes to Morton, June 17, 1850, Morton Papers, LCP; Gliddon to Squier, Nov. 11, 1850, Squier Papers, LC; *Charleston Courier,* May 28, 1850; Bachman, "Correspondence of the Courier." Advice to Morton in the controversy came from Nott (to Morton, May 4, July 25, 1850, Morton Papers, LCP) and even from the editors of the *Charleston Medical Journal,* who were not above offering various helpful hints (Cain and Porcher to Morton, Dec. 28, 1850, Morton Papers, LCP).

12. Nott to L. R. Gibbes, Nov. 21, 1850, L. R. Gibbes Papers, LC; R. W. Gibbes to Morton, Apr. 10, 1850, Morton Papers, LCP; "The Doctrine of the Unity of the Human Race . . . ," *American Journal of Science,* 2d ser., XI (1851), 302; "The Doctrine of the Unity of the Human Race . . . ," *Southern Quarterly Review,* XVII (1850), 250.

13. Morton to Squier, Apr. 30, 1851, Squier Papers, LC; Morton to Lewis W. [*sic*] Gibbes, Jan. 31, 1851, L. R. Gibbes Papers, LC. Morton's article for Schoolcraft appeared as "Physical Type of the American Indians," in Henry R. Schoolcraft, *Information Respecting the History, Condition and Prospects of the Indian Tribes of the United States . . .* (Philadelphia, 1852), Part II, pp. 315–31. Morton's article did not appear in Baird's *Encyclopaedia* (6 vols.; New York, 1852–53). On Morton's proposed "Elements of Ethnography" see Nott to Morton, July 25, 1850, Morton Papers, LCP, and Henry S. Patterson, "Memoir of the Life and Scientific Labors of Samuel George Morton," in J. C. Nott and George R. Gliddon, *Types of Mankind . . .* (Philadelphia, 1854), pp. xvii–lvii.

14. "Death of Dr. Samuel George Morton," *New York Daily Tribune,* May 20, 1851; Brantz Mayer to Squier, June 20, 1851; Nott to Squier, May 24, 1851, Squier Papers, LC. Quotations from the religious paper are from an unidentified clipping in Morton Papers, APS.

15. R[obert] W. G[ibbes], "Death of Samuel George Morton, M.D.," *Charleston Medical Journal,* VI (1851), 594–98.

"A Perfect Hair"

1. Quirk Ogee, LL.C. [James Ewing Cooley], *Extracts from Humbugiana; or, The World's Convention. A Satire. In Four Parts* ("Gotham: Published by Gas, Green & Ginger, Shinglesign Square. XVIII.XLVII [i.e., 1847]"). The book was dedicated to "George Rigamarole Gliddon."

2. Gliddon, "Proposal" (Boston, 1850), a three-page prospectus for the Boston

lectures; "Types of Mankind," *Presbyterian Magazine,* IV (1854), 285–89; Gliddon, "Letter from Mr. Gliddon about the Papyrus found on the Boston Mummy," Boston *Daily Evening Transcript,* Aug. 22, 1850. One writer suggested that the error probably originated at the mummifying establishment, where care was not always taken to put female bodies in female coffins, and added, "The error of Mr. Gliddon, which caused so much amusement in Boston . . . should [not] at all detract from his well deserved reputation as an Egyptian scholar" (William C. Prime, *Boat Life in Egypt and Nubia* [New York, 1857], p. 265).

3. A[lexander] D. Bache, "Remarks of Prof. A. D. Bache, President of the Association, upon the Meeting of the American Association at Charleston, S.C., March, 1850," *Proceedings,* AAAS, III (1850), 158–65. The custom was to give local scientists as much publicity as possible. Thus most of the prominent Southern scientists who were not already members were elected at this meeting.

4. *Proceedings,* AAAS, III (1850), 34–38.

5. This and the two paragraphs following are based on Nott, "An Examination of the Physical History of the Jews, in its bearings on the Question of the Unity of the Races," *Proceedings,* AAAS, III (1850), 98–106. William Gilmore Simms, editor of the *Southern Quarterly Review,* printed Nott's paper —N.S., I (1850), 426–51—then, rejecting another article on the subject of the unity of man by John Young Bassett (Sir William Osler's "Alabama Student"), explained, "It will be impossible to suffer the one subject to absorb too large a proportion of our pages" (Simms to John Young Bassett, June 1, 1850, John Y. Bassett Papers, Southern Historical Collection, University of North Carolina Library).

6. The "scientific correspondent at the North" was probably Morton, for Nott had written to ask whether he knew "any thing of the Pedigree of President Roberts of Liberia . . . . is he *Hybrid* or not?" (Nott to Morton, Sept. 27, 1849, Morton Papers, LCP).

7. Agassiz, [A correction of some mis-statements], *Proceedings,* AAAS, III (1850), 106–7; and see [Edwin P. Whipple], "Recollections of Agassiz," *Harper's,* LIX (1879), 97–110.

8. P. A. Browne, "A Microscopic Examination and description of some of the Piles of the head of Albinos," *Proceedings,* AAAS, III (1850), 108–14.

9. Browne to Childs & Peterson, May 28, 1858, Autograph Collection of the Historical Society of Pennsylvania; Browne, "An Address, Intended to Promote a Geological and Mineralogical Survey of Pennsylvania . . ." (Philadelphia, 1826); Ellis P. Oberholtzer, *Philadelphia: A History of the City and Its People, a Record of 225 Years* (4 vols.; Philadelphia, [1912]), II, 19, 198–99; Harold D. Eberlein and Cortlandt Van Dyke Hubbard, "The American 'Vauxhall' of the Federal Era," *Pennsylvania Magazine of History and Biography,* LXVIII (1944), 150–74; J. Thomas Scharf and Thompson Westcott, *History of Philadelphia, 1609–1884* (3 vols.; Philadelphia, 1884), I, 616, 644; Browne, *An Attempt to Discover some of the Laws which Gov-*

ern Animal Torpidity and Hibernation . . . (Philadelphia, 1847), title page; Samuel Breck, "A Collection of Puns and Witticisms of Judge Richard Peters (Copied from the manuscript of Samuel Breck)," *Pennsylvania Magazine of History and Biography*, XXV (1901), 366–69.

10. Browne to Haldeman, Jan. 4, 1849, Haldeman Papers, ANSP; Browne and Montroville W. Dickeson, *Trichographia Mammalium; or, Descriptions and Drawings of the Hair of the Mammalia* (Philadelphia, 1848); Browne, *The Classification of Mankind, by the Hair and Wool of their Heads, with an Answer to Dr. Prichard's Assertion, that 'The Covering of the Head of the Negro is Hair, . . . and Not Wool'* . . . (Philadelphia, 1850), pp. 1, 8, 20; *Proceedings* ANSP, V (1851), 145–46.

11. Browne, *The Classification of Mankind*, p. 13; Browne, "Examination of the Hair of the Head of a mummy, unrolled in Philadelphia in Jan., 1851," *Charleston Medical Journal*, VI (1851), 371–72; Browne, "Examination and Description of the Hair of the Head of the North American Indians, and Its Comparison with that of Other Varieties of Men," in Schoolcraft, *Information Respecting the History . . . of the Indian Tribes* . . . (5 vols.; Philadelphia, 1851–55), Part III, pp. 375–93.

    One modern pathologist considers the properties of the Negro's hair "even more characteristic of the Negro than is the color of the skin, because other races may be quite as dark (East Indians), but no other than this race or intermixtures with it has the typical woolly or kinky hair as a stable feature." But woolly hair does not always appear concomitantly with skin color and may occur "congenitally in people identified as white." The hair of human races differs in cross-section, length, weight, and chemistry, although evidently not in the number of hair-scales. On this subject see Julian Herman Lewis, *The Biology of the Negro* (Chicago, 1942), pp. 61–68.

12. Browne, *The Classification of Mankind, by the Hair and Wool of their Heads, with the Nomenclature of Human Hybrids* (Philadelphia, 1852). The German anatomist, Carl Vogt, a strong believer in the diversity of the human species, was later to cite such terms as these as evidence of the widespread acceptance of hybridization and specific distinction among the human races (Vogt, *Lectures on Man: His Place in Creation, and in the History of the Earth* [London, 1864], p. 437).

13. "The Hair Theory of Peter A. Brown [*sic*]," New York *Evening Post*, May 4, 1854. See also "The Hair and Wool of the Different Species of Man," *United States Magazine and Democratic Review*, N.S., XXVII (1850), 451–56; "Physical Character of the Negro," De Bow's *Review*, IX (1850), 231.

14. Browne, *The Classification of Mankind . . . with an Answer to Dr. Prichard's Assertion*, p. 8.

15. Browne, "Examination and Description"; *The Classification of Mankind . . . with the Nomenclature of Human Hybrids;* Browne to Haldeman, Oct. 8, 1851, Haldeman Papers, ANSP.

16. Browne to Haldeman, May 22, 1851, Haldeman Papers, ANSP; Browne to Morton, Mar. 14, 1850, Morton Papers, LCP. For Morton and Nott's limited

use of Browne's findings see Morton, "Notes on Hybridity, designed as a further Supplement . . . ," *Charleston Medical Journal,* VI (1851), 301–8, and Nott, "A Summary of the Latest Scientific Facts Bearing upon the Question of Unity or Plurality of Species," in H[enry] Hotz (trans.), *The Moral and Intellectual Diversity of Races. . . . From the French of Count A. de Gobineau* (Philadelphia, 1856), 463–512.

In 1854 Robert W. Gibbes was called as an expert witness in a trial in which a slave girl, "suspicioned by some parties to be an Indian," brought suit for her freedom. Gibbes stated that Negro hair was wool, could be felted, and was "eccentrically elliptical" (W[illiam] S[tump] Forwood, "The Negro—a Distinct Species," *Medical and Surgical Reporter,* X [1857], 225–34).

17. Gibbes to Morton, Mar. 31, 1850 (and see Gibbes to B. L. C. Wailes, Apr. 12, 1850, Benjamin Leonard Covington Wailes Papers, Duke University Library); Nott to Morton, May 4, 1850, Morton Papers, LCP. Nott had heard of the proposed book from Robert Gibbes. Agassiz never published such a work.

18. Joseph Le Conte, *The Autobiography of Joseph Le Conte,* ed. William D. Armes (New York, 1903), p. 140; Bache to L. R. Gibbes, May 30, 1850, L. R. Gibbes Papers, LC. On the clerical attack on Agassiz see John Torrey to Asa Gray, Aug. 27–30, 1850; John Carey to Gray, Aug. 26, 1850, Historic Letter File, Harvard University Herbarium. Francis Parkman wrote to Squier about Agassiz: "The Orthodox are at him . . . , raising a great outcry about impiety. . . . If they could, they would serve him as the Church served Galileo" (Parkman to Squier, Apr. 2, 1850, in *Letters from Francis Parkman to E. G. Squier, with Biographical Notes and a Bibliography of E. G. Squier,* ed. Don C. Seitz (Cedar Rapids, Iowa, 1911), pp. 38–40.

Kicking Up a "Dam[d] Fuss Generally"

1. Nott to Squier, Mar. 26, 1851, Squier Papers, LC.
2. Simms to Henry Rowe Schoolcraft, Mar. 8, [1851], in *Letters of William Gilmore Simms,* ed. Mary C. Oliphant Simms, Alfred T. Odell, and T. C. Duncan Eaves (5 vols.; Columbia, S.C., 1952–55), III, 101–2; [J. D. B. De Bow], "Physical Character of the Negro," *De Bow's Review,* IX (1850), 231; [De Bow], "Ethnological Researches—Is the African and Caucasian of Common Origin?" *ibid.,* pp. 243–45.
3. J. C. Nott, "Ancient and Scripture Chronology," *Southern Quarterly Review,* N.S., II (1850), 385–426. This was also published separately as *Chronology, Ancient and Scriptural . . .* (Charleston, 1850).
4. Lyell, *Principles of Geology* (9th ed.; New York, 1853), p. 660. Neanderthal Man was uncovered in 1856 but its significance was not generally accepted until after publication of the *Origin of Species* in 1859. On the whole question of contemporary attitudes toward chronology see the forthcoming work by Francis C. Haber, *Revolution in the Concept of Historical Time: A Study in the Relationship between Biblical Chronology and the*

Rise of Modern Science, to be published by the Johns Hopkins Press in 1960.

5. J. C. N[ott], "Diversity of the Human Race," De Bow's *Review*, X (1851), 113–32.

6. Mobile, 1850; reprinted as "Nature and Destiny of the Negro," De Bow's *Review*, X (1851), 329–32. I have been unable to find a copy of the original edition and have relied on De Bow's reprint.

7. Gliddon to John R. Bartlett, Nov. 21, 1853, Bartlett Papers, JCB; Nott to Squier, Sept. 26, 1852, Squier Papers, LC; William T. Hamilton, *The 'Friend of Moses'; or, A Defence of the Pentateuch as the Production of Moses and an Inspired Document, against the Objections of Modern Skepticism* (New York, 1852), pp. 453–54. In 1825, when he was a minister in New Jersey, Hamilton (1798–1884) had preached an antislavery sermon for the American Colonization Society (*A Word for the African* ... [Newark, 1825]), but in Alabama in 1844 he took as his subject *The Duties of Masters and Slaves respectively: or, Domestic Servitude as Sanctioned by the Bible* ... (Mobile, 1845). Yet in *The 'Friend of Moses*,' Hamilton came as near as any of the defenders of the unity of man to asserting the equality of the Negro. He had known black men capable of delivering "appropriate" and "touching" addresses and of conducting arguments "with great tact and ability" and was unable to find "in comparison with the white man, any essential inferiority of intellect native to the negro." He consistently argued not only for the unity, but also for the equality of man. But he did not state the fatal conclusion that slavery therefore must be abolished. He did not mention slavery in this work (*ibid.*, p. 471).

8. This and the paragraph following are based on J. C. Nott, "Geographical Distribution of Animals and the Races of Man," *New Orleans Medical and Surgical Journal*, IX (1853), 727–46. See also [J. C.] N[ott], "Aboriginal Races of America," *Southern Quarterly Review*, N.S., VIII (1853), 59–92.

9. For one of Cartwright's many articles in defense of slavery, written in his usual strain of brutal facetiousness, see his widely reprinted "Report on the Diseases and Physical Peculiarities of the Negro Race ...," *New Orleans Medical and Surgical Journal*, VII (1851), 691–715.

The Watchman's Response

1. Gliddon to Squier, Oct. 23, 1851; Nott to Squier, Mar. 26, 1851, Squier Papers, LC.

2. Nott to Squier, Mar. 26, 1851, Squier Papers, LC.

3. Nott to Squier, Sept. 26, 1852, Squier Papers, LC.

4. Nott and Gliddon, *Types of Mankind* ... (Philadelphia, 1855), pp. 81, 503.

5. Luke Burke, editor of the positivistic *London Ethnological Journal* and friend of Nott and Gliddon, admitted that *Types of Mankind* was not "a classic production in science," that controversy was "its end and aim," but, he said, "controversy is the natural position of Ethnology at the present moment, especially in the United States. 'Types of Mankind' was written

for the times, for the very day, for the American public . . ." (Burke, "Strictures on Dr. Bachman's paper entitled 'An Examination of Prof. Agassiz's Sketch of the Natural Provinces of the Animal World . . .' [Communicated by Dr. J. C. Nott, of Mobile]," *Charleston Medical Journal*, XI [1856], 433–58).

6. Gliddon to John R. Bartlett, Nov. 21, 1853, Bartlett Papers, JCB; Bachman, "Types of Mankind. . . ," *Charleston Medical Journal*, IX (1854), 627–59; Gliddon to Squier, Apr. 6, 9, 1854, Squier Papers, LC.

7. [E. G. Squier], "Notices of New Books. Science of Man and Nations, Types of Mankind," *New York Herald*, Apr. 23, 1854.

8. Gliddon, who had earlier suggested that Squier "think over what reviewers you can influence," was elated at Squier's review and thought him "by G—d, the pluckiest man I ever knew." Nott, equally pleased, thought Squier's review "altogether the best thing I have ever seen from your pen" (Gliddon to Squier, Mar. 7, Apr. 24, 1854; Nott to Squier, Apr. 30, 1854, Squier Papers, LC).

9. "Types of Mankind," *Presbyterian Magazine*, IV (1854), 284–89. See "Progress of Infidelity," *Daily Richmond Enquirer*, Apr. 29, 1854, in which the editor, having dutifully expressed his disapproval of *Types of Mankind*, warned the defenders of Christianity that if "they seek shelter behind the dogmas of bigotry, and by discouraging freedom of inquiry, betray an apprehension of the revelations of science, they will suffer as much by their pusillanimity, as by a positive repulse."

10. "Is Man One or Many?" *Putnam's Monthly*, IV (1854), 1–14. This and the following paragraph are based on this review.

11. "Types of Mankind," *Presbyterian Quarterly Review*, XIII (1854), 177–217. This and the five paragraphs following are based on this review. Gliddon suffered much ridicule from the small group of scholarly theologians in the United States. See, for example, S[amuel] R[eufs], "Mr. Gliddon's Biblical Criticisms," *Christian Examiner*, LVII (1854), 340–64.

12. The reviewer of *Types of Mankind* for the *Southern Literary Messenger* also believed that it was "at once an influential, as well as dangerous production" and objected that its doctrine sundered "the common tie of human sympathy." He referred the reader to Bachman (William Archer Cocke, "Types of Mankind," *Southern Literary Messenger*, XX [1854], 66–68).

13. Alonzo Potter, *Lectures on the Evidences of Christianity. Delivered in Philadelphia, by Clergymen of the Protestant Episcopal Church, in the Fall and Winter of 1853–4* (Philadelphia, 1855), pp. 53–54.

14. "A.L.," "On the Unity of the Human Race," *Southern Quarterly Review*, X (1854), 273–304. "Names venerable" probably refers to Prichard, whose views on unity the reviewer discusses.

15. James D. Dana, "Science and the Bible: A Review of 'The Six Days of Creation' of Prof. Tayler Lewis," *Bibliotheca Sacra*, XIII (1856), 80–130, 631–56; XIV (1857), 388–412, 461–524. Agassiz replied to Dana that he did not "regret contributing" to *Types of Mankind*. "Nott is a man after my

heart, for whose private character I have the highest regard. He is a true man, and if you knew what he has had to suffer in Mobile from the criminations of bigots . . . you would not wonder at his enemity [*sic*] to such men. He has dealt with them in about the same manner as you have with Prof. Lewis. All the difference is that he has no sympathy with their church. But I know him to be a man of truth and faith. Gliddon is coarse, especially in his utterance and has allowed his resentments to mislead him to personalities which all his friends blame. But I would rather meet a man like him, who knows as much as he does about antiquity and who cares to investigate it, than any of those who shut their eyes against evidence" ([Louis Agassiz], to J. D. Dana, [July 18, 1856], James Dwight Dana Scientific Correspondence, Sterling Library, Yale University).

16. In its original form, this was a paper read before the Montreal Meeting of the AAAS in 1857 (Dana, "Thoughts on Species," *Proceedings,* AAAS, XI [1857], 96–109), but it first appeared in published form in the same volume of the *Bibliotheca Sacra* in which appeared also the last part of his attack on Lewis (XIV [1857], 854–74). The fact that he published it in the organ of the Andover School of Congregational theology and in such proximity to his attack on Lewis can hardly be considered coincidental. The theological presuppositions of his argument for unity of mankind are most evident.

17. John William Draper, *Human Physiology, Statical and Dynamical; or, The Conditions and Course of the Life of Man* (New York, 1856), pp. 565, 568. For biography of Draper see Donald Fleming, *John William Draper and the Religion of Science* (Philadelphia, 1950).

18. Nott to Squier, Apr. 10, Sept. 18, 1854, Squier Papers, LC.

19. Bachman, "Types of Mankind," *Charleston Medical Journal,* IX (1854), 627–59. Nott always refused to recognize Bachman as a scientist and complained to Joseph Leidy in 1855, "If his articles were read only by naturalists they would do no harm, but they are read & intended for the people, & biggots—I think it is the duty of some one occasionally to roll back these masses of filth from the road of science" (Nott to Leidy, July 29, 1855, Leidy Papers, ANSP).

20. Bachman, "An Examination of a few of the statements of Prof. Agassiz in his 'Sketch of the natural provinces of the animal world, and their relation to the different types of men,'" *Charleston Medical Journal,* IX (1854), 790–806.

21. Bachman, "An Examination of Prof. Agassiz's Sketch of the Natural Provinces of the Animal World, and their relation to the different Types of Man, with a Tableau accompanying the Sketch," *Charleston Medical Journal,* X (1855), 482–534.

22. Bachman, "An Examination of a few of the statements."

23. Bachman, "Types of Mankind."

24. Bachman, "An Examination of Prof. Agassiz's Sketch." This and the paragraph following are based on this article. Henry Rowe Schoolcraft, never

on good terms with Nott, Gliddon, and Squier, wrote Bachman to thank him for his review of *Types of Mankind,* in Schoolcraft's opinion "a patch work of infidel papers" (Schoolcraft to Bachman, Sept. 23, 1854, Bachman Papers, Charleston Museum).

25. Nott, "Communication from Dr. Nott, of Mobile, Ala.," *Charleston Medical Journal,* IX (1854), 862–64; Nott, "Reply to Dr. Bachman's Review of Agassiz's Natural Provinces," *Charleston Medical Journal,* X (1855), 753–67. See also Burke, "Strictures on Dr. Bachman's Paper."

26. This and the quotation which follows are from Gliddon to Squier, Apr. 24, 1854, Squier Papers, LC.

"Agitators Often Do Much Good"

1. Nott to Squier, Apr. 10, 30, Oct. 5, 1854, Squier Papers, LC.

2. Nott to [Joseph Leidy], Oct. 4, 1854, Leidy Papers, ANSP; Gliddon to Squier, Sept. 9, Nov. 15, Dec. 20, 1854, Jan. 8, 1855, Squier Papers, LC; Gliddon, "The Monogenists and the Polygenists," in Nott and Gliddon, *Indigenous Races of the Earth* . . . (Philadelphia, 1857), pp. 402–602. Many had wanted command of the camel experiment, but, Gliddon asked, "Does any one of them know 'k—— my a——' in Arabic? . . . Was any one of them capable of drawing up *my* plan, or executing it as it should be done? Time will show!" Gliddon to Squier, July 8, 1855, Squier Papers, LC. For Gliddon's contributions to the famous camel experiment see John Russell Bartlett, *Personal Narrative of Explorations and Incidents in Texas, New Mexico, California, Sonora, and Chihuahua, connected with the United States Boundary Commission, during the years 1850, '51, '52, and '53* (2 vols.; New York, 1854), II, 576–77; and George P. Marsh, *The Camel: His Organization, Habits and Uses Considered with Reference to His Introduction into the United States* (Boston, 1856), *passim.*

3. Nott to Squier, July 27, 1858, Squier Papers, LC; H[enry] Hotz (trans.), *The Moral and Intellectual Diversity of Races, with Particular Reference to Their Respective Influence in the Civil and Political History of Mankind, From the French of Count A. de Gobineau* (Philadelphia, 1856), pp. ix, 17, 19, 24, 33, 76–81, 463–512. This and the two paragraphs following are based on this work. (Gobineau's work was first published in Paris, 1853–55.)

4. Nott to Squier, Mar. 1, Apr. 26, 1857; Squier Papers, LC; Nott to [Leidy], Apr. 6, 1856, Leidy Papers, ANSP. Nott and Leidy maintained a close acquaintance during the fifties. Somewhat of a skeptic in religion, Leidy, though reluctant to commit himself publicly, probably adhered to the views of the multiple creationists. See Leidy's contribution to *Indigenous Races,* pp. xvi–xix; Nott's Appendix to Hotz, *Moral and Intellectual Diversity of Races;* Nott, "Reply to Dr. Bachman's Review."

5. [James D. B. De Bow], "The Earth and Its Indigenous Races," *De Bow's Review,* XXIII (1857), 70–77.

6. [Bennet Dowler], "Indigenous Races of the Earth," *New Orleans Medical and Surgical Journal,* XIV (1857), 138–42.

7. W[illiam] S[tump] Forwood, "The Negro—a Distinct Species," *Medical and Surgical Reporter,* X (1857), 225–34; "Senex," "Is the Negro a Distinct Species? Answered in the Negative. In reply to an Article by W. S. Forwood, M.D.," *Medical and Surgical Reporter,* X (1857), 288–301.

8. Abraham Coles, "A Critique on Nott and Gliddon's Ethnological Works. With some remarks on an article by W. S. Forwood, M.D., entitled 'The Negro—a Distinct Species,'" *Medical and Surgical Reporter,* X (1857), 417–49. This and the five paragraphs following are based on this article.

9. In common with other critics of the doctrine of diversity, Coles handled gingerly both Agassiz and Morton. This is probably accounted for by both their scientific renown and their lack of vehemence in attacking Scripture.

10. Nott to Squier, Apr. 10, 1854, July 1, 1857, Squier Papers, LC; [John Lawrence Le Conte] to father, June 9, 1857, Le Conte Papers, APS.

11. H[enry] S. Sanford to Squier, Nov. 17, 1857, Papers of E. G. Squier relating to the Honduras Interoceanic Railway, LC; Brantz Mayer to Squier, Mar. 18, 1858; Nott to Squier, Dec. 4, 7, 15, 24, 1857, Squier Papers, LC; Leidy, [Resolution offered to the Academy on the death of Gliddon], *Proceedings,* ANSP, IX (1857), 203.

12. Squier to parents, Oct. 30, 1856, Squier Papers, New-York Historical Society.

13. Nott to Hammond, June 3, 1850, Nov. 7, 1858, Hammond Papers, LC. Nott established the Medical School of Alabama, which opened in November, 1859.

14. Nott, "A Natural History of Dogs," *New Orleans Medical and Surgical Journal,* XV (1858), 484–500; "Influence of Anatomy on the March of Civilization," *New Orleans Medical and Surgical Journal,* XV (1858), 64–77.

15. Nott to Squier, Aug. 22, 1860, Squier Papers, LC.

16. Nott to Squier, May 3, 1861, Squier Papers, LC. "Certainly," Nott exclaimed, puzzled at the attitude of the Lincoln administration, "Certainly, you do not expect to conquer us & make us vassals!—This idea is too absurd to be entertained by any sane mind, that co[m]prehends the Anglo Saxon Character."

"The Old Roman"

1. Ravenel to Lewis R. Gibbes, June 10, 1861, Lewis R. Gibbes Papers, Charleston Museum.

2. Bachman to [J. A.] Brown, Feb. 3, 1860, Bachman Papers, Charleston Museum; [Catherine L. Bachman], *John Bachman . . .* (Charleston, S.C., 1888), pp. 363, 381, 392, 402; *Harper's Weekly,* V (1851), 33–34; Jefferson Davis, *The Rise and Fall of the Confederate Government* (2 vols.; New York, 1881), II, 709–17.

3. For the story of this tumultuous marriage see Madeleine B. Stern, *Purple Passage: The Life of Mrs. Frank Leslie* (Norman, Okla., 1953).

4. William H. Russell, *My Diary North and South* (Boston, 1863), pp. 190–91, 225–26 (entries for May 11, 18, 1861).

5. Kenneth R. H. Mackenzie, "The Life and Anthropological Labours of Dr. Nott of Mobile . . . ," *Anthropological Review*, VI (1868), lxxix–lxxxiii; Nott, "Dr. J. C. Nott . . . ," *Anthropological Review*, VI (1868), 450–52; *The War of the Rebellion: A Compilation of the Official Records of the Union and Confederate Armies* (Washington, 1880–1901), 1st ser., XVII, Part 2, 649; X, 469; Emmett B. Carmichael, "Josiah Clark Nott," *Bulletin of the History of Medicine*, XXII (1948), 249–62; Nott to Squier, Dec. 5, 1865, Squier Papers, LC. See also "Our Southern Correspondence," *National Intelligencer*, Dec. 9, 1865.

Brigadier General James St. Clair Morton died leading an attack at Petersburg, June 17, 1864.

6. [Asa Gray], "Darwin on the Origin of Species," *Atlantic Monthly*, VI (1860), 109–16, 229–39; [Asa Gray], "Darwin and His Reviewers," *ibid.*, pp. 406–25. Gray himself, though determined to maintain an open mind on the matter, continued to believe in a special creation for mankind and for perhaps some other species.

W[illiam] H[enry] Anderson, *Biographical Sketch of Dr. J. C. Nott* (Mobile, 1877). Dr. William Polk, who also knew Nott, said that "he was broad enough . . . to accept to the full all of Darwin's views and conclusions" ("Josiah C. Nott," *American Journal of Obstetrics*, vol. LXVII [1913], 957–8). Nott displayed great enthusiasm for Herbert Spencer's *Illustrations of Universal Progress* (New York, 1864) in which Spencer applied evolutionary doctrine to all phenomena (Nott to Squier, Sept. 27, 1868, Squier Papers, LC).

7. Nott, "The Problem of the Black Races," *De Bow's Review*, N.S., I (1866), 266–70; "Instincts of Races," *New Orleans Medical and Surgical Journal*, XIX (1866), 1–16, 145–56.

8. Nott to Squier, Jan. 12, 1866, May 28, 1868, May 26, Oct. 7, 1872, Squier Papers, LC; Nott to Leidy, July 2, Nov. 3, 1867, Leidy Papers, CPP; [Josiah C. Nott], "Female Surgery: Correspondence," *New Orleans Medical and Surgical Journal*, XXI (1868), 82–86; Thomas Addis Emmet, *Incidents of My Life, Professional—Literary—Social, with Services in the Cause of Ireland* (New York, 1911), pp. 199–200; Anderson, *Biographical Sketch of Dr. J. C. Nott*.

9. Nott to [Squier], Mar. 8, 1849, Squier Papers, LC.

The Problem of the Free Hybrid

1. Gray to [Francis] Boott, Jan. 16, 1860, Lyell Album, APS; and see E. C. Agassiz, *Louis Agassiz: His Life and Correspondence* (2 vols.; Boston, 1886), I, 372.

2. Howe to Agassiz, Aug. 3, 1863, Agassiz Papers, Houghton Library. For

biographies of Howe see Edward E. Allen, "Samuel Gridley Howe," DAB; and Harold Schwartz, *Samuel Gridley Howe: Social Reformer, 1801–1876* (Cambridge, Mass., 1956). The Schwartz volume is particularly useful on the period of Howe's work with the Commission. I am indebted to Mr. Edward Lurie for bringing to my notice both the Agassiz-Howe correspondence and the Schwartz volume when the latter was an unpublished doctoral dissertation at Harvard.

Agassiz's letters to Howe are: Aug. 6, 9, 10, 11, 15, 1863, Agassiz Papers, Houghton Library. The last letter is unfinished and unsigned. Those of August 9 and 10 appear, carefully edited, in E. C. Agassiz, *Louis Agassiz*.

3. Agassiz to Howe, Aug. 9, 1863.
4. Agassiz to Howe, Aug. 10, 1863.
5. Agassiz to Howe, Aug. 9, 1863.
6. Agassiz to Howe, Aug. 9, 10, 1863.
7. David Macrae, *The Americans at Home* (2 vols.; Edinburgh, 1870), II, 322.

"Notwithstanding Mrs. Grundy"

1. Schoolcraft to Bachman, Sept. 23, 1854, Bachman Papers, Charleston Museum.
2. Squier to parents, Oct. 20, 1856, Squier Papers, New-York Historical Society; Kenneth R. H. Mackenzie, "The Life and Anthropological Labours of Dr. Nott of Mobile . . . ," *Anthropological Review*, VI (1868), lxxix–lxxxiii; J[ames] L[awrence] Cabell, *The Testimony of Modern Science to the Unity of Mankind* . . . (New York, 1859), p. 275 n.; Norton to Squier, Apr. 29, 1849, Squier Papers, LC.
3. Howe to Agassiz, Aug. 18, 1863, Agassiz Papers, Houghton Library. This letter, except for a postscript, is not written in Howe's hand, although it is initialed by him.
4. "The Whig and the 'Types of Mankind,' " Richmond *Enquirer*, July 6, 1854. This was brought to my attention by Avery Craven, *The Coming of the Civil War* (New York, 1942), p. 168.
5. J[ohn] Augustine Smith, "A Sketch of a Lecture on the Different Races of Men . . . ," issued with Charles Lyell, *Lectures on Geology, Delivered at the Broadway Tabernacle . . . , Reported for the New-York Tribune* (New York, 1843).
6. A[sa] G[ray], "Review of Darwin's Theory of the Origin of Species by Means of Natural Selection," *American Journal of Science*, 2d ser., XXIX (1860), 153–84.
7. Gliddon to Squier, Apr. 22, 1851, Squier Papers, LC.

Index

Index

Boston Society of Natural History, 42
Boston *Transcript*, 147
Botta, Paul, 90
Boudin, Jean C. M., 80, 90, 174
Bowditch, Henry I., 102, 146
Brachycephalism. *See* Retzius, Anders
Bradford, Alexander, 11
Brown, John, 189
Browne, Peter A., 149–55
Bruno, Giordano, 112, 180
Buffon, G. L. L., 10, 11, 15, 34, 43, 114, 139, 142
Bunsen, Baron Christian, 47, 118, 141, 157
Burke, Luke, 118

Cabell, James Lawrence, vii
Caldwell, Charles, 19–22; on adaptation of man, 21; attacks S. S. Smith, 20–23; on *Crania Americana*, 39; on Henry Moss, 5–6; on phrenology, 20, 37; on revelation and science, 21, 22
Calhoun, John C., 53, 61–65, 154
Camper, Pieter, 25
Carpenter, William B., M.D., 73–74
Cartwright, Samuel A., M.D., vii, 160
Caucasian race: as distinct species, 81, 88; hair of, 151; superiority of, 160. *See also* Races of man
Census, U.S., of 1840, 58–66, 71
Cephalic index. *See* Retzius, Anders
Chambers, Robert, 24, 89
Champollion, Jean François, 70
Charleston Literary Society, 53, 104, 124, 125, 126
Charleston Medical Journal, 126, 143, 144, 170
Chinese, 175
Christian Examiner, 73, 74, 104, 109
Chronology, 88, 167–68; Bachman on, 132; biblical, 30, 50, 75, 122, 156–58, 164–68, 178; and Darwinism, 186; Egyptian, 42, 50, 70, 120, 156–58, 167–68; of man, 140; of Mound Builders, 87; of races, 106
Civil War, U.S., 184
Coles, Abraham, 177–80
Collins, John, 30
Combe, George, 30, 35, 36, 37
Commercial Review of the South and West. See De Bow's *Review.*
Connecticut Academy of Science, 83
Conway, Moncure, 110–12
Cooper, Thomas, 19
Crania Aegyptiaca, 51–53, 90, 124. *See also* Morton, Samuel George

Crania Americana, 25, 45, 62, 88, 90, 121, 125; publication of, 30; reviews of, 39–40. *See also* Morton, Samuel George
Craniology, 120. *See also* Morton, Samuel George
Creation, 77, 107–9; biblical, 17, 18–19, 118, 120–21, 122, 132–33, 139; economy of, 4, 31, 89, 117, 132, 133, 137, 138; and equality, 2–3; of man, 4–5, 16, 31, 43, 138, 169, 170, 171–72
Curtis, Moses Ashley, 75–77, 78, 79–80
Cuvier, Georges, 10, 24, 43, 102, 142, 157

Dana, James Dwight, 102, 169–70
Darwin, Charles, 3, 89, 93, 114, 192; and "American School," 195–96; on chronology of organic development, 186; "Historical Sketch" of, 116; on hybridization, 117; on new breed of cattle, 129; Nott's reaction to, 183, 185, 187
Darwinism, 185–87; Agassiz's reaction to, 189; and "American School," 186, 188, 195–96; Gray's reaction to, 189; Nott's reaction to, 185, 187
D'Avenne, Prisse, 47, 174
Davis, Alexander Jackson, 47
Davis, Edwin H., M.D., 82, 83, 84, 85, 97
Davis, Jefferson, 161
De Bow, James D. B., 118, 156, 158, 176
De Bow's *Review*, 80, 155
Declaration of Independence: and abolition, 55; Abraham Coles on, 178; Moncure Conway on, 111; and Gliddon, 181; Jefferson on effects of, 23; meaning of, 2, 5; Nott on, 183; relation of, to science, 2, 109; and slavery, 57–58
Delafield, John 11
Deluge, 157, 168
Descent of Man, 196
Development hypotheses, 24–25, 89, 108
De Wette, Wilhelm M. L., 118, 121
Dewey, Orville, 73
Dickeson, Montroville W., 83
Dickson, Samuel H., M.D., 74, 123
Doctrine of the Unity of the Human Race Examined on the Principles of Science, 125, 143
Dogs, chronology of, 140
"Dolichocephalism," *See* Retzius, Anders
Douglas, Stephen A., 57
Dowler, Bennet, M.D., 176–77
Draper, John William, 170

Eaton, Amos, 26
Edwards, Governor, 37

Egypt, 97, 106; chronology of, 118; ethnology of, 51, 70; monuments of, 117, 141; Negroes in, 50

Egyptology, 47, 70, 88, 140

Eichhorn, Johann Gottfried, 121

Emancipation, 190

Emerson, R. W., 84, 102

Emmet, Thomas Addis, M.D., 187

Equality, vii, 56–57; Jeffersonian concept of, 2; racial, 2–3; and science, 3, 11

Eskimos, 98

Essay on the Causes of the Variety of Complexion and Figure in the Human Species, 4, 177

Essay concerning Human Understanding, 182

Ethnology, 99, 164

Everett, Edward, 49, 146

"Facial angle," 25

Forry, Samuel, 39–40

Forwood, William S., M.D., 177

France, 61

Franklin, Benjamin, 34

Freedmen's Bureau, 186, 187

"Friend of Moses," The, 159

Frothingham, Nathan Langdon, 109–10, 157

Fugitive Slave Law, 194

Gärtner, Karl Friedrich, 114

Galileo, 158, 164, 169, 180

Gall, Franz, 35, 38

Gallatin, Albert, 83, 97–98

Genetics, 196

Gibbes, Lewis R., 123, 154, 184

Gibbes, Robert W., M.D., 91, 143, 144, 154

Gibson, William, 36

Gliddon, Anastasia, 48

Gliddon, Anne, 48, 90, 181

Gliddon, Catherine, 48

Gliddon, George R., 73, 80, 81, 82, 88, 89, 97, 98, 100, 104, 113, 118, 122, 142, 143, 148, 151, 153, 157, 159, 161, 173, 186, 188, 194, 196; and *Ancient Monuments of the Mississippi Valley,* 87; and John C. Calhoun, 62, 64; career of, 45–50; on chronology, 50; and *Crania Aegyptiaca,* 51, 52, 53; death of, 180–81; on death of Morton, 144; on Egyptian chronology, 70, 120; and *Indigenous Races,* 175–76, 177, 178, 179; lectures of, on Egypt, 46–50, 145–47; on Negroes and Egyptians, 50; reports to

Morton, 90–92; and *Types of Mankind,* 162, 163, 165, 167, 169, 170, 174, 177, 178, 193

Gliddon, Henry, 90

Gliddon, John (father of George R.), 45, 47

Gliddon, John (brother of George R.), 48

Gobineau, Arthur de, 174, 175

Gould, Augustus A., 146

Gray, Asa, 75, 79, 102, 107; on Agassiz's lectures, 104; on Darwinism, 185–86, 189, 196; on theory of multiple origin of races, 195

Great Britain, 61

Haight, Richard K., 45

Hair, as racial characteristic, 150, 151–53

Haldeman, S. S., 116, 150, 153

Hamilton, Thomas, 54, 56

Hamilton, William T., 159

Hammond, James Henry, 52–53, 63, 77, 80, 182

Harlan, Richard, 10, 25

Hartshorne, Joseph, M.D., 36

Haviland, John, 47

Hayward, George, M.D., 146

Head shape. *See* Craniology

Henry, Joseph, 84, 102, 153, 169

Herbert, William, 116

Heredity, 128

Hildreth, Samuel P., 27, 28

Hitchcock, Edward, 26, 169

Hodgson, William Brown, 52, 53

Holbrook, John Edwards, 53, 87, 123, 124

Holmes, Francis S., 123

Holmes, Oliver Wendell, M.D., 96, 146

Holmes, Robert S., M.D., 26

Honduras Inter-Oceanic Railway, 180

Hotz, Henry, 174, 175

Houghton, Douglass, 28

Howard, Gen. Oliver Otis, 186

Howe, Samuel Gridley, M.D., 37, 189–90, 193–94

Hudson, Henry Norman, 146

Humboldt, Alexander, 87–88

Hunt, Leigh, 48

Hunt, Thornton, 48

Hunter, John, 10, 16, 114

Hunt's Merchants' Magazine, 59

Hybridity, 76, 77, 143

Hybridization, 67, 112, 114–18, 120, 125, 126, 127–28, 131, 137, 138, 139, 141, 152, 162, 190, 191, 195. *See also* Races of man, mixture of

Morton, Mrs. Samuel George, 161
Moss, Henry, 5–6, 13
Moultrie, James, M.D., 123
Mound Builders, 85, 97, 120; antiquity of, 85–86; crania of, 83–84; hair of, 152; Morton on, 32–33; origin of, 10–11, 86–87. *See also* Indian
Mulattoes, 66–68, 76

Nasmyth, Alexander, 28
National Institute, 52
Negroes: anatomical peculiarities of, 67–68; antiquity of, 106; color of, 13; compared to Indians, 34–35; cranial capacity of, 148; danger of emancipation to, 195; Darwinism and, 186; as distinct species, 73, 81, 88, 115; in Egypt, 50, 51, 97; hair of, 151, 152, 153; and idea of equality, 2–3, 55, 136, 191; inferiority of, 8, 18, 34–35, 80, 100, 103, 110–12, 144, 158–59, 160, 172, 175, 177, 187; insanity among, 58–60; interbreeding with whites, 189–91; Jefferson on, 12; natural increase of, 185; origin of, 5–8, 15, 104, 156; phrenological character of, 35–36; as variety of human species, 131, 134, 172. *See also* Census, U.S., of 1840; Slavery
New York Evening Post, 152
New York Tribune, 144
Newton, Isaac, 138, 155
North American Review, 85
Norton, Andrews, 118, 121
Norton, Charles Eliot, 85, 193
Nott, Abraham, 65
Nott, Eliphalet, 65
Nott, Henry Junius, 65
Nott, Josiah Clark, M.D., 65–72, 73, 74, 75, 76, 77, 78–79, 80–81, 82, 83, 87, 88, 89, 93, 98, 109, 113, 118–21, 122–23, 124, 125, 131, 135, 142–43, 144, 147, 153, 154, 155, 157, 158–60, 161–62, 164–65, 169, 170, 171, 173, 174–76, 177, 178, 179, 180, 181, 182–83, 184–85, 189, 192, 193, 194, 196; on abolition, 158–59; on biblical chronology, 156–57; on biblical creation, 120–21; on chronology, 78; on Darwinism, 185, 186; death of, 188; on geographical distribution of species, 160; on interbreeding, 72; on Jews, 147–48; on mulattoes, 66–68; on Negro, 67–68, 80–81; 148; on organic variation, 79; on origin of races, 69–71, 81, 119–20; on race characteristics, 119–20; on race mixture, 81, 158–59; on religious bigotry, 68; on religion and sci-ence, 119, 163; on revelation, 69; on slavery, 80–81, 149, 158–59, 160
Nuttall, Thomas, 49

Origin of Species, 116, 189
Orthognathism. *See* Retzius, Anders
Owen, Richard, 116
Owen, Robert, 48

Page, T. J., 28
Palfrey, John Gorham, 49
Parker, Theodore, 146
Parkman, Francis, 95
Parrish, Joseph, M.D., 26
Patterson, Henry S., M.D., 163, 170
Pauthier, Jean Pierre, 90
Peale's Museum, 47
Peirce, Benjamin, 146
Philology, 98
Phrenology, 20, 29, 35, 36–37, 39
Physick, Philip Syng, M.D., 65
Pickering, Charles, 97, 100, 113, 146; on origin of man, 92–93; and U.S. Exploring Expedition, 92–96; and Charles Wilkes, 94–95
Pickering, John, 95
Piddington, Henry, 28
Pitcher, Zina, 27, 28
Porcher, Frederick Peyre, M.D., 123
Potter, Alonzo, 168–69
Presbyterian Magazine, 165
Presbyterian Quarterly Review, 166
Prescott, William H., 83, 146
Prichard, James Cowles, 39, 51–52, 53, 114, 116
Priest, Josiah, 11
Priestley, Joseph, 19
Prognathism. *See* Retzius, Anders
Pulszky, Francis, 176
Putnam's Monthly, 165, 166–67

Quetelet, L. A. D., 25

Races of man: criteria of, 4, 5, 6, 9, 43; hereditary transmission of characteristics of, 9–10; mixture of, 81, 158–59; 160, 190–91 (*see also* Hybridization); origin of, 5–8, 10, 12, 15–16, 18–19, 20, 31, 33, 40, 41, 89, 93, 101–2, 107, 109, 110–12, 114, 115, 119–20, 131, 133, 157, 158, 163, 166, 178–79, 192; persistence of characteristics in, 30, 33, 40, 41, 51, 88, 119–20, 182–83; as separate species, 92, 166, 177, 178, 182, 186; as single species, 2–3, 4, 5, 173

Index

Races of Man and Their Geographical Distribution, 95-96
Rafinesque, Constantine, 11, 13
Ravenel, Edmund, 27, 123, 184
Ravenel, Henry William, 123
Ray, Isaac, 37
Ray, John, 43, 114
Reed, Walter, 65
Religion: conflict of, with science, 69, 119, 122-23, 134, 164, 165-66, 168, 173, 177, 178-80, 193, 194; as rationale for slavery, 194. See also Creation
Retzius, Anders, 25, 38, 51
Richmond Enquirer, 194
Roberts, Joseph J., 148
Robertson, William, 34
Rogers, Thomas, 25
Rosellini, Hippolyte, 70
Ruschenberger, William S.W., 28
Rush, Benjamin, M.D., 2, 6-7, 10, 12-13
Russell, William Howard, 184-85

St. Hilaire, Geoffroy, 24, 187
Savagism, 8
Schoolcraft, Henry Rowe, 143, 192
Secession, 183
"Senex," 177
Silliman, Benjamin, 26, 37, 49, 83, 102, 153, 169
Silliman, Benjamin, Jr., 113-14, 169
Silliman's Journal. See American Journal of Science
Simms, William Gilmore, 155, 156
Sketches of the History of Man, 15
Slavery, 53; antiquity of, 51; attitude of South toward, 54-55; Bachman on, 172; and Census of 1840, 60, 61, 62-63; Abraham Coles on, 177-78; Moncure Conway on, 110-12; defense of, 54-58; effect on Negro, 8, 36, 80-81; in Egypt, 62; Nott on, 149, 158-59, 160, 185; popular opposition to, in Massachusetts, 13-14; Benjamin Rush on, 12-13; S. S. Smith on, 12; and theory of multiple origins of race, 193-94; as violation of natural rights, 13-14; Charles White on, 17
Smith, John Augustine, M.D., 18-19, 103, 195
Smith, Samuel Stanhope, 3-10, 14, 17, 19, 22, 23, 33, 34, 72, 98, 132, 170, 177; enumeration of races, 11; on equality, 3; on hereditary transmission of race characteristics, 9-10; on Henry Moss, 5; on Negro, 8; on origin of races, 5-7, 8, 9;

on races as single species, 4-12; on slavery, 12
Smith, William, 55
Smithsonian Institution, 84, 88, 153
Sömmering, Samuel T. von, 10
South Carolina Ordinance of Secession, 184
Southern Quarterly Review, 143, 155, 156, 169
Southern Rights Association, 158
Sparks, Jared, 84, 146
Species: geographical distribution of, 88-89, 117-18, 129, 139, 140, 160, 171, 182; immutability of, 3, 24, 127, 131; origin of, vii, 115-18, 127, 132-34, 138, 140; variation of, 128-29
Species criteria: adaptability as, 7; existence of gradation as, 4; interbreeding as, 4, 19, 43-44, 127; interfertility as, 15, 16, 135
Spontaneous generation of organisms, 3
Spurzheim, Johann, 35, 36
Squier, Ephraim G., 81, 82-88, 97, 109, 113, 118, 122, 124, 138, 143, 161, 162, 170, 174, 176, 183, 185, 187, 188; on antiquity of Indian Mounds, 85-86; assists Nott, 120; in Central America, 155, 180; on chronology, 164; death of, 184; on ethnology, 98-99, 164; on Negroes and slavery, 192-93; on origin of Mound Builders, 86-87, 88; on philology, 98; on relations between North and South, 181-82; on Types of Mankind, 163-64
Squier, Rev. Joel, 82
Stephens, John Lloyd, 45, 47
Stewart, Thomas S., 47
Stone, Frank, 48
Stowe, Calvin, 191
Stowe, Harriet Beecher, 191
Strain, Isaac G., 28
Strauss, David Friedrich, 118, 121
Stuart, Moses, 121
Sullivant, Joseph, 28
Sumner, Charles, 146

Tappan, Arthur, 95
Tappan, Benjamin, 28, 95
Tappan, Lewis, 95
Texas, annexation of, 61
Theology, and theory of multiple creations of man, 110, 111-12
Tiedemann, Friedrich, 29
Torrey, John, 102, 103-4, 169
Types of Mankind, 161-73, 174, 176, 177, 178, 186, 192, 193